Operational Amplifiers and Linear Integrated Circuits

THE PWS–KENT SERIES IN TECHNOLOGY

Operational Amplifiers
and
Linear Integrated Circuits

=== *SECOND EDITION* ===

Jefferson C. Boyce

Formerly of
Allan Hancock College
Santa Maria, California

PWS-KENT Publishing Company
Boston

PWS–KENT
Publishing Company

20 Park Plaza
Boston, Massachusetts 02116

PWS–KENT Publishing Company is a division of Wadsworth, Inc.

Library of Congress Cataloging-in-Publication Data

Boyce, Jefferson C.
    Operational amplifiers and linear integrated circuits / Jefferson
C. Boyce.—2nd ed.
        p.   cm.
    Bibliography: p.
    Includes index.
    ISBN 0-534-91472-1
    1. Operational amplifiers.   2. Linear integrated circuits.
I. Title
TK7871.58.06B67   1988   88-2474
621.3815′35—dc19   CIP

Printed in the United States of America
88 89 90 91 92——10 9 8 7 6 5 4 3 2 1

Sponsoring Editor: Robert Prior
Editorial Assistant: Mary Thomas
Production: Technical Texts, Inc.
Interior and Cover Design: Sylvia Dovner
Cover Image: Slide Graphics of New England
Typesetting: Compset, Inc.
Cover Printing: New England Book Components, Inc.
Printing and Binding: Halliday Lithograph

Acknowledgments *Figures 5–6 and 6–8:* Redrawn from manufacturer's specification sheets with permission. Fairchild Camera & Instrument Corporation, Mountain View, CA. *Figures 5–9, 5–10, 5–13, and 5–14:* Redrawn from

(Continued page 508)

Preface

Operational Amplifiers and Linear Integrated Circuits, Second Edition, explores a fascinating facet of electronics in a rather interesting manner. The functional approach, with deemphasis of advanced mathematics, is used. That is, the basic function of amplification is considered as a "block" that modifies incoming information according to certain ground rules. Once the amplification function is established, oscillation criteria can be examined. Then the whole world of electronics is at our fingertips.

The functional approach to any device considers the analysis of a complex system and explanation of its operation based on the functions of components. It is not the detailed operation of nonidentifiable components.

Modern technology has placed us in a position where we may not be able to remove and replace—much less identify—some of the major components of an electronic system. The operational amplifier and linear integrated circuit are examples. From an interest viewpoint, it may be worthwhile to know what is going on inside the package, but nothing can be done if one of the internal components malfunctions. Therefore, the important thing is the function of the package based on its total electrical characteristics. In using the functional approach, attention is focused on such things as input and output resistance, gain, and frequency/phase response. The reaction of this package to external stimuli and common electrical and electronic component connections is the subject of this book. Graphical and algebraic methods support the functional approach adequately, resulting in an understandable and highly applicable text.

We all see the designers' approaches to functional analysis daily. The calculator, for example, has become a package, since little can be done to fix it if it malfunctions. Hand calculators are inexpensive enough to throw away when the battery wears out. The same goes for pocket AM/FM radios, flashlights, and cigarette lighters. Maybe Detroit is even thinking about disposable products. One day we may be "throwing away" our cars because they are too expensive to repair.

It is assumed that the reader has completed studies in AC and DC circuits, active devices and circuits, and digital fundamentals. The reader should also be able to accomplish the following:

1. Solve basic DC series, parallel, and series-parallel circuit problems using both algebraic and graphical methods.
2. Solve basic AC series, parallel, and series-parallel circuit problems showing phase and amplitude relationships with vectors and algebraic solutions.
3. Show DC and AC voltage and current relationships in basic amplifiers, oscillators, and power supplies.
4. Recognize common digital circuits and show input/output waveforms with Boolean equations and truth tables.

Basic formulas are given in Appendix B. It is recommended that these formulas be reviewed prior to beginning Chapter 1. The information in Appendix B lays the groundwork for understanding the remainder of the book. Should difficulty be encountered during review of basic fundamentals, it is suggested that the many texts shown in the Bibliography be referenced.

Just a few basic facts will allow us to understand the many applications of operational amplifiers and linear integrated circuits. In Chapter 1, we review amplification from a systems viewpoint. The details of what is happening inside the amplifier are shown to be relatively unimportant. Only the input/output details are needed. Chapter 2 provides discussion of operational amplifier DC specifications and the three basic circuit configurations. In Chapter 3, the basic circuit configurations are then used in DC applications such as typical amplifiers and voltage regulators.

Chapter 4 expands our knowledge to AC specifications and circuits so that more complex applications can be investigated. Audio amplifiers are discussed in Chapter 5, and high-frequency amplifiers are described in Chapter 6. Chapters 7 and 8 are devoted to explanations of filters. Chapter 7 provides the basics and shows how operational amplifiers can improve simple filters. Advanced active filters are explained in Chapter 8.

Op-amp–based and integrated circuit waveform generation circuits are the subject of Chapter 9. Both sinusoidal and nonsinusoidal oscillators are shown, with many variations developed to demonstrate the versatility of the operational amplifier. Chapter 10 refers back to the original purpose for operational amplifiers, as mathematical operations using op amps are investigated. Special-purpose operational amplifiers and their applications are detailed in Chapter 11. Comparators, instrumentation amplifiers, current difference amplifiers, and the like are mentioned as they relate to the subject of operational amplifiers.

Chapter 12 shows how operational amplifiers can improve the characteristics of semiconductor devices such as diodes and transistors. Chapter 12 also shows that transistors and other semiconductor devices can be used for control of operational amplifiers and for extension of the capabilities of operational amplifiers. Chapters 13 and 14 investigate the use of special linear integrated circuits. Analog/digital conversion is the subject of Chapter 13, while Chapter 14 investigates phase-locked loops. Last, but surely not least, Chapter 15 provides a further look at the applications of various types of operational amplifiers. These applications are typical and provide an overview of the world of operational amplifiers.

Chapters 13 and 14 are new to the second edition of this text. The "old reliables," like the 741 operational amplifier, remain in this edition. The concepts haven't changed, and the 741 is readily available and inexpensive. Newer operational amplifiers and linear integrated circuits merely increase speed, power handling capability, and functional complexity. This second edition also includes sample computer programs (Appendix C), which may be used to solve some of the simple equations used with operational amplifiers and linear integrated circuits.

Specification sheets, application notes, and technical manuals contributed much to the development of this book. The following manufacturers generously allowed use of technical information and specifications:

Fairchild Camera & Instrument Corporation
National Semiconductor Corporation
Precision Monolithics, Inc.
RCA Solid State Division
Signetics Corporation
Siliconix, Inc.
Exar Corporation

Their contribution to the material in this book is gratefully acknowledged. Any inaccuracies that may have resulted from the author's interpretation of manufacturers' data is solely the responsibility of the author. The use of data sheets and other manufacturers' information as supplements to this book is highly recommended.

A word of thanks also to those who reviewed the second edition manuscript: Stephen F. Judy, Eastern Maine Vocational Technical Institute, Bangor; Robert Reaves, Durham Technical Community College, Durham, North Carolina; Nicholas Karayanakis, University of North Florida, Jacksonville; Perry R. Gotschal, Williamsport Area Community College, Williamsport, Pennsylvania; Andrew M. Flock, Hickok Technical Institute, Cleveland, Ohio.

In conclusion, the support of my loving wife, Betty, has once again allowed another book to evolve. There is no doubt that her recognition of the conditions necessary for successful completion of a manuscript, and her willingness to establish those conditions, made this book possible. Any success that this book achieves is willingly dedicated to Betty.

Contents

Amplification

OBJECTIVES   After studying Chapter 1, you will be able to

1. Define amplification.
2. Discuss the advantages of integrated circuit amplifiers over discrete-component amplifiers.
3. Calculate the relationship between the source of information to be amplified and the input characteristic of an amplifier.
4. Calculate the relationship between the output characteristic of an amplifier and the load connected to the amplifier.
5. Identify the characteristics of an ideal amplifier and how closely it can be approximated.
6. Discuss the effect of negative feedback on amplification.
7. Define operational amplifier.
8. Name the functional blocks that make up an operational amplifier, and discuss their functions.
9. List the characteristics of a differential amplifier.
10. Discuss the similarities and differences between bipolar and FET operational amplifiers.

INTRODUCTION

As technology advances, more and more electronic operations are performed using functional modules such as **integrated circuits** (ICs) rather than discrete components. The amplification function, which is basic to *all* linear integrated circuits, is a typical example. In preparation for discussion of **operational amplifiers**, this chapter reviews the subject of amplification with emphasis on amplifiers as systems, rather than a collection of components. As will be seen from the basic calculations used to discuss both ideal and practical amplifiers—with and without **feedback**—a detailed analysis of components is not required for an understanding of amplifier operation. It is necessary to understand only the basic characteristics and configurations shown in this chapter in order to apply operational amplifiers to many diverse circuits and systems.

BASIC AMPLIFIERS

Everywhere we look in electronics—from small pocket radios to massive space satellites—we find a functional circuit called an *amplifier*. We will begin our discussion of amplification by investigating the basic concepts and characteristics of amplifiers.

Basic Amplifier Concepts

Amplification is the control of a large amount of voltage, current, or power by a smaller amount of voltage, current, or power. Figure 1–1 shows the amplification process in block diagram form. The large amount of voltage, current, or power comes from a power source such as a battery. Inserted between the controlling power device and the load that uses the power is the amplifying device. The power source supplies its full capability to the amplifier. However, the load receives no power from the power source through the amplifier until a control input is provided. The control input determines how much of the energy from the power source is applied to the load.

A typical example is the tape deck or stereo in a home or car. In a car, for example, the power source is the car's battery. The controlling power to the amplifier is derived from sound stored on the tape and is very weak. The output of the amplifier usually feeds a loudspeaker and is often quite strong. With no tape operating, no sound comes from the

Figure 1–1

Amplification Process

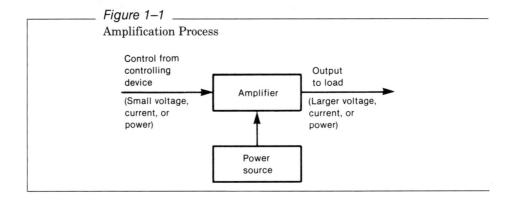

loudspeaker, even though battery power is connected. When the tape is operating, the small amount of controlling power from the tape causes a large amount of power to be routed from the battery to the loudspeaker. Thus, amplification has taken place. Remember, *an amplifier merely controls the power from the power source.* The amplifier does not originate any power; it is a control device.

Basic Amplifier Characteristics

When we talk about amplifiers, there are a few basic characteristics to be considered. The recognized symbol for an amplifier is shown in Figure 1–2, along with its primary characteristics. It should be noted at this point that it does not matter *how* amplification is performed. An amplifier may be made from vacuum tubes, transistors, or integrated circuits. *Any* amplifier can be considered as a "gain package" that has an input resistance (impedance), amplification (gain), and an output resistance (impedance).

Input resistance is the resistance seen by the signal or controlling power source "looking into" the amplifier input terminals. **Output resistance** is the resistance seen by the load "looking back into" the output terminals. Impedance is used in place of resistance when frequencies are present at which capacitive and/or inductive reactance are of importance. The amplification or gain (A) of the amplifier is the number by which the input voltage (V_i) is multiplied to obtain the output

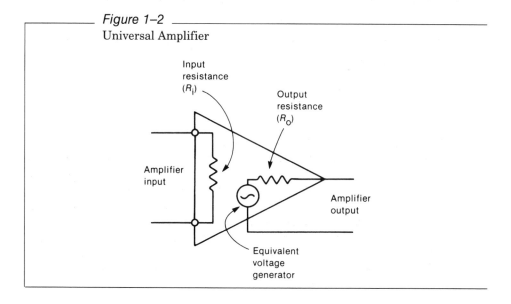

Figure 1–2

Universal Amplifier

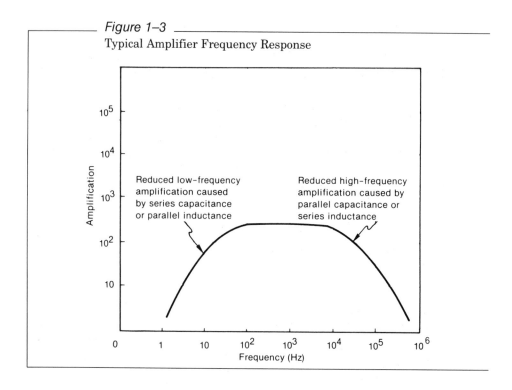

Figure 1-3

Typical Amplifier Frequency Response

voltage (V_o). That is, $V_o = A \times V_i$, so $A = V_o/V_i$. The output of the amplifier is considered equivalent to a voltage generator in series with the output resistance. The voltage output of the equivalent generator is A multiplied by the input voltage.

All amplifiers have a gain characteristic that varies with the *frequency* of the input signal. Any capacitive reactances in series with or inductive reactances in parallel with the signal path through the amplifier will affect the low-frequency gain characteristic. Inductive reactances in series with or capacitive reactances in parallel with the signal path affect the high-frequency gain characteristic. A sample gain characteristic or *frequency response* graph is shown in Figure 1-3.

Direct coupling between stages of an amplifier can effectively remove the low-frequency "droop" in gain. Until integrated circuits were perfected, direct coupling was very difficult to achieve when large amounts of amplification were needed. Temperature changes caused drastic changes in the characteristics of devices that used tubes and transistors. The result was highly unstable direct-coupled amplifiers. Integrated circuit construction of amplifiers allowed better control of device characteristics. Improvement in high-frequency gain characteristics was achieved by careful design and layout of vacuum tube and transistor amplifiers. Integrated circuits allowed much smaller amplifiers, and inductance and capacitance effects became less evident. Still, some problems do exist, and external components may need to be added to achieve the desired frequency response of an amplifier.

Indirectly, the subject of this entire book is amplification. It is extremely important that the basic idea of amplification is understood. Without this understanding, it may be difficult to deal with much of the information that follows. The key concept is: *The amplifier does not originate power; it only controls power.*

—————— AMPLIFIER CALCULATIONS ——————

Much can be learned about amplifier operation by performing a few basic calculations and by using graphs. Only basic algebra is required to calculate the characteristics of an amplifier's operation.

Ideal Amplifiers

Let's use the model amplifier in Figure 1–4 to demonstrate amplifier operation. We will assign an input resistance (R_i) of 1 MΩ (megohm), an output resistance (R_o) of 100 kΩ (kilohms), and a voltage gain of -250. The minus sign merely indicates that there is phase reversal between the input and the output, as would occur in a single-stage inverting amplifier. If a perfect signal source (one whose internal resistance is 0 Ω) is used, then all the source voltage appears at the input of the amplifier. For example, a perfect signal source furnishing 1 mV (millivolt) would provide the full 1 mV to the amplifier input. Furthermore, if a load is not connected to the output of the amplifier, the output will be 250 mV.

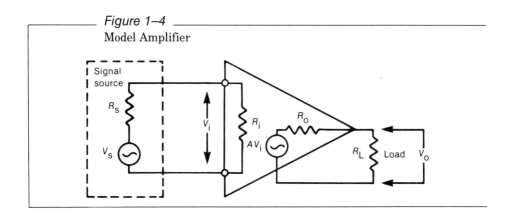

Figure 1–4
Model Amplifier

With no load connected, no current will flow through the output resistance of the amplifier, and no voltage drop will occur. The full output of the equivalent voltage generator (A times the input voltage) is available. The output voltage is calculated as follows:

$$V_s = 1 \text{ mV}$$

$$V_i = V_s = 1 \text{ mV (no losses)}$$

$$V_o = A \times V_i = (250)(1) = 250 \text{ mV}$$

where

V_s = the signal source voltage
V_i = the input voltage
V_o = the output voltage
A = the voltage gain

Practical Amplifiers

To be realistic, however, there are very few perfect signal sources. They all have some internal resistance. For our purposes, we will assign a value of 10 kΩ for the internal resistance of the signal source. Let's also connect a load of 50 kΩ to the output of the amplifier. Will these changes affect the voltage gain of the complete circuit? The actual amplifier input voltage will be less than the voltage of the source because of voltage divider action. See Figure 1–4. Note that when the internal resistance of the source is small compared with the input resistance of the amplifier, very little signal is lost. In the case we are discussing, the input signal is 0.99 mV, still very nearly 1 mV. At the output, however, it is a different story. The output of the amplifier's equivalent generator is applied to a voltage divider consisting of the output resistance of the amplifier and the external load. The output would now be calculated as follows:

$$V_s = 1 \text{ mV}$$

$$V_i = V_s \times \frac{R_i}{R_i + R_s} = 0.99 \text{ mV}$$

$$V_o = (A \times V_i) \frac{R_L}{R_L + R_o} = 82.5 \text{ mV}$$

These calculations show that the loaded output is only 82.5 mV—which is quite a difference from 250 mV. Nevertheless, it is realistic. It is very difficult to obtain the full theoretical gain from an amplifier that must supply a load.

Table 1–1

Effect of Changing Input Resistance

R_i (Ω)	V_i (mV)
1 k	0.091
5 k	0.333
10 k	0.500
50 k	0.833
100 k	0.909
500 k	0.980
1 M	0.990
5 M	0.998

Assumptions:

$$V_i = V_s \times \frac{R_i}{R_i + R_s} \qquad V_s = 1 \text{ mV} \qquad R_s = 10 \text{ k}\Omega$$

When a signal source is connected to the input and a load to the output of an amplifier, things begin to happen. First of all, the input voltage to the amplifier is no longer necessarily the voltage of the signal source. The internal resistance of the signal source in conjunction with the input resistance of the amplifier forms a voltage divider. A portion of the signal source voltage is dropped across the source's internal resistance. Thus the actual input voltage to the amplifier may be less than expected. As long as the input resistance of the amplifier is large in respect to the internal resistance of the signal source, there will be minimal losses. A good rule of thumb says that the input resistance of the amplifier should be greater than 10 times the source resistance. The input voltage to an amplifier with various input resistances (and a fixed source resistance) is shown in Table 1–1. (Refer to Figure 1–4).

A similar situation occurs when a load resistance is connected to the output of an amplifier. The source of voltage now is the equivalent voltage generator of the amplifier. Its voltage value is the input voltage times the amplification (gain) of the amplifier. The equivalent generator's output is applied to the load through the output resistance of the amplifier. Its voltage is divided between the output resistance of the amplifier and the load resistance, depending on the relative values of resistance. As may be seen in Figure 1–4, lower values of load resistance result in greater voltage losses in the amplifier. The net result is less than the theoretical amplification in practical amplifiers. Only when the load is infinitely high will the theoretical amplification be obtained. Numerical examples verifying these statements about output resistance are shown in Table 1–2 (see also Figure 1–4).

Table 1–2
Effect of Changing Load Resistance

R_L (Ω)	V_o (mV)
1 k	2.48
5 k	11.9
10 k	22.7
50 k	83.3
100 k	125
500 k	208
1 M	227
5 M	245

Assumptions:

$$V_o = (A \times V_i) \frac{R_L}{R_L + R_o} \qquad V_i = 1 \text{ mV} \qquad R_o = 100 \text{ k}\Omega$$

$$A = 250$$

IDEAL AMPLIFIER

From what we have just seen, it looks as if what is needed is an amplifier with infinite input resistance, zero output resistance, and infinite gain. If we had infinite input resistance, then we would not have to worry about the internal resistance of the signal source. We could connect an amplifier to *any* signal source and not drop any signal voltage internal to the source. With zero output resistance, any size of load resistance could be connected. No signal voltage drop internal to the amplifier would occur, and we could take full advantage of the amplifier's gain. Infinite gain would allow us to amplify even the weakest of signals to a usable value.

But is infinite input resistance achievable? Actually, it isn't, although amplifiers can be designed with input resistances on the order of a million megohms, which is close enough to infinite resistance for most users. But do we really want infinite input resistance? When there is such high input resistance, very small leakage currents can create severe problems. Just a picoampere or so of current can be considered as a signal. High-grade insulation and special construction techniques are required for all amplifiers with very high input resistance. The problems are not insurmountable but do require attention.

Zero output resistance is not easy to get either, but we do have amplifiers with less than 100 Ω output resistance. Generally, when output resistance gets very low, the amplifier uses lots of power. Provisions must be made to dissipate the heat generated and to protect the components against that heat. High-power amplifiers tend to be bulky and require large power supplies. Often, external components such as power transistors are used with solid-state amplifiers to obtain the necessary low resistance and added power capability.

Infinite gain is also not an everyday occurrence. Looking at the specifications for modern amplifiers reveals that gains on the order of more than a million are not uncommon. Actually, such high gains are not very useful. Only 1 μV (microvolt) of random noise would be amplified to a full volt. Even with the best of precautions, high-gain amplifiers tend to be unstable. However, we will find shortly that very high gain can be put to use.

The ideal amplifier would also maintain its gain from DC to infinitely high frequencies. This parameter cannot be achieved in reality. Every amplifier has an upper frequency limit that is determined by its construction and application. There is much to be said about frequency response in ensuing paragraphs and chapters.

FEEDBACK

Feedback is a technique used to modify the performance of amplifier circuits. *Positive feedback* is generally used when increased gain or oscillation is desired. Positive feedback is discussed in detail in later chapters where oscillation and oscillators are explained. *Negative feedback* is commonly used to improve stability and linearity in amplifier

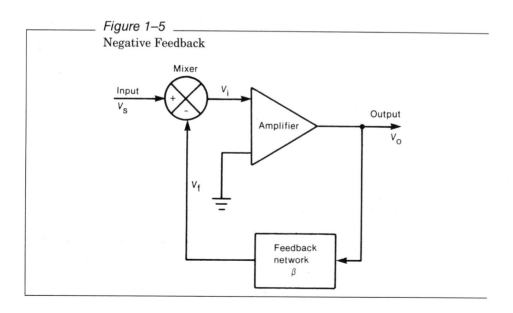

Figure 1–5
Negative Feedback

circuits. Negative feedback is discussed in almost all of the remaining chapters.

Figure 1–5 shows the concepts of negative feedback. A portion of the amplifier's output is returned to the input and combined with the incoming signal. The fed-back signal, however, is opposite in phase to the input signal and *subtracts* from the incoming signal in the mixer. The net result is that the amplifier perceives a smaller input signal than is really present. The amplifier circuit appears to have less gain than it did without feedback. Although this may seem to be undesirable, some desirable side effects do occur. Let's investigate amplifier operation with feedback to see what happens.

Feedback Calculations

Without feedback, the gain (A) of an amplifier is expressed as $A = V_o/V_i$, where $V_i = V_s$ in Figure 1–5. With feedback, gain is still equal to the ratio of output voltage to input voltage, except that $V_i = V_s - V_f$. Note the minus sign for V_f; the feedback voltage is out of phase with the input signal. Also note that $V_f = (\beta)(V_o)$, where β is the percentage of V_o fed back. With this information, we can develop the formula for amplifier gain with feedback (A_{fb}). We begin the calculations as follows:

$$V_o = (A)(V_i) = (A)(V_s - V_f) = (A)[V_s - (\beta \times V_o)]$$
$$= (A \times V_s) - (A \times \beta \times V_o)$$

Then we factor and rearrange terms so that

$$V_o + (A \times \beta \times V_o) = A \times V_s$$
$$V_o \times [1 + (A \times \beta)] = A \times V_s$$
$$\frac{V_o}{V_s} = \frac{A}{1 + (A \times \beta)}$$

But

$$\frac{V_o}{V_s} = A_{fb}$$

so

$$A_{fb} = \frac{A}{1 + (A \times \beta)}$$

which is approximately $A/(A \times \beta)$ when $(A \times \beta)$ is much greater than 1. Then,

$$A_{fb} \approx 1/\beta \qquad \text{(1-1)}$$

Thus, in an amplifier with relatively large **open-loop gain** (A), the **closed-loop gain** (A_{fb}) is determined almost entirely by the **feedback factor** (β). Open-loop gain is sometimes represented by A_{ol} and closed-loop gain by A_{cl}.

Let's assume an amplifer with open-loop gain of 90 and a feedback factor of 0.1. According to the equations just developed,

$$A_{fb} = \frac{A}{1 + (A \times \beta)} = \frac{90}{1 + (90 \times 0.1)} = \frac{90}{10} = 9$$

In simplified (approximate) form,

$$A_{fb} \approx 1/\beta \approx 1/0.1 \approx 10$$

A difference of about 10% is seen, but when ($A \times \beta$) is much larger, the difference gets much smaller. See Example 1–1.

Example 1–1

An amplifier has an open-loop gain of 900 and a feedback factor of 0.1. Determine the closed-loop gain by the complete and the approximate formulas.

Solution

$$A_{fb} = \frac{A}{1 + (A \times \beta)} = \frac{900}{1 + (900 \times 0.1)} = \frac{900}{91} = 9.89$$

$$A_{fb} \approx \frac{1}{\beta} \approx \frac{1}{0.1} = 10$$

As demonstrated in Example 1–1, when ($A \times \beta$) becomes large, the difference between the complete and approximate formulas becomes smaller.

Advantages of Feedback

So much for the gain reduction. Now let's see what good comes from negative feedback. Assume that the gain of an amplifier without feedback changes from 90 to 100. This represents a change of about 11%. If the same amplifier used the feedback factor just discussed, the gain would change from 9 to only 9.1, a change of about 1%. Thus an amplifier with negative feedback tends to be *more stable* than one without.

Much mathematical manipulation also shows some good side effects as far as input and output resistances are concerned. The input resistance (R_i) is *increased* by the factor $1 + (A \times \beta)$, while the output resistance (R_o) is *decreased* by the same factor. Higher amplifier input resistance loads signal sources less. Lower output resistance makes the amplifier less susceptible to load variations. Furthermore, although gain has been reduced, the frequency response of the amplifier has been improved. Generally, then, negative feedback has more pluses than minuses. Many examples of negative feedback will be seen in the remainder of this book.

OPERATIONAL AMPLIFIERS

Operational amplifiers (op amps) are a special type of amplifier, usually constructed in integrated circuit (IC) form. Each operational amplifier is a complete amplifier *system* having very high amplification (gain), high input resistance, and low output resistance. An operational amplifier comes very close to being a truly universal and ideal amplifier.

The term *operational amplifier* is derived from a group of high-performance *DC* amplifiers originally designed for use in analog computers. These amplifiers were used in conjunction with resistors, capacitors, and inductors to perform mathematical operations. The original operational amplifiers were constructed using vacuum tubes. In the early 1960s, transistors were used in operational amplifier design. By the late 1960s, however, IC technology had developed integrated circuit operational amplifiers.

Today only a small number of the manufactured operational amplifiers are used to perform analog computer operations. Any circuit that can use amplification can use the operational amplifier. Radios,

---

Figure 1–6

Standard Operational Amplifier Symbol

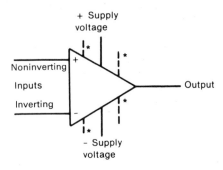

*Special control and inputs/outputs

televisions, stereos, test instruments, machine controls, and many other devices use operational amplifiers in place of discrete components such as transistors and resistors. Operational amplifier applications are limited only by the imagination of the designer.

The standard symbol for an operational amplifier is shown in Figure 1–6. A triangular symbol is used, with the inputs on the flat side and the output on the opposite point. The position of the + and the − inputs may be reversed for drawing clarity. Supply voltage(s) are shown

Figure 1–7

Type 741 Operational Amplifier Packaging

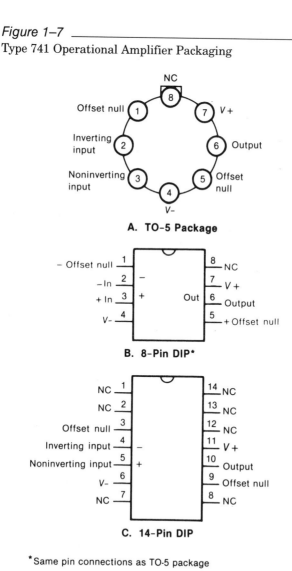

A. TO-5 Package

B. 8-Pin DIP*

C. 14-Pin DIP

*Same pin connections as TO-5 package

for information only. Usually, the supply voltage connections are omitted from diagrams. It should always be assumed, though, that correct supply voltages are applied.

Operational amplifiers are available in several different case styles. Figure 1–7A shows the commonly used packaging for a type 741 and many other operational amplifiers. Typical pin connections are shown in Figures 1–7B and 1–7C. Because of its wide availability and low cost, a type 741 operational amplifier has been selected as an example here. After the basic concepts and calculations associated with operational amplifiers have been explained, other types of operational amplifiers will be discussed. The type 741 operational amplifier is available in most of the common case styles, so comparisons may be made. The unfamiliar terms used here will be explained in the next section.

PRACTICAL OPERATIONAL AMPLIFIER

The operational amplifier tries to achieve the characteristics attributed to an ideal amplifier. Perhaps the best way to see what a real-life operational amplifier can do is to consult the specifications for a typical operational amplifier.

General Amplifier Characteristics

One of the most typical of all operational amplifiers is the 741. Rather than discuss the intricacies of the many different operational amplifiers so early in our studies, we will use this old but reliable op amp for our example. As we delve deeper into applications of the operational amplifier, we can investigate the improved and updated devices.

Checking the electrical characteristics of the 741 operational amplifier (Appendix A) reveals that it has an input resistance of 2 MΩ, an output resistance of 75 Ω, and an open-loop gain of 200,000. It is definitely *not* an ideal amplifier. Let's see what it has inside that keeps it from being ideal.

Amplifier Analysis

We are not going to make a detailed analysis of the **equivalent circuit** of an operational amplifier. That is really no longer necessary because we cannot do anything about changing parts in the circuit. A quarter-inch square chip is just too small to work on. It will help, however, if we can visualize what is going on inside the chip. A functional block diagram of a typical operational amplifier is shown in Figure 1–8 for this

_20014646_

Figure 1–8
Operational Amplifier

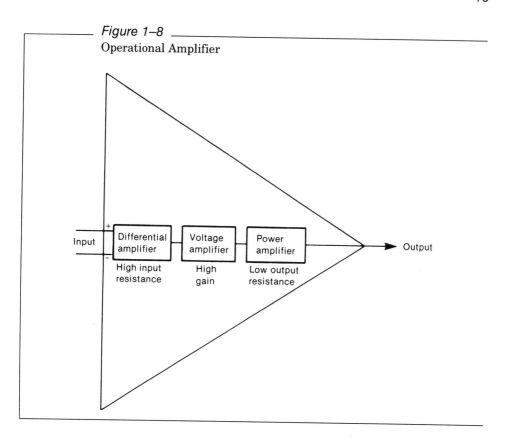

purpose. Some operational amplifiers are less complex; some, more complex. But the functions shown in Figure 1–8 are generally included.

The first stage in almost all operational amplifiers is a differential amplifier. A **differential amplifier** has two inputs and an output that results from the amplified *difference* between the two inputs. (Some differential amplifiers have two outputs, but most of those employed in op amps use only one.) The output will be in phase with the noninverting (+) input and opposite in phase to the inverting (−) input. Careful design establishes an input resistance greater than 1 MΩ with bipolar transistor input stages. Field effect transistor input stages can have input resistances on the order of a million megohms. The differential input stage, then, is the primary factor in determining input resistance.

Although the differential amplifier may have some gain, another **voltage amplifier** stage is often added to provide the "super" gain of most operational amplifiers. The second gain stage uses conventional solid-stage technology to boost the overall operational amplifier gain to its high value. Impedance matching between the differential amplifier and the output stage is also accomplished in the second gain stage.

The output stage of an operational amplifier is almost invariably a **power amplifier**. Its primary function is to supply power to the load at a low impedance. Conventional integrated circuit power-amplifier techniques are used.

Now, when we look at the operational amplifier, we can get a better idea of what is happening. Signals applied to the input are amplified in the differential amplifier, and the output to the second gain stage is the amplified difference between the two inputs. Further amplification and impedance matching occurs in the second gain stage. The output stage supplies the power at the low impedance required for practical operation of the op amp. The output is in phase with the noninverting (+) input and out of phase with the inverting (−) input.

Despite all the advantages gained with the use of operational amplifiers, one disadvantage must be discussed. As with *any* amplifier circuit, high gain or amplification can result in unstable operation if certain precautions are not taken. With operational amplifiers in particular, the routing of connecting wires must be done carefully. If the output of an operational amplifier is somehow (such as by wire routing) allowed to affect the amplifier's input, unstable operation may occur. Furthermore, the long lengths of connecting wire used to connect power to operational amplifiers can make an otherwise satisfactory power source appear quite unsatisfactory. On every operational amplifier, good design practices place bypass capacitors at each point where power is applied to the device. If care is taken with wire routing and adequate power source bypassing is used, stable operation will in all likelihood be the rule rather than the exception.

─────── *OPERATIONAL AMPLIFIER TYPES* ───────

Today's operational amplifiers are almost entirely integrated circuit devices. They are manufactured using the techniques originally developed (and then improved) for transistor construction. Although quite fascinating, the subject has been well covered in many existing publications. The Bibliography contains many references for the reader interested in learning about IC design and manufacturing techniques.

Our interest in this book leans more toward what kinds of operational amplifiers and linear integrated circuits are available. That is, what types of semiconductor devices are used during manufacture? If we restrict discussion to this topic, it is relatively easy. Later, we can talk about *functionally different* types of op amps. For now, though, we'll focus on the manufacturing classification.

The techniques used to manufacture the early operational amplifiers and linear integrated circuits were derived from transistor manufacturing techniques. Active devices on the ICs were **bipolar junction transistors**, a natural evolution from common transistors. Resistor requirements were often met by biasing transistors so that their collector-emitter resistances replaced discrete resistors. Improved manufacturing techniques resulted in improved bipolar IC operational amplifiers, and many of today's op amps are completely bipolar in construction.

Unipolar (field effect transistor) techniques were used to improve on some of the input characteristics of bipolar op amps. Input impedance, noise, and other problems practically disappeared with FET-input operational amplifiers. Both junction field effect transistors (JFETs) and metal-oxide semiconductor field effect transistors (MOSFETs) are used as op amp input stages.

Bipolar and unipolar techniques are often combined to obtain the best of both worlds. JFET or MOSFET input stages provide high input impedance and low noise, while bipolar junction transistors supply gain and low output impedance. As new requirements appear on the scene, new op amps and linear integrated circuits are designed to fill the need. No attempt is made in this book to discuss all types of op amps. The most common types are used during explanation of op amp and linear integrated circuit operation, and their specific characteristics are covered at that time. New designs are usually adequately covered in technical data available from op amp manufacturers. This valuable source of information should be used to keep abreast of the rapidly changing integrated circuit field.

────────── *SUMMARY* ──────────────────────────

Amplification is merely the control of a large amount of voltage, current, or power by a small amount of voltage, current, or power. Any amplifier—whether it is constructed from vacuum tubes, transistors, or integrated circuits—can be considered as a "gain package" that has input impedance, amplification, and output impedance. The gain characteristic is often frequency-sensitive, which results in decreased gain at various frequencies. Calculations show that an ideal amplifier should have very high input impedance, infinite gain at all frequencies, and very low output impedance. Before the appearance of operational amplifiers, none of these characteristics were easily attainable. Operational amplifiers, however, using feedback, can provide both very high input impedance and very low output impedance. The frequency sensitivity of the gain characteristic is not perfect, but with careful circuit design very high gain over a broad range of frequencies can be obtained.

Operational amplifiers are complete amplifier systems in a single integrated circuit package. Consisting of the equivalent of many transistors and resistors, operational amplifiers may be analyzed as containing an input differential amplifier, an intermediate high-gain amplifier, and an output power amplifier. Both bipolar and field effect transistors are employed to supply desired characteristics.

Considering operational amplifiers as a gain package will allow the study of applications to proceed smoothly. Each of the applications discussed here builds on the gain-package concept.

QUESTIONS

1. Define amplification.

2. List and define the three primary amplifier characteristics common to all types of amplifiers.

3. Explain why integrated circuit amplifiers are replacing discrete-component amplifiers.

4. Discuss the relationship between input signal source resistance and amplifier input resistance.

5. Discuss the relationship between load resistance and amplifier output resistance.

6. Explain the difference(s) between an ideal amplifier and practical amplifiers.

7. List the advantages and disadvantages of negative feedback.

8. Why is closed-loop gain less than open-loop gain?

9. Define operational amplifier.

10. What are the common types of packages that house operational amplifiers?

11. Draw a block diagram showing the major stages of an operational amplifier. Explain the function of each block.

12. Define differential amplifier, and give its primary characteristics.

13. Compare and contrast bipolar and FET operational amplifiers.

PROBLEMS

1. An operational amplifier has an input resistance of 2 MΩ, an output resistance of 100 Ω, and an open-loop gain of 100,000. Find the output voltage with an input of 0.5 mV from a source with an internal resistance of 100,000 Ω. The load resistance is 10,000 Ω.

2. Repeat Problem 1 with a source resistance of 1 MΩ.

3. Repeat Problem 1 with a load resistance of 100 Ω.

4. The amplifier described in Problem 1 is connected in the circuit of Figure 1–5. β is 0.5. Find V_f for the conditions in Problem 1.

5. In Problem 4, find V_f if the source resistance is 1 MΩ.

6. In Problem 4, find V_f if the load resistance is 100 Ω.

2

DC Specifications
and Circuits

OBJECTIVES   After studying Chapter 2, you will be able to

1. Define open-loop gain, in phase, and out of phase.
2. Explain the difference between open-loop gain and difference-mode gain, if any.
3. Discuss why common-mode gain should be zero.
4. List the typical value of open-loop gain, input resistance, and output resistance for a type 741 operational amplifier.
5. Define input offset voltage, and explain how it is counteracted.
6. Explain the reason for input bias current and its effect.
7. Discuss why maximum ratings are important.
8. Show the relationship between saturation voltage and supply voltage.
9. Show where electrical specifications for operational amplifiers can be found.
10. Describe the characteristics of a voltage follower, a noninverting amplifier, and an inverting amplifier.

INTRODUCTION

Although the technician may not need to be able to design electronic systems using operational amplifiers and linear integrated circuits, it is advisable to be knowledgeable of amplifier and linear integrated circuit characteristics. A typical specification sheet for an operational amplifier (Appendix A) contains much more information than most nondesign people need. Some of the specifications are required for everyday use and troubleshooting. Others help explain the operation and applications of operational amplifiers and linear integrated circuits.

In preparation for analysis and troubleshooting of operational amplifier circuits, Chapter 2 discusses basic specifications and circuit configurations. Not all the items in the op amp specification sheet are discussed in this chapter. Only the characteristics that help explain principles of operation will be used. In later chapters, as the more detailed specifications are encountered, additional characteristics are discussed.

GAIN SPECIFICATIONS

One of the most important specifications for any operational amplifier is the number used to describe its amplification, or gain. Unfortunately, practical amplifiers do not have the infinite gain of ideal amplifiers. Three different types of gain are used to describe operational amplifiers: open-loop gain, difference-mode gain, and common-mode gain. This information is summarized in Figure 2–1. Note that the information in Figure 2–1 assumes DC input and output, very high input resistance, and very low output resistance. AC characteristics are discussed shortly.

Open-Loop Gain

Open-loop gain (A_{ol}) is defined simply as the output voltage divided by the input voltage. That is,

$$A_{ol} = \frac{V_o}{V_i} \tag{2–1}$$

When connected as shown in Figure 2–1A, the output will be *in phase* with the input. That is, the output voltage will change in a positive direction when the input voltage changes in a positive direction. Likewise, when the input voltage changes in a negative direction, the output voltage will also change in a negative direction. The − input of an operational amplifier is sometimes grounded, and the signal is applied to the + input to be compatible with common signal sources. Output and input signals remain in phase under these conditions. It is also possible to ground the + input and apply the signal to the − input of the operational amplifier. Output, then, is *out of phase* with the input. That is, the output voltage will change in a negative direction when the input voltage changes in a positive direction, and vice versa.

Open-loop gain is very high (typically 200,000 in the case of the type 741 shown in Appendix A) in operational amplifiers. It is common to see open-loop gain specifications much greater than 1,000,000 as

Figure 2–1
Amplifier Gain

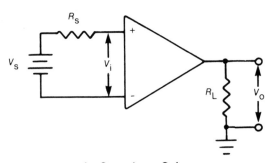

A. Open–Loop Gain

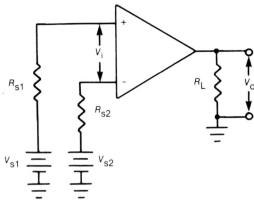

B. Difference–Mode Gain

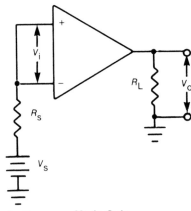

C. Common–Mode Gain

technology advances. The open-loop configuration is seldom used in operational amplifiers because of stability problems. An example will show one of the many problems that can occur. When operated with supply voltages of $+15$ V and -15 V, the output voltage can typically vary between $+13$ V and -13 V without radically distorting the shape of the input signal. With a typical gain of 200,000, therefore, an input signal no larger than about 65 μV can be tolerated, as shown in the calculations of Example 2–1.

_____ *Example 2–1* _____

What is the maximum input voltage to an op amp with a gain of 200,000 if the output cannot exceed 13 V?

Solution

$$V_i = \frac{V_o}{A_{ol}} = \frac{13}{200,000} = 65 \ \mu V$$

Unwanted random signal variations (called *noise*) often exceed 65 μV in electronic systems. Thus, the operational amplifier would be *saturated* with the input noise and not be able to respond to input signals. A solution to the problem of open-loop gain will be seen shortly.

Difference-Mode Gain

Another input method is shown in Figure 2–1B. Two separate input sources are connected. One supplies the $+$ input, while the other is connected to the $-$ input. Gain is still output voltage divided by input voltage, but here input voltage is the *difference* between the two inputs. This gain is called **difference-mode gain** (A_{dm}) and is the same as open-loop gain:

$$A_{dm} = \frac{V_o}{V_i}$$

where $V_i = V_{s1} - V_{s2}$. Thus,

$$A_{dm} = \frac{V_o}{V_{s1} - V_{s2}} \tag{2–2}$$

Common-Mode Gain

If both $+$ and $-$ inputs are connected to the *same* input source, the common-mode configuration results, as shown in Figure 2–1C. Output voltage divided by input voltage still yields gain, but in this case the **common-mode gain** (A_{cm}) will (theoretically) be zero. That is,

$$A_{cm} = \frac{V_o}{V_i} = 0$$

where $V_i = V_1 - V_2 = 0$, since *both inputs have the same voltage applied.* However, because of imperfect balance in the input stages of the operational amplifier, V_i will not be zero, and there will always be some output. It will be very small, but it will be present.

The common-mode performance of an operational amplifier is sometimes expressed as the **common-mode rejection ratio (CMRR)**, which is the ratio of open-loop gain (A_{ol}) to common-mode gain (A_{cm}):

$$\text{CMRR} = \frac{A_{ol}}{A_{cm}} \qquad (2\text{–}3)$$

The CMRR is *ideally infinite,* since A_{cm} is ideally zero. In practice, A_{cm} has a finite though small value, and the CMRR thus has a noninfinite but very large value. A CMRR on the order of 10,000 to 40,000 is not unusual. CMRR is often expressed in decibels (dB), as shown in the calculations of Example 2–2. See Appendix B for dB formulas.

Example 2–2

Calculate the CMRR in dB for CMRRs of 10,000 and 40,000.

Solution

$$\text{CMRR} = 20 \log \frac{A_{ol}}{A_{cm}} = 20 \log 10,000 = (20)\,(4) = 80 \text{ dB}$$

$$\text{CMRR} = 20 \log \frac{A_{ol}}{A_{cm}} = 20 \log 40,000 = (20)\,(4.6) = 92 \text{ dB}$$

Advanced operational amplifiers have CMRRs much greater than 100 dB.

It should be noted that the characteristics just discussed are typical parameters. Each of the gain values, the output voltage variations, and so on are all subject to wide differences due to manufacturing tolerances. Furthermore, gain, for example, depends on supply voltage, output load resistance, temperature, and so forth. Graphs representing these many variations are shown in the typical specification sheets of Appendix A.

INPUT AND OUTPUT RESISTANCE CHARACTERISTICS

The input and output resistance (impedance) characteristics of operational amplifiers are almost as important as the gain characteristics. Most specification sheets provide the typical input resistance (R_i) and the output resistance (R_o). These are the numbers used by the circuit designers during the initial design stage of new circuits. These values are DC parameters, and it should be recognized that AC applications must also include any reactive components such as input capacitance. However, the reactive components are not important during our initial discussion of operational amplifiers. When high-frequency AC applications are shown, more information will be presented concerning the effects of input and output capacitance. Meanwhile, let's just consider the operational amplifier as shown in Figure 1–4, with only resistive input and output characteristics.

Practical amplifiers do not have the infinite input resistance and zero output resistance of the ideal amplifier. The specification sheet for the type 741 operational amplifier (Appendix A) lists a typical input resistance (R_i) of 2 MΩ. For all practical purposes, the input resistance specification is the resistance that would be measured between the two input terminals of the operational amplifier. Bipolar IC operational amplifiers have input resistances ranging from a few hundred thousand ohms to many megohms. FET-input operational amplifiers boast input resistance values into the thousands of megohms. Because of the wide variation in input resistance between various types of operational amplifiers, specification sheets should be consulted when it becomes necessary to replace an operational amplifier with a different type. As is apparent, selection of an op amp with low input resistance to replace an op amp that has a high input resistance could adversely affect equipment operation.

Nonzero output resistance (R_o) is a characteristic of practical operational amplifiers. Most practical operational amplifiers have output resistances near or below 100 Ω. The type 741 operational amplifier specification shows a typical output resistance of 75 Ω. As with the input resistance specification, replacement operational amplifiers should have similar output resistance ratings.

Input and output characteristics are also closely related to temperature and supply voltage variations. See the typical specification sheets in Appendix A for graphs showing input and output parameter variations.

ERROR SOURCES

As we investigate the operational amplifier in greater detail, we find more and more that it is an imperfect device. It does not have infinite gain, nor does it have infinite input or zero output resistance. A number of other imperfections also lead to results other than those expected in theory.

Input Offset Voltage

For example, we would expect that zero input would result in zero output. However, because of inherent unbalance in the differential amplifier stage of the operational amplifier, zero output does not always result from zero input. The inputs of the operational amplifier may be shorted (zero volts), yet there may still be a few millivolts appearing at the output. The voltage that must be applied to the input terminals to cause zero output voltage is called the **input offset voltage** (V_{io}). Bipolar-input operational amplifiers generally have lower input offset voltage characteristics than FET-input devices do. It is easier during manufacture to match the active devices in the differential amplifiers of bipolar circuits. General-purpose bipolar operational amplifiers have input offset voltage characteristics of from a few millivolts to as little as 25 μV (microvolts) or less. Comparative FET operational amplifiers are generally rated in tens of millivolts. Special care in manufacture will provide input offset voltage ratings in the vicinity of 1 mV for FET operational amplifiers. There are, of course, exceptions to any rule. Designers have been able to develop, at greater cost, FET operational amplifiers that challenge the input offset voltage superiority of bipolar-input operational amplifiers. Generally, however, bipolar-input operational amplifiers are superior to FET operational amplifiers in low input offset voltage.

Input offset voltage errors may be balanced out in most operational amplifiers. Terminals are provided for connection of a potentiometer to _null_ the effect of the unbalanced differential amplifier stage. It is merely necessary to short the input terminals (zero volts) and adjust the output voltage to zero. Unfortunately, the input offset voltage is sensitive to temperature changes and to aging. Occasional readjustment of the balancing potentiometer may be necessary if zero output with zero input is critical to the circuit.

Input Bias and Offset Currents

Input bias current must also be examined. Each of the inputs to the operational amplifier requires a small but finite current to operate the input stage. In bipolar operational amplifiers, this current is in the nanoampere range because of very high input resistance. FET-input operational amplifiers have even smaller input bias currents. The published specifications, unfortunately, are average values, and there will almost always be a difference between the input bias currents of an operational amplifier. This difference is called the **input offset current** and must be compensated with external components. Techniques for accomplishing these compensations are shown later.

OTHER SPECIFICATIONS

All operational amplifiers are designed to operate at certain *maximum ratings*. These ratings are the conditions that the operational amplifier can tolerate without the possibility of destruction. A manufacturer's specification sheets usually define such maximum ratings as supply voltage, operating temperature, power dissipation, input voltage, and so on. The designer generally considers these factors during circuit design. However, malfunctions may cause some of the maximum ratings to be exceeded, with resultant failure of the operational amplifier. *The most common difficulty* arises when power supply voltages exceed maximum ratings due to equipment failure or temperature extremes. Technicians should be alert to these possibilities when troubleshooting failed equipment containing operational amplifiers.

The maximum output voltage that the operational amplifier can supply while still responding linearly to input voltage change is called the **saturation voltage**, or **output voltage swing**. Symmetry is usually implied. That is, the output voltage has an equal positive and negative saturation voltage. The meaning and implications of saturation voltage will become clearer as actual circuit applications of operational amplifiers are shown.

Most modern operational amplifiers can tolerate a short circuit at the output terminal. Internal circuitry limits the maximum current to a value that will prevent excessive power dissipation under even these most extreme conditions. The **output short-circuit current** rating defines the maximum output current that the operational amplifier can deliver. When replacing a defective operational amplifier, this rating should be observed, since the designer may have considered the amplifier to be "short-circuit proof."

Another source of potential error is the power supply used by an operational amplifier. If the magnitude of the power supply voltage(s) varies, or if noise is present along with the DC supply voltage(s), an output voltage change occurs. This **supply voltage sensitivity** has an effect similar to an input offset voltage error. Specification sheets provide a rating in microvolts per volt. For example, a typical **supply voltage rejection ratio** for the type 741 operational amplifier is 30 μV/V, which means that if the power supply voltage changes 1 V, it will have the same effect as a 30 μV input offset voltage change. Modern operational amplifiers have supply voltage rejection ratios as low as 1 μV/ V. Thus, power supply sensitivity must also be taken into consideration when replacing operational amplifiers in sensitive equipment.

Most of the electrical specifications and operating characteristics found in Appendix A are determined at a given test temperature and with the noted supply voltages. When operated at any other temperature or supply voltage, the characteristics may be different. Many operational amplifiers are designed to be used with symmetrical + and − supply voltages. The type 741 op amp, for example, typically operates with +15 V and −15 V supplies. Although the supply voltages may be shown on schematic diagrams, they are often not shown. Unless specific precautions are taken, many operational amplifiers will not operate properly with a single supply. (Single-supply operation is discussed in a later chapter.) Remember that, on all schematic diagrams, power is assumed to be provided in accordance with specifications. Be sure you are familiar with those specifications before you begin to analyze or troubleshoot operational amplifier circuits.

Numerous other characteristics will be noted as the specification sheets in Appendix A are used. The characteristics mentioned to this point are those characteristics that are of importance when discussing principles of operation of op amps with DC inputs and outputs. As AC applications are discussed in later chapters, the specific operational amplifier characteristics will be explained.

───── BASIC OPERATIONAL AMPLIFIER CIRCUITS ─

All operational amplifier applications are based on only three circuit configurations, which is not an unusual situation; it has been seen in the application of other active devices such as transistors and vacuum tubes. For example, bipolar transistor circuits may be classified as common-base, common-emitter, or common-collector configurations. All applications of bipolar transistors fit in one way or another into these three classifications.

Voltage Follower

The first of the basic op amp configurations to be discussed is the **voltage follower**, or isolation amplifier. Figure 2–2 shows the basic concepts of the voltage follower. The input to be amplified is applied to the noninverting (+) input. A direct connection is made between the output of the op amp and the inverting (−) input.

A good understanding of the operation of the voltage follower re-

---
Figure 2–2
Voltage Follower

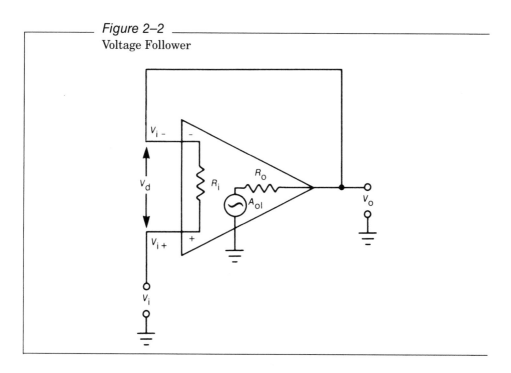

---

quires two very important assumptions. These assumptions are used throughout the remainder of the book, so be sure you understand them. First, as mentioned earlier, only a very small voltage difference between the inverting and noninverting inputs is necessary to obtain operational amplifier action. Just a few millivolts of voltage difference is adequate to cause complete amplifier saturation. For all practical purposes, then, the inverting and noninverting inputs may be considered equal even though there may be a few millivolts difference. The differential voltage (V_d) is thus assumed to be zero. *Assumption 1,* therefore (in terms of Figure 2–2), is as follows:

$$V_{i+} = V_{i-} \quad \text{or} \quad V_d = 0$$

That is, *it is assumed that there is no voltage difference between the inverting and noninverting inputs (V_{i-}, V_{i+}) of an operational amplifier.*

Secondly, *the input currents to both the inverting and noninverting inputs are considered zero.* The input resistance of the op amp is so high that any input current that flows is for all practical purposes nonexistent. *Assumption 2,* then (in terms of Figure 2–2), is as follows:

$$I_{i+} = I_{i-} = 0$$

If the voltage differential between the inverting and the noninverting inputs is zero, then both inputs must have the same input voltage. Since the inverting input is connected directly to the op amp output, the output voltage is the same as the input voltage. Therefore, the closed-loop voltage gain (A_{cl}) of the voltage follower is unity. This closed-loop gain can be mathematically calculated as follows (use Figure 2–2 for reference):

$$V_o = (A_{ol})(V_d)$$

so

$$V_d = \frac{V_o}{A_{ol}}$$

$$V_i = V_d + V_o = \frac{V_o}{A_{ol}} + V_o = \left(\frac{1}{A_{ol}} + 1\right)V_o$$

Then, because A_{ol} is very large and $1/A_{ol}$ can, therefore, be disregarded,

$$V_i = V_o$$

$$A_{cl} = \frac{V_o}{V_i} = \frac{V_i}{V_i} = 1 \tag{2-4}$$

With a voltage gain of 1, the voltage follower may not seem to be a very worthwhile configuration. But let's see what else happens when we feed the output directly back to the input of an op amp.

We can use assumptions 1 and 2 to determine the effect of negative feedback on input resistance. If the voltage differential between the op amp inputs is very small and the current flow into the inputs is almost nonexistent, it is reasonable to suppose that there is high resistance. In fact, since the fed-back output voltage maintains the input voltage differential very near to zero, the input resistance will be very high. The input resistance of a voltage follower is mathematically determined as follows (see Figure 2–2 for reference):

$$I_i = \frac{V_i}{R_i'}$$

where R_i' is the voltage follower input resistance, and

$$I_i = \frac{V_d}{R_i}$$

where R_i is the op amp input resistance. Solving for R_i',

$$R_i' = (V_i)\frac{R_i}{V_d}$$

But

$$V_d = \frac{V_o}{A_{ol}}$$

Therefore,

$$R_i' = \frac{V_i}{V_o}(A_{ol})(R_i)$$

But in a voltage follower,

$$\frac{V_i}{V_o} = 1$$

Therefore,

$$R_i' = A_{ol} \times R_i \qquad\qquad (2\text{--}5)$$

Equation 2–5 may be used to calculate the input resistance of a voltage follower, as shown in Example 2–3.

_____ *Example 2–3* _____

The input resistance of a type 741 op amp is 2 MΩ, and its open-loop gain is 200,000. Calculate its input resistance when connected in the voltage follower configuration.

Solution

$$R_i' = A_{ol} \times R_i = 200{,}000 \times 2 \text{ M}\Omega = 400{,}000 \text{ M}\Omega$$

The extremely high input resistance of a voltage follower makes it very useful when minimum loading of other circuits is a requirement.

Coupled with a very high input resistance is a very low output resistance. The voltage follower's output resistance (R_i') is reduced by the open-loop gain factor:

$$R_i' = \frac{R_o}{A_{ol}} \qquad\qquad (2\text{–}6)$$

Thus, the 75 Ω output resistance of the type 741 op amp is reduced by a factor of 200,000. For all practical purposes, then, the output resistance of a voltage follower is zero. Thus, the voltage follower may be used to isolate a low-resistance load from a high-resistance source. Applications of the voltage followers are shown in Chapter 3.

The negative feedback, furthermore, stabilizes the otherwise unstable op amp. When the op amp is used in an open-loop configuration, small changes in supply voltage, temperature, and so on result in large output changes. Unfortunately, such changes are not related to the input to be amplified. But, by returning the op amp output to its input (out of phase), the voltage follower becomes an amplifier with a stable unity gain, high input resistance, and low output resistance.

Noninverting Amplifier

When more than unity gain is required, a **noninverting amplifier**, as shown in Figure 2–3, may be used. The noninverting amplifier is very

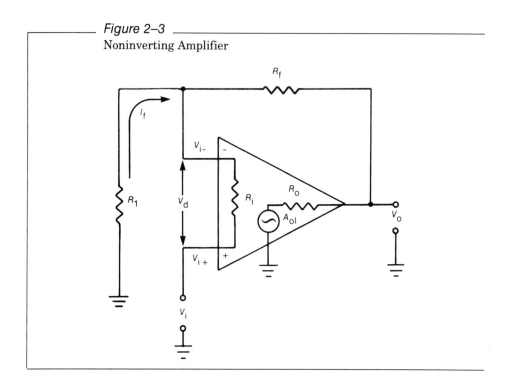

Figure 2–3
Noninverting Amplifier

much like the voltage follower. Instead of all the output being fed back to the input out of phase, only a part of the output is used. The input to be amplified is applied to the noninverting (+) input, while the feedback is applied to the inverting (−) input. Resistors R_f and R_1 act as a voltage divider that determines how much output is to be fed back. The percentage of output fed back is called **β (beta)**. β was discussed in Chapter 1 (see Figure 1–5).

Assumptions concerning equal-voltage inputs and zero-current inputs are used as they were in discussion of the voltage follower. For example, the differential input voltage must still be zero. In the noninverting amplifier, however, the voltage divider values make it necessary for the output voltage to rise well above the input voltage. The mathematical derivation of the simplified closed-loop gain formula is as follows (use Figure 2–3 for reference):

$$I_f = \frac{V_i}{R_1}$$

because $V_{i-} = V_{i+} = V_i$. Since 0 current flows in the op amp inputs (assumption 2), all of I_f flows through R_f. The potential causing I_f is V_o, so

$$V_o = (I_f)(R_1 + R_f)$$

Therefore,

$$V_o = \frac{V_i}{R_1}(R_1 + R_f) = V_i\left(1 + \frac{R_f}{R_1}\right)$$

$$\frac{V_o}{V_i} = 1 + \frac{R_f}{R_1}$$

or, since $A_{cl} = V_o/V_i$,

$$A_{cl} = 1 + \frac{R_f}{R_1}$$

But

$$\beta = \frac{R_1}{R_1 + R_f}$$

and

$$\frac{1}{\beta} = \frac{R_1 + R_f}{R_1} = 1 + \frac{R_f}{R_1}$$

Therefore,

$$A_{cl} = \frac{1}{\beta} \qquad\qquad (2\text{--}7)$$

Note that no mention is made of the open-loop gain of the op amp. When the open-loop gain is much greater than the closed-loop gain, only the voltage divider resistors are instrumental in determining gain. Closed-loop gain can vary from as little as 1 to more than 1000 using reasonably priced op amps.

Occasionally the term **loop gain** appears. Loop gain (A_l) is the *reduction* of open-loop gain by the closed-loop gain. It is the ratio of open-loop gain to closed-loop gain and is used in many op amp calculations:

$$A_l = \frac{A_{ol}}{A_{cl}} = A_{ol} \times \beta \qquad\qquad (2\text{--}8)$$

In fact, the input resistance (R_i') of the noninverting amplifier is obtained by multiplying the input resistance of the op amp without feedback by the loop gain:

$$R_i' = R_i \times A_l \qquad\qquad (2\text{--}9)$$

The input resistance, therefore, is high but less than that of the voltage follower.

Output resistance (R_i') of the noninverting amplifier is reduced in the same manner as with the voltage follower. It is obtained by dividing the nonfeedback output resistance by the loop gain:

$$R_i' = \frac{R_o}{A_l} \qquad\qquad (2\text{--}10)$$

Once again, this parameter results in higher output resistance than that supplied by the voltage follower but much less than that supplied by the open-loop amplifier configuration.

For most general-purpose op amps, some limitations apply. For example, the voltage divider $R_1 + R_f$ should not be less than 1 kΩ nor more than about 100 kΩ. If less than 1 kΩ, too much current will be

_____ *Table 2–1* _____
Noninverting Amplifier Calculations

R_f	β	A_{cl}	A_1	R_i'	R_o'
1 kΩ	0.5	2	100,000	2×10^{11} Ω	0.00075 Ω
10 kΩ	0.091	11	18,200	3.64×10^{10} Ω	0.004 Ω
47 kΩ	0.021	47.62	4,200	8.4×10^{9} Ω	0.018 Ω
82 kΩ	0.012	83.33	2,400	4.8×10^{9} Ω	0.03 Ω
100 kΩ	0.0099	101	1,980	3.96×10^{9} Ω	0.038 Ω

Assumptions (refer to Figure 2–3):
$R_i = 2$ MΩ $R_o = 75$ Ω $A_{ol} = 200,000$ $R_1 = 1$ kΩ
Typical calculations for $R_f = 10$ kΩ:
$\beta = R_1/(R_1 + R_f) = 1/(1 + 10) = 1/11 = 0.091$ $A_{cl} = 1/\beta = 1/0.091 = 11$
$A_1 = A_{ol}\beta = (200,000)(0.091) = 18,200$
$R_i' = R_i A_1 = (2 \times 10^6)(18,200) = 3.64 \times 10^{10}$ Ω
$R_o' = R_o/A_1 = 75/18,200 = 0.004$ Ω

required from the output of the op amp. If greater than about 100 kΩ, the input resistance of the op amp becomes a factor, and the simplified equations are not completely valid. The upper limit is less of a problem with FET-input and high-resistance-input bipolar operational amplifiers. Closed-loop gain should not exceed about 1000 to maintain stable operation. The minimum gain, of course, is 1 when R_f is zero (output connected directly to inverting input). This special case of the noninverting amplifier becomes the previously discussed voltage follower. Table 2–1 shows typical calculations demonstrating the formulas for noninverting amplifiers and the resulting circuit parameters. Appendix C (program 1) contains a BASIC computer program that calculates noninverting amplifier gain.

Inverting Amplifier

The final op amp configuration to be discussed is the **inverting amplifier**. As shown in Figure 2–4, the input to be amplified is connected to the inverting ($-$) input, while the noninverting ($+$) input is grounded. The output, then, will be 180 degrees out of phase with the input. Note that the feedback from output to input via R_f is applied to the inverting input along with the input to be amplified. Since the feedback is out of phase, it will cancel some of the input. The net result will look like a smaller input signal at the inverting input terminal, with a resultant reduction in amplification. Once again, when the open-loop gain of the op amp is high compared to the closed-loop gain, only the feedback resistances R_f and R_1 are used for gain calculations. Depending on the R_f/R_1 ratio, closed-loop gain may range from less than 1 to a very high

Figure 2–4
Inverting Amplifier

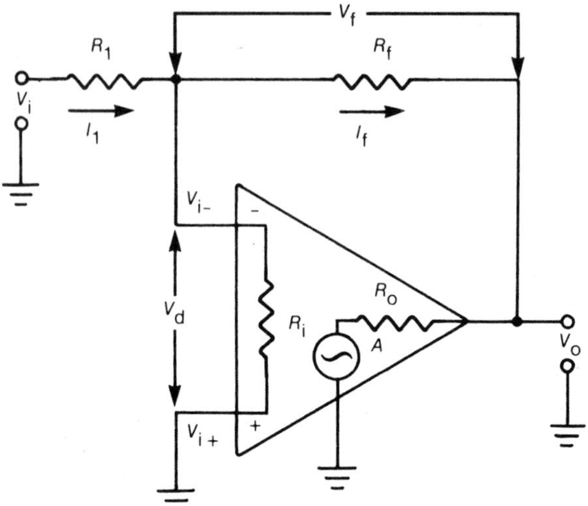

value. The mathematical derivations of inverting amplifier equations
are as follows (use Figure 2–4 for reference).

Since the + input is grounded, by assumption 1, $V_{i+} = V_{i-} = 0$.
The − input also appears to be grounded, so $V_{i-} = 0$. Therefore,

$$V_f = V_o$$

$$I_1 = \frac{V_i}{R_1}$$

$$I_f = \frac{V_o}{R_f}$$

And since, by assumption 2, no current flows in op amp inputs,

$$I_1 = -I_f$$

With V_{i-} at 0 V, $-I_f$ flowing through R_f causes V_o to be negative. Thus,
V_o is out of phase with V_i (inverted):

$$\frac{V_i}{R_1} = \frac{-V_o}{R_f}$$

or

$$V_o = -\left(\frac{R_f}{R_1}\right) \times V_i$$

$$\frac{V_o}{V_i} = -\left(\frac{R_f}{R_1}\right)$$

or

$$A_{cl} = \left(\frac{R_f}{R_1}\right) \qquad \textbf{(2–11A)}$$

But

$$\beta = \frac{R_1}{R_f}$$

Therefore,

$$A_{cl} = -\left(\frac{1}{\beta}\right) \qquad \textbf{(2–11B)}$$

$$A_1 = \frac{A_{ol}}{A_{cl}} = A_{ol} \times \beta \qquad \textbf{(2–11C)}$$

The input resistance (R_i') of the inverting amplifier is approximately equal to the value of R_1. This statement can be justified by assuming, as we have done before, that the voltage differential between the inverting ($-$) and noninverting ($+$) input is zero. If the $+$ input is grounded (zero volts), then the $-$ input will also be at zero volts or will appear to be grounded. (This is sometimes called a **virtual ground**.) Therefore, as far as the input signal is concerned, R_1 is the input resistance of the circuit. Care must be taken in the use of the inverting amplifier to ensure that its low input resistance does not upset other circuits to which it is connected.

As with the noninverting amplifier configuration, the output resistance of the inverting amplifier is reduced by the loop gain:

$$R_i' = \frac{R_o}{A_1} \qquad \textbf{(2–12)}$$

The sample calculations in Table 2–2 demonstrate the techniques used to explain the operation of an inverting amplifier and show some typical

Table 2–2

Inverting Amplifier Calculations

R_f	β	A_{cl}	A_1	R'_i	R'_o
1 kΩ	1	1	200,000	1 kΩ	0.000375 Ω
10 kΩ	0.1	10	20,000	1 kΩ	0.00375 Ω
47 kΩ	0.021	47	4,200	1 kΩ	0.018 Ω
82 kΩ	0.012	82	2,400	1 kΩ	0.03 Ω
100 kΩ	0.01	100	2,000	1 kΩ	0.0375 Ω

Assumptions (refer to Figure 2–4):
$A_{ol} = 200,000$　　　$R_1 = 1\text{ k}\Omega$　　　$R_i = 2\text{ M}\Omega$　　　$R_o = 75\ \Omega$
Typical calculations for $R_f = 10\text{ k}\Omega$:
$\beta = R_1/R_f = 1/10 = 0.1$　　　$A_{cl} = -1/\beta = -1/0.1 = 10$
$A_1 = A_{ol}\beta = (200{,}000)(0.1) = 20{,}000$　　　$R'_i = R_1 = 1\text{ k}\Omega$
$R'_o = R_o/A_1 = 75/20{,}000 = 0.00375\ \Omega$

parameter values. Appendix C (program 2) contains a BASIC computer program that calculates inverting amplifier gain.

SUMMARY

Gain, or amplification, is one of the most important specifications for any operational amplifier. Open-loop gain describes the ratio of output voltage to input voltage. Difference-mode gain is also the ratio of output voltage to input voltage, but the input voltage is the difference between the two inputs of an operational amplifier. Common-mode gain is, once again, output voltage divided by input voltage, but both operational amplifier inputs are connected together. Common-mode gain should be zero. The common-mode performance of an op amp is often expressed as the common-mode rejection ratio (CMRR). It should be noted that the output voltage of any op amp circuit cannot exceed the supply voltage. When the output voltage approaches the supply voltage, saturation occurs.

Operational amplifiers typically have input resistances on the order of many megohms and output resistances below 100 ohms. Further nonperfect amplifier characteristics are found in operational amplifiers. For example, zero input does not result in zero output. An input offset voltage exists because of inherent unbalance in the differential amplifier stage, which causes a small output even with the input terminals short-circuited. Input bias and offset currents flow and, even though they may be in the range of only nanoamperes, cause output errors.

Three basic configurations for operational amplifier circuits are used. The voltage follower circuit has unity gain, almost infinite input resistance, and almost zero output resistance. A noninverting amplifier circuit has gain that is a function of a feedback network, high but not almost-infinite input resistance, and almost-zero output resistance. The inverting amplifier configuration also uses feedback to control gain, a relatively low input resistance, and very low output resistance.

Op amp calculations often take advantage of two assumptions to simplify the mathematics involved. First, both op amp inputs are assumed to be equal, so that the differential input voltage is zero. Second, equal currents are assumed to be flowing in both input circuits. Realistic circuit characteristics are obtained with these assumptions without excessive mathematical manipulations.

QUESTIONS

1. Define open-loop gain.

2. What determines the phase relationship between the output and input of an operational amplifier?

3. List the following typical specifications for a type 741 op amp: (a) open-loop gain, (b) input resistance, and (c) output resistance.

4. Under what circumstances would you use difference-mode gain rather than open-loop gain?

5. What is the typical CMRR of a type 741 op amp? Where would you find this information for a different type of op amp?

6. What factors can affect gain, input resistance, output resistance, and so forth?

7. When would you use input impedance in place of input resistance?

8. Is there any advantage to using a FET op amp in place of a bipolar op amp? Explain.

9. What factors can cause a nonzero output from an op amp when the input is zero?

10. Compare typical input offset voltages for bipolar and FET op amps.

11. How is input offset voltage counteracted in op amp circuits?

12. What is input offset current, and how does it affect op amp circuits?

13. Why must op amp maximum ratings not be exceeded?

14. Define the following terms: (a) saturation voltage, (b) output voltage swing, (c) output short-circuit current, and (d) supply voltage sensitivity.

15. Why can the voltage difference between the inverting and noninverting inputs of an op amp be considered to be zero?

16. Why can it be assumed that zero input current flows in an op amp?

17. Draw a schematic diagram of an op amp connected in the voltage follower configuration.

18. Explain why the closed-loop gain of a voltage follower is unity.

19. Explain the high input resistance and low output resistance of the voltage follower.

20. Draw a schematic diagram of an op amp connected in the noninverting amplifier configuration.

21. Why doesn't the open-loop gain of an op amp have any appreciable effect on the closed-loop gain of a noninverting amplifier?

22. Define loop gain, and explain its significance.

23. Discuss the input and output resistance of a noninverting amplifier.

24. Draw a schematic diagram of an op amp connected in the inverting amplifier configuration.

25. What determines the closed-loop gain of an inverting amplifier? Explain.

26. Why is the input resistance of an inverting amplifier low compared to either the voltage follower or the noninverting amplifier?

27. Are there any other *practical* configurations in which to connect operational amplifiers? If so, draw a schematic diagram and explain.

═══ PROBLEMS ═══

1. Assume an operational amplifier with open-loop gain of 100,000, input resistance of 4 MΩ, and output resistance of 100 Ω. Calculate the closed-loop gain, input resistance, and output resistance for the op amp connected in the voltage follower configuration.

2. If R_f = 100,000 Ω and R_1 = 10,000 Ω, calculate the closed-loop gain, input resistance, and output resistance for an op amp with open-loop gain of 100,000 connected in the noninverting amplifier configuration.

3. Repeat Problem 2 for the inverting amplifier configuration.

4. Repeat Problem 2 for the noninverting amplifier configuration if R_f = 47,000 Ω and R_1 = 27,000 Ω.

5. Calculate the closed-loop gain, input resistance, and output resistance for an inverting amplifier configuration using the conditions in Problem 4.

6. Assume an op amp with an open-loop gain of 125 dB, input resistance of 6 MΩ, and output resistance of 70 Ω. Calculate the closed-loop gain, input resistance, and output resistance for the op amp connected in the voltage follower configuration.

7. If $R_f = 47{,}000\ \Omega$ and $R_1 = 27{,}000\ \Omega$, calculate the closed-loop gain, input resistance, and output resistance for an op amp with an open-loop gain of 125 dB connected in the noninverting amplifier configuration.

8. Repeat Problem 7 for the inverting amplifier configuration.

3

DC Applications

OBJECTIVES   After studying Chapter 3, you will be able to

1. Define transducer, thermistor, and thermocouple.
2. Describe how thermistors and thermocouples operate.
3. Show how a bipolar transistor base-emitter junction voltage change with temperature can be converted to either degrees Fahrenheit or degrees Celsius.
4. Describe how to improve the current and voltage sensitivity of a moving-coil meter movement.
5. Calculate regulation percentage.
6. Explain the concept of how a series pass transistor can regulate voltage.
7. Explain the characteristics of a voltage regulator using operational amplifiers and pass transistors.
8. Show how to increase the current handling characteristics of voltage regulators.
9. Explain the concept of shunt regulators.
10. Explain the concept of switching regulators.
11. Show what can be done with integrated circuit voltage regulators.

INTRODUCTION

Now that we have covered the basic concepts concerning DC circuits and specifications, we can examine some op amp applications. Since operational amplifiers are *direct-coupled,* they may be used where amplification of DC voltages and currents is required. This chapter investigates the use of op amps in temperature-measurement devices, electrical/electronic measuring instruments, and devices that regulate voltage or current.

TEMPERATURE MEASUREMENT

A simple yet useful application of op amps as DC amplifiers can be found in electronic thermometers. The first thing we need to know is how changes in temperature can be converted into an electrical quantity that can be amplified by an op amp. Early electric thermometers used either thermistors or thermocouples as *temperature transducers*. A **transducer** is a device that converts one form of energy into another.

Thermistors

A **thermistor** is a temperature-sensitive resistor whose primary function is to change resistance with changing temperature. Generally, thermistors have a negative coefficient, meaning that resistance decreases as temperature increases, as shown in Figure 3–1A. (There are some thermistors with a positive temperature coefficient, but they are not as popular.) Figure 3–1B shows a thermistor (T) connected in a simple series voltage divider circuit. Because the resistance change of the thermistor is nonlinear, the current change (and the associated voltage drop across R) is nonlinear. Analog or digital meters used to measure the voltage drop across R must, therefore, be calibrated specifically for the thermistor and circuit in use. Furthermore, as temperature increases and resistance decreases, current increases in the circuit. As with any resistor, increasing current causes increasing power dissipation. The thermistor, therefore, must dissipate more heat. Self-heating of the thermistor generates further nonlinearities. Combinations of series, parallel, and series-parallel resistive networks can be used to "linearize" thermistor resistance changes. Self-heating can also be prevented by operating thermistors at relatively low current levels.

Thermocouples

Thermocouples consist of two dissimilar metals joined at one end. A voltage is developed when there is a temperature difference between the joined end and the unjoined ends of the two wires. All dissimilar metals exhibit this *thermoelectric effect*, although relatively few are used. When such matters as melting point of the metals, corrosive atmospheres in which measurements are made, voltage output, linearity, and the like are considered, the choice is narrowed. The characteristics curve for a common iron-constantan thermocouple is shown in Figure 3–2. Thermocouples are used over a wide temperature range. Their linearity is comparable to or better than thermistors, but the voltage available for

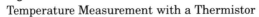

Figure 3–1
Temperature Measurement with a Thermistor

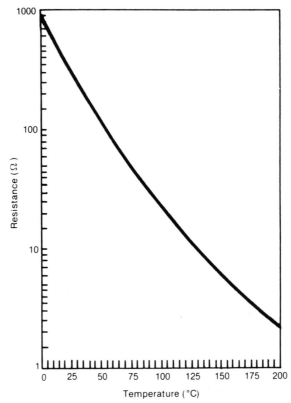

A. Thermistor Characteristic

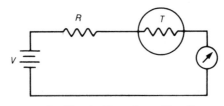

B. Simple Thermistor Circuit

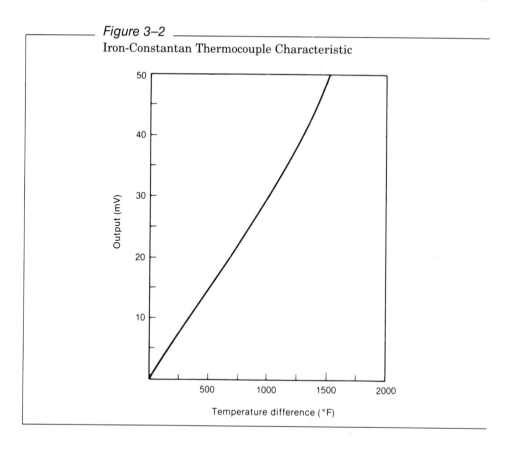

Figure 3–2

Iron-Constantan Thermocouple Characteristic

indication is quite low. Note that for temperatures below 500°F, the output of the thermocouple is less than 15 mV. Either very sensitive indicators or some form of amplification must be provided to make thermocouple temperature measurement practical.

Solid-State Temperature Transducers

Now let's see what solid-state technology can do for us. Note that one of the problems that had to be solved with early transistors was that of temperature sensitivity. The forward-biased base-emitter junction responded very predictably to changes in temperature. Such changes caused unwanted collector current changes. Designers solved the problem by using degenerative (negative) feedback, but we are going to take advantage of that temperature sensitivity.

By shorting the collector and base, the transistor base-emitter behaves like a **diode** with the characteristics shown in Figure 3–3A.

Figure 3–3
Semiconductor Temperature Sensor

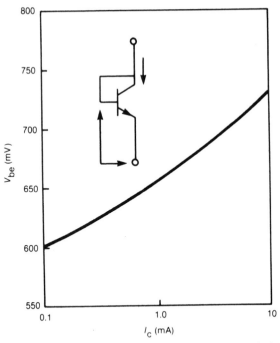

A. Diode–Connected Transistor Characteristic

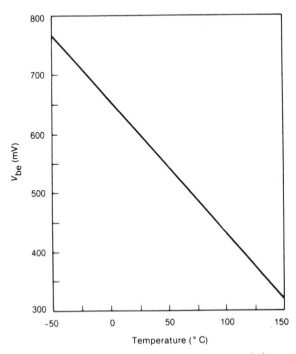

B. V_{be} versus Temperature Characteristic

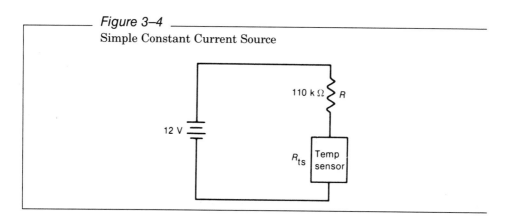

Figure 3–4

Simple Constant Current Source

Note that the base-emitter voltage increases as the collector current (I_c) increases. Furthermore, if temperature increases, the base-emitter voltage decreases. By maintaining constant current, we can use the variation in base-emitter voltage as an indication of temperature. Figure 3–3B shows the variation of base-emitter voltage over a wide temperature range. (Constant current is assumed.) The base-emitter voltage (V_{be}) may be calculated accurately by means of the following formula:

$$V_{be} = (V_{be} \text{ at } 25°C) + (TC) \times (T - 25°C) \qquad (3–1)$$

where

T = temperature of interest

TC = temperature coefficient = $-2.25 + (0.0033) \times (V_{be} - 600)$

Maximum linearity and accuracy of a temperature-measuring device using a semiconductor junction requires that a constant current be maintained through the junction as temperature varies. The scheme shown in Figure 3–4 approximates a **constant current source**. The following Ohm's law calculations show a current variation of only 4 μA over the entire relevant temperature range.

For a typical sensor at 25°C and I = 100 μA,

$$V_{be} = 600 \text{ mV}$$

$$\Delta V_{be} = -2.25 \text{ mV/°C}$$

Then, at $-40°C$,

$$V_{be} = 746.25 \text{ mV}$$

$$V_R = V - V_{be} = 12 - 0.74625 = 11.25375 \text{ V}$$

and by Ohm's law,

$$I_{40} = \frac{V_R}{R} = \frac{11.25375}{110,000} = 102 \ \mu A$$

$$R_{ts} = \frac{V_{ts}}{I} = \frac{746.25 \times 10^{-3}}{102 \times 10^{-6}} = 7316 \ \Omega$$

And, at $+150°C$,

$$V_{be} = 318.75 \ mV$$

$$V_R = V - V_{be} = 12 - 0.31875 = 11.68125 \ V$$

and by Ohm's law,

$$I_{150} = \frac{V_R}{R} = \frac{11.68125}{110,000} = 106 \ \mu A$$

$$R_{ts} = \frac{V_{ts}}{I} = \frac{318.75 \times 10^{-3}}{106 \times 10^{-6}} = 3007 \ \Omega$$

So

$$I_{150} - I_{40} = 106 - 102$$

$$\Delta I = 4 \ \mu A$$

where

ΔV_{be} = change in voltage across the base-emitter junction
V_R = voltage drop across series resistor
R_{ts} = resistance of temperature sensor
V_{ts} = voltage drop across temperature sensor
$V_{ts} = V_{be}$

Such small current variations have negligible effect on V_{be}. Therefore, the graph of Figure 3–3B may be used with confidence that *only* temperature variations will cause appreciable change in base-emitter voltage. If greater accuracy is required, an actual constant-current source (to be discussed later) may be used.

An Electronic Thermometer

Now what can be used to provide an indication of the temperature variation? More than a 425 mV change occurs from $-40°C$ to $+150°C$. That is about 1/2 V change, which could be measured by a conventional meter

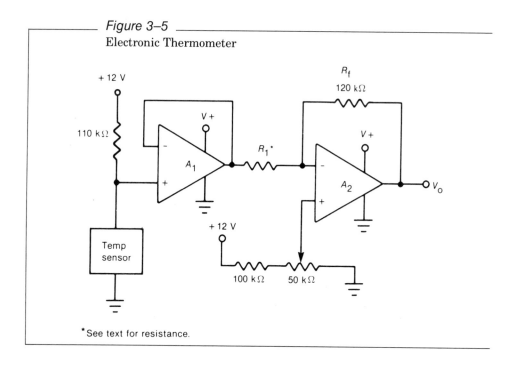

Figure 3–5

Electronic Thermometer

*See text for resistance.

with its scale calibrated for temperature indication. But we must be cautious. The Ohm's law calculations have shown that the base-emitter junction resistance (R_{ts}) is fairly high at the selected current level. (The actual values are from about 3 kΩ to 7.3 kΩ.) Most conventional meters would have relatively low resistance, and the resultant load on the diode would upset the current-voltage relationship. Op amps can be used here.

Figure 3–5 is a diagram of a temperature-measuring device using the base-emitter junction of a transistor as a sensing device. Op amps isolate the sensing device from the indicating instrument and scale the output to conventional values. Note first that the sensing device and its associated power source are the same as just discussed. The voltage across the diode is applied to the noninverting input of A_1. Output of A_1 is fed back to the inverting input. The result is a voltage follower, with its output the same as its input. However, the very high input resistance of the voltage follower does not load the temperature sensor. The very low output resistance of the voltage follower allows connection of almost *any* load without appreciably changing the output voltage. Thus, we could connect almost any measuring instrument to the output of the voltage follower and read the voltage equivalent of the measured temperature.

A_2 and associated components are used to convert the output of A_1 to a voltage that correlates with actual temperature. For example, at

25°C (77°F), voltage follower output is 600 mV. If we select the ratio of R_f to R_1 and adjust the 50 kΩ resistor, the output voltage can be "shifted" to 250 mV, which is more closely correlated with 25°C.

Modern Temperature Transducers

The trend in temperature measurement appears to be one of including both the sensor and the associated op amps on a single IC. Figure 3–6 is representative of temperature transducers in common use. Three separate functions are included on the IC. Power applied to the chip is regulated by an on-chip **voltage regulator** to a stable reference voltage. The regulator on the chip under discussion regulates to approximately 6.8 V. The sensor section of the IC contains not only a sensor but also a built-in op amp. Sensor output is fixed at − 10 mV/°K. The Celsius and Kelvin temperature scales are similar, except that the Kelvin scale uses − 273° as a reference, while the Celsius scale uses 0°. Sensor output, thus, is − 2.73 V at 0°C. The internal op amp has the sensor output applied to its noninverting input. The inverting input is brought out to a connection on the IC so that gain may be controlled. Gains from unity

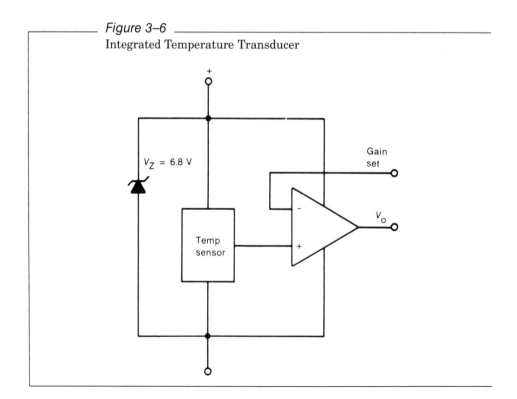

Figure 3–6

Integrated Temperature Transducer

up to about 100 may be established by feedback resistors, or the high open-loop gain may be used.

Thus, an IC that directly senses temperature and provides a linear, buffered output is available. It is no longer necessary to provide separate op amps to obtain this function. With less components, reliability is improved and cost is lowered. It should be noted, however, that the basic principles of op amps have been applied generously in the temperature transducer.

METERS

Op amps allow relatively inexpensive meter movements to be used where high sensitivity and minimum circuit loading are required. In electronics, we often find that measuring instruments upset circuit conditions. Many inexpensive meter movements load the circuits, and it is necessary to use more expensive electronic meters to obtain accurate results. Let's examine a typical situation of voltage measurement.

Increasing Meter Input Resistance

The **sensitivity** of many nonelectronic voltmeters is 20,000 Ω/V. That is, if the voltmeter had a 1 V position on the range switch, it would present a resistance (R_M) of 20,000 Ω to any circuit being measured. Calculations associated with measuring voltages in the simple DC voltage divider of Figure 3–7A are as follows:

$$V_{R_2} = \left(\frac{R_2}{R_1 + R_2}\right)(V) = \left(\frac{1}{9 + 1}\right)(10) = 1 \text{ V}$$

Thus, when the meter is not connected, the calculated voltage drop across R_2 is 1 V. With the meter loading the circuit, as shown in Figure 3–7B, only 0.02 V appears across R_2:

$$R_x = \frac{R_2 R_M}{R_2 + R_M} = \frac{(1 \times 10^6)(20 \times 10^3)}{(1 \times 10^6) + (20 \times 10^3)} = 19,608 \ \Omega$$

$$V_{R_x} = \left(\frac{R_x}{R_1 + R_x}\right)(V) = \left(\frac{19,608}{9,019,608}\right)(10) = 0.02 \text{ V}$$

where R_x = the resistance of R_2 in parallel with R_M.

If a voltage follower is inserted between the circuit and the meter (Figure 3–7C), the discrepancy disappears. As noted in Chapter 2, the input resistance of a voltage follower is on the order of 400,000 MΩ (using a type 741 op amp). The high input resistance of the voltage follower

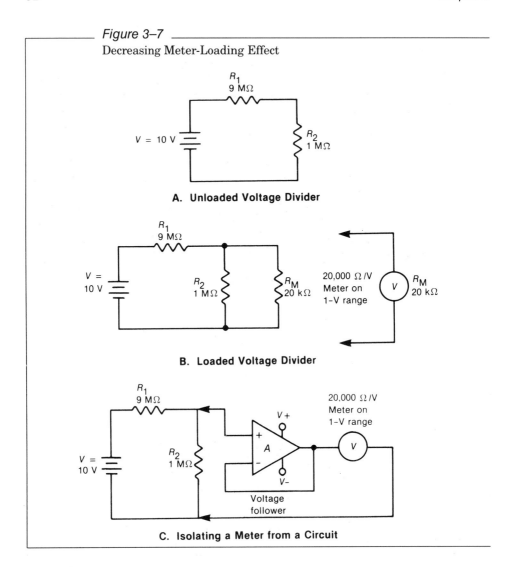

Figure 3–7

Decreasing Meter-Loading Effect

A. Unloaded Voltage Divider

B. Loaded Voltage Divider

C. Isolating a Meter from a Circuit

does not modify the divider-resistance ratio, and the voltage division remains the same. Connecting the meter to the output of the op amp has no loading effect because of the extremely low output impedance of the op amp. The unity gain of the op amp thus makes the input voltage at a high impedance available at the output with a low impedance.

Improving Meter Voltage Sensitivity

It is necessary at times to use a basic meter movement and increase not only its apparent resistance but also its **voltage sensitivity**. For ex-

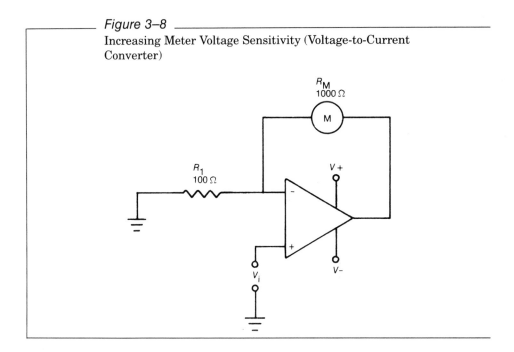

Figure 3–8

Increasing Meter Voltage Sensitivity (Voltage-to-Current Converter)

ample, it may be necessary to convert a 0-1 V full-scale meter to read 0-100 mV full scale in order to measure small voltages in the 0-100 mV range. The common D'Arsonval meter movement is a current-operated device. Resistance is also associated with the moving coil of the meter. For example, a 100 μA movement is usually associated with a resistance of 1000 Ω. With the full-scale deflection current of 100 μA flowing through the moving coil, a 0.1 V drop will occur. Thus, the *voltage sensitivity* of the movement is 0.1 V. A noninverting op amp can be used to increase the voltage sensitivity.

The clue to this apparent magic is found in the derivation of the closed-loop gain formula (Equation 2–7). Referring to Figure 3–8, $I_f = V_i/R_1$. The equation shows that the current flowing in the feedback resistance is *independent* of the feedback resistance. Only the input voltage and R_1 determine I_f. Let's replace R_f with the 1000 Ω resistance of the 100 μA meter and make $R_1 = 100 \Omega$. See Figure 3–8. Solving for V_i,

$$V_i = I_f \times R_1 = 0.1 \text{ mA} \times 0.1 \text{ k}\Omega = 0.01 \text{ V}$$

Thus, it only takes 0.01 V input to cause 100 μA of current to flow through the meter movement. The voltage sensitivity of the movement has been increased by a factor of 10, or the ratio of R_f to R_1. It should be noted that the meter-resistance term does not appear in the preceding calculation. The current through the meter is completely independent of the meter resistance. Therefore, any 100 μA meter movement could be placed in the feedback path without affecting the circuit operation.

The circuit arrangement of Figure 3–8 is known as a **voltage-to-current converter**. We are not interested in the output voltage, only the feedback current. Input resistance of the voltage-to-current converter is not as high as for the voltage follower but is still many hundreds of megohms. The op amp once again has improved the performance of an existing electronic device.

Current-to-Voltage Converters

Current-to-voltage converters also find many applications in op amp circuits. Figure 3–9 will help explain the concepts of the current-to-voltage converter. If the I_i terminals are connected in a circuit in which current is flowing, current will attempt to flow through the op amp input circuits. However, it may be recalled that both the inverting and noninverting input currents are equal and zero. Current must be fed through R_f to balance the input current (I_i). Therefore, the output voltage must assume a value sufficient to cause I_f to flow in R_f. Thus,

$$I_i = \frac{V_o}{R_f} \quad \text{or} \quad V_o = I_i \times R_f$$

Input current has been converted to an output voltage.

If we are to use this circuit to measure current, what effect will it have when inserted in a current-carrying circuit? Current-measuring devices should, ideally, offer zero resistance to the circuit being measured. Is the current-to-voltage converter such a device? Let's apply

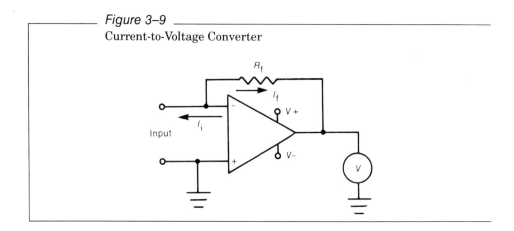

Figure 3–9

Current-to-Voltage Converter

some of the facts we know about op amps and determine the input resistance of the current-to-voltage converter. We have already met the
requirement that input currents be equal and zero. Another important
factor is that the voltage difference between the inverting and noninverting inputs be zero. If the noninverting input is grounded (zero volts),
then the inverting input must be at a virtual ground (zero volts). In
other words, there is no apparent voltage drop across the input of the
current-to-voltage circuit. The apparent resistance is 0 Ω. Actually,
the voltage difference can never quite be zero, and a small resistance on
the order of a fraction of an ohm exists. In practical applications, the
current-to-voltage converter is superior to conventional low current am-
meters. Output voltage and resistance factors can be calculated as
shown in Example 3–1.

_____ *Example 3–1* _____

In Figure 3–9, $R_f = 10 \text{ k}\Omega$, and $I_i = 1 \text{ mA}$. Calculate output voltage V_o
and input resistance R_i.

Solution

Output voltage calculation:

$$V_o = -R_f I_i = -(10 \times 10^3) \times (1 \times 10^{-3}) = 10 \text{ V}$$

Input resistance calculation:

$$R_i = \frac{R_f}{(A_{ol} + 1)}$$

Assuming $A_{ol} = 200{,}000$,

$$R_i = \frac{(10 \times 10^3)}{(200{,}000 + 1)} = 0.05 \ \Omega$$

_____ *VOLTAGE REGULATION* _____

Before the subject of op amp applications to **voltage regulation**
is discussed, perhaps we should review the general concepts of regulation. A typical DC power supply is shown in Figure 3–10. The voltage V
measured at the terminals of the supply is V_s *if* nothing but the measuring instrument is connected (Figure 3–10A). (It is assumed that the
measuring instrument consumes no power from the supply.) When a

Figure 3–10

Effect of Load on Power Supply Output

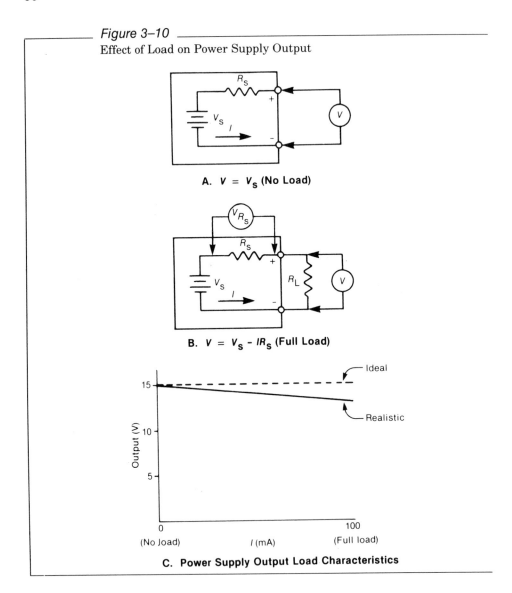

A. $V = V_S$ (No Load)

B. $V = V_S - IR_S$ (Full Load)

C. **Power Supply Output Load Characteristics**

load is connected to the terminals, however, it is a different matter. Current flows in the circuit; and, according to Kirchhoff's law, the sum of the voltage drops across all resistors in the circuit must equal the applied voltage. One of the resistors is the load (R_L), while the other is the internal resistance (R_s) of the power supply. Note that the terminals of the power supply do not allow access directly to the "battery." Any voltage drop that occurs across the internal resistance of the supply must *reduce* the actual voltage available to the load. See Figure 3–10B. Therefore, the no-load voltage (V_{nl}) will be higher than the full-load voltage (V_{fl}). Example 3–2 shows how to calculate the full-load voltage.

Example 3–2

In Figure 3–10B, $V_s = 15$ V, $R_s = 15\ \Omega$, and $R_L = 150\ \Omega$. Calculate the full-load voltage V_{fl}.

Solution

By Kirchhoff's law,

$$V_{fl} = V_s - (I \times R_s) = 15 - (I \times R_s) = 15 - \left(\frac{V_s}{R_L + R_s}\right) \times R_s$$

$$= 15 - \left(\frac{15}{150 + 15}\right) \times 15 = 15 - 1.36 = 13.64 \text{ V}$$

A graph of the variation in output voltage of the power supply with changes in load current is shown in Figure 3–10C. An *ideal* power supply output is also shown for reference. Power supplies are often rated in terms of a *regulation percentage*, which is calculated as follows:

$$\% \text{ regulation} = \left(\frac{V_{nl} - V_{fl}}{V_{fl}}\right) \times 100 \qquad (3\text{–}2)$$

Substituting the information determined in Example 3–2,

$$\% \text{ regulation} = \left(\frac{15 - 13.64}{13.64}\right) \times 100 = 9.97\%$$

Now let's perform similar calculations with the internal resistance of the power supply assumed to be 5 ohms.

Example 3–3

In Figure 3–10B, $V_s = 15$ V, $R_s = 5\ \Omega$, and $R_L = 150\ \Omega$. Calculate the full-load voltage V_{fl} and the regulation percentage.

Solution

By Kirchhoff's law,

$$V_{fl} = V_s - V_{R_s} = V_s - (I \times R_s) = 15 - (0.0968)(5)$$

$$= 15 - 0.485 = 14.52 \text{ V}$$

continued

(Example 3–3 continued)

Substituting the information determined,

$$\% \text{ regulation} = \left(\frac{15 - 14.52}{14.52}\right) \times 100 = 3.3\%$$

From the calculations in Example 3-3, it can be seen that one of the primary factors determining the regulation of a power supply is the internal resistance. Power supplies with good regulation have low internal resistance and small numbers for their regulation percentage, as will be seen shortly.

Manual Control

If the equipment we are using requires that a specific voltage be maintained as different loads are connected, we could vary R_1 to keep the load voltage constant as shown in Figure 3–11.

Figure 3–11
Manual Voltage Control

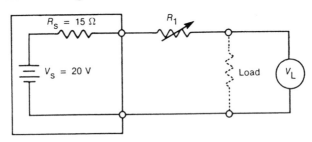

Example 3–4

Our imaginary requirements will be that the voltage applied to the equipment (load) is 15 V even though the equivalent resistance of the load may be as low as 100 Ω or as high as 500 Ω. The power supply is rated at $V_s = 20$ V, and $R_s = 15$ Ω. Calculate the value of the series resistor R_1 when $V_L = 15$ V and $R_L = 500$ Ω.

Solution 1

For $R_L = 500$ Ω and $V_L = 15$ V,

$$I_T = \frac{V_L}{R_L} = \frac{15}{500} = 30 \text{ mA}$$

$$V_{R_s} = I_T R_s = (0.03)(15) = 0.45 \text{ V}$$

$$V_{R_1} = V_s - V_{R_s} - V_{R_L} = 20 - 0.45 - 15 = 4.55 \text{ V}$$

$$R_1 = \frac{V_{R_1}}{I_T} = \frac{4.55}{0.03} = 151.67 \ \Omega$$

The power rating (P_1) of R_1 will be as follows:

$$P_1 = V_{R_1} I_T = (4.55)(0.03) = 0.137 \text{ W}$$

where

$V_L = V_{R_L}$ = voltage appearing across load resistor

I_T = total current in circuit

V_{R_s} = voltage appearing across resistance of source (internal resistance of power supply)

Solution 2

If the value of R_L is changed to 100 Ω, V_L will drop immediately to 7.5 V. For $R_L = 100 \ \Omega$,

$$V_L = (V_s)\left(\frac{R_L}{R_T}\right) = (20)\left(\frac{100}{266.7}\right) = 7.5 \text{ V}$$

where R_T = total circuit resistance—that is, $R_s + R_1 + R_L$.

Solution 3

Calculate the value of R_1 for $R_L = 100 \ \Omega$ and $V_L = 15$ V.

$$I_T = \frac{V_L}{R_L} = \frac{15}{100} = 150 \text{ mA}$$

$$V_{R_s} = I_T R_s = (0.15)(15) = 2.25 \text{ V}$$

$$V_{R_1} = V_s - V_{R_s} - V_{R_L} = 20 - 2.25 - 15 = 2.75 \text{ V}$$

$$R_1 = \frac{V_{R_1}}{I_T} = \frac{2.75}{0.15} = 18.3 \ \Omega$$

The power rating (P_1) of R_1 will be as follows:

$$P_1 = V_{R_1} I_T = (2.75)(0.15) = 0.4 \text{ W}$$

It should be noted that the power rating of R_1 is an important factor. Wattage dissipation of R_1 varied from 0.137 W with a 500 Ω load to 0.4 W with the 100 Ω load. These power requirements are easily met when small current is flowing through a load. When currents above 0.5 A are used with integrated circuits, however, the wattage rating of the adjustable series resistor can become a problem. Furthermore, this method of regulation requires someone to constantly monitor the instrument showing V_L and to adjust the series resistor each time a change occurs. This procedure is impractical not only because it requires constant attention, but because the operator may not be able to correct the changes rapidly enough.

Simple Transistorized Regulator

An automatic method of adjusting the series resistance to compensate for changes in load resistance makes use of the characteristics of transistors. When we studied transistors, we learned that collector current was a function not only of the amplification of the transistor (β) but also of the base current. Increasing base current caused increasing collector current, while decreasing base current decreased the collector current. Base current was increased by increasing the base-emitter voltage. Decreasing the base-emitter voltage decreased base current. Another way of looking at it is that increasing base-emitter voltage increases transistor conduction (decreases its collector-emitter resistance). The opposite is also true—that is, decreasing base-emitter voltage increases collector-emitter resistance. Without worrying about actual voltages, currents, or resistances, let's analyze the schematic diagram in Figure 3–12 to see how the basic series voltage regulator works.

Transistor Q_1 acts as the series variable resistor that was used in Figure 3–11. As already mentioned, it will be necessary to vary the base-

Figure 3–12

Series Transistorized Regulator

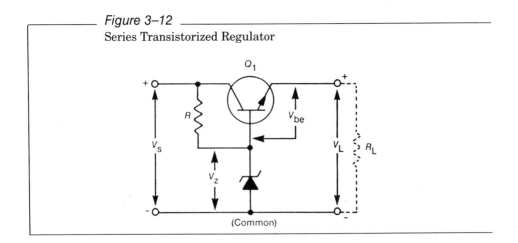

emitter voltage in order to cause the transistor to act as a variable re-sistor. The clue to the circuit's operation is the **zener diode**. A zener diode is, by itself, somewhat of a voltage regulator. Within the range of its operation, it will maintain a relatively constant voltage with chang-ing load current. We will use the zener diode as a reference to maintain the voltage between the transistor's base and common (−) constant. Re-sistor R establishes the normal operating current through the zener diode.

Now let's take a look at the regulator's output. If we consider only the output part of the circuit, Kirchhoff's law tells us that

$$V_{\mathrm{L}} = V_z + V_{\mathrm{be}}$$

where V_z is the voltage of the zener diode. Assuming that Q_1 is a silicon transistor, V_{be} is about 0.6 V. Thus, the output voltage will be the voltage of the zener diode plus 0.6 V. Any difference between the voltage from the unregulated source V_s and V_{L} appears across Q_1—that is, from col-lector to emitter. As we have seen, any change in R_{L} will cause a change in V_{L} due to current changes and subsequent changes in voltage drop across the series resistance. Assume a reduction in R_{L}, which is equiv-alent to an increase in current. The current increase will cause an additional voltage drop across Q_1, and V_{L} will decrease. When V_{L} de-creases, the base-emitter voltage of Q_1 increases (the base is held con-stant by the zener diode). Increased base-emitter voltage causes decreased collector-emitter resistance (increased current), and V_{L} in-creases. In a like manner, increasing R_{L} and the subsequent rise in volt-age due to decreased load current will be countered by an increased col-lector-emitter resistance. V_{L} returns to almost the original value immediately.

The regulator of Figure 3–12 reduces the effective resistance of the voltage source to just a few ohms, which means a better regulation percentage, but it is still not perfect. Perfection cannot be reached, of course, but regulation percentages on the order of 0.001% and internal resistances of just a few milliohms are attainable when op amps are used.

Op Amp Voltage Regulators

One of the reasons that the regulator of Figure 3–12 is not perfect is that the change in output voltage is not completely compensated by the **series pass transistor**. It would require *infinite* amplification to pro-vide a perfect voltage regulator. We can come close to attaining infinite gain with an op amp. In fact, a voltage regulator is nothing more than

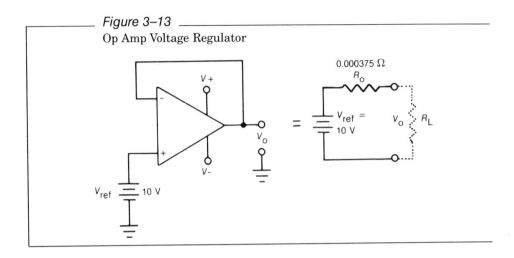

Figure 3–13
Op Amp Voltage Regulator

an op amp with high current capability. Let's first examine the op amp as a low-current-capability regulator before we go on.

The basic voltage follower discussed in Chapter 2 is the simplest of all voltage regulators, or constant voltage sources. As connected in Figure 3–13, the output of the voltage follower will be the same as the voltage applied to the noninverting input. It was shown in Chapter 2 that the op amp output followed the input. One of the rules for op amp operation is that the difference between the inverting and noninverting inputs has to be zero. Since the op amp output is fed back to the inverting input, the output has to be the same voltage as the noninverting input in order to maintain the input differential at zero volts. Recall (from Equation 2–6) that the output impedance of the voltage follower (R_i') is equal to the output resistance of the op amp divided by the open-loop gain ($R_i' = R_o/A_{ol}$). For the type 741 op amp, the output resistance is 75 Ω and the open-loop gain is typically 200,000. Therefore, the output resistance of the voltage follower is 75/200,000, or 0.000375 Ω. The voltage follower equivalent circuit is shown in Figure 3–13.

Voltage regulators using op amps have an excellent regulation percentage. We may not exceed the output current capability of the op amp, however. In the case of the type 741 op amp, the maximum output current rating is 5 mA. Let's do some calculations to see what kind of regulation percentage we can expect. To make it easy, we will assume a 10 V output requirement using a type 741 op amp. The *reference voltage* (V_{ref}) will thus be 10 V, and the minimum R_L consistent with a 5 mA current maximum will be 2000 Ω. Voltage variations from no load to full load, along with regulation percentage calculations, are shown.

_____ Example 3–5 _____

In Figure 3–13, assume $R_L = 2 \text{ k}\Omega$ and $V_{ref} = 10$ V. Calculate the regulation percentage.

Solution

$$I = \frac{V_o}{R_o + R_L} = \frac{10}{2000 + 0.000375} = 0.0049999 \text{ A} \approx 5 \text{ mA}$$

$$V_{nl} = 10 \text{ V}$$

$$V_{fl} = V_{nl} - IR_o = 10 - (0.005)(0.000375) = 10 - 0.000001875$$
$$= 9.999998125 \text{ V}$$

Substituting the information just determined,

$$\% \text{ regulation} = \left(\frac{V_{nl} - V_{fl}}{V_{fl}}\right) \times 100 = \left(\frac{10 - 9.999998125}{9.999998125}\right) \times 100$$
$$= 0.00001875\%$$

The regulation percentage may also be calculated as follows:

$$\% \text{ regulation} = \frac{R_o}{(A_{ol})(\beta)(R_L)} \times 100 \qquad \text{(3–3)}$$

where

R_o = op amp open-loop output resistance

A_{ol} = op amp open-loop gain

β = percentage of output fed back to input

R_L = smallest value of load resistance (maximum current)

The regulation percentage for the voltage follower should be verified using Equation 3–3.

Note that for all practical purposes, the output voltage is 10 V and the regulation percentage is zero. Any load variation within the current rating of the op amp will thus cause no apparent output voltage change.

There are other factors, however, that *may* result in output voltage changes. The op amp voltage regulator is only as good as the stability of V_{ref}. If a battery is used as V_{ref}, V_o will be constant as long as V_{ref} is constant. Even with practically zero current flowing from the battery (the input resistance of the voltage follower is extremely high), variations will occur due to chemical deterioration. A zener diode could be

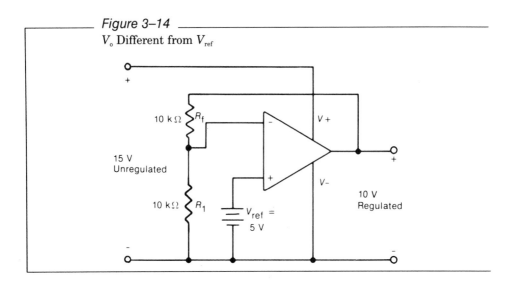

Figure 3–14

V_o Different from V_{ref}

used as V_{ref}, but its voltage can vary with temperature and current changes. For better accuracy, **reference diodes** (specially designed and manufactured zener diodes) may be used. They are less sensitive to temperature and current changes. Precision references that include temperature stabilizing circuitry on the same IC chip as the reference diode will provide even more accuracy and stability. The primary point with the op amp voltage regulator, however, is that the stability of its output voltage is more dependent on stability of the reference voltage than it is on variations in the output load.

If some output voltage other than the reference voltage is desired, it is only necessary to modify the feedback from output to inverting input. Just pace a resistive divider in the feedback path, making the circuit into the typical noninverting amplifier. All that was discussed concerning the noninverting amplifier in Chapter 2 still holds true. Specifically, the input voltage differential must be zero volts. That means, for example, that the inverting input of the circuit in Figure 3–14 must be equal to the reference voltage at the noninverting input. If the reference voltage is 5 V, and the resistive divider is made up of two 10 kΩ resistors as shown, the output will be forced to 10 V. The divider in the feedback path reduces the voltage at the inverting input to 5 V, which establishes the required input differential of zero volts. We now have a 10 V voltage regulator. Because of the smaller feedback factor, the output resistance has increased by a factor of two, as has the regulation percentage. However, the values are still so small that both output resistance and regulation percentage can still be considered zero. Typical calculations are shown in Example 3–6.

_____ *Example 3–6* _____

Calculate the output resistance R_o and the regulation percentage for the circuit of Figure 3–14 if $V_{ref} = 5$ V and $R_f = R_1 = 10$ kΩ. Assume $A_{ol} = 200,000$.

Solution

According to Equation 2–10,

$$R'_i = \frac{R_o}{(A_{ol})(\beta)}$$

where

$$\beta = \frac{R_1}{R_1 + R_f} = \frac{10,000}{10,000 + 10,000} = \frac{1}{2}$$

$$R'_i = \frac{75}{(200,000)(0.5)} = 0.00075 \ \Omega$$

Substituting the information just determined,

$$\% \text{ regulation} = \frac{R_o}{(A_{ol})(\beta)(R_L)} \times 100 = \frac{75}{(200,000)(0.5)(2000)} \times 100$$

$$= 0.0000375\%$$

Increasing Regulator Current Capability

If we need more than 5 mA of load current, there are a number of different choices. Two of the choices will be discussed now. The third, that of using a voltage regulator IC, will be delayed until later in the chapter. One of the ways to obtain a higher current capability for the voltage-regulated power supply is to use an op amp with greater current output. Op amps with output current ratings greater than 1 A are available. They are costly, however, and the more common method uses inexpensive op amps and discrete components, as shown in Figure 3–15.

An **emitter follower** added to the simple op amp voltage regulator will increase its current capability. The emitter follower connection for a bipolar transistor, remember, has a voltage gain of approximately unity but can have appreciable current gain. For our purpose, let's assume a beta, or current gain, of 100. The collector current (I_c) of a transistor is equal to β times the base current (I_b):

$$I_c = (\beta) \times (I_b)$$

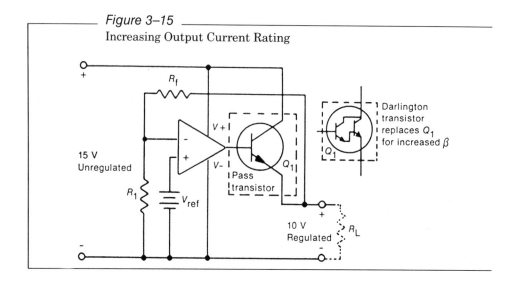

Figure 3–15

Increasing Output Current Rating

For all practical purposes, the emitter current—hence the load current (I_L) in our example—and the collector current are the same. Thus, the load current will be β times the base current that is available from the op amp (that is, $I_L = β \times I_b$). The 5 mA output of the op amp, therefore, will be stepped up to 5 mA times 100, or 500 mA.

All that we have really done is to add a *current* amplification stage to the op amp. The voltage gain has not changed appreciably. Note that the feedback network still connects from output to inverting input. The added current booster is included within the feedback loop. Thus, the overall circuit will regulate to the previously determined value of 10 V. How well will it regulate? As stated earlier, the regulation percentage is pretty much determined by the internal resistance of the regulating circuit. In the case of an emitter follower, its output resistance is approximately equal to the resistance at the base of the transistor divided by the β of the transistor. The 75 Ω output resistance of the type 741 op amp thus is reduced by a factor of 100 (the β of the series pass transistor). With feedback applied through R_f and R_1, the output resistance is further reduced by the amount of loop gain. The following calculations show that the series pass transistor results in improved output resistance:

$$R_i' = \frac{R_o}{(β_{Q_1})(1 + A_{ol}β)} = \frac{75}{(100)[1 + (200,000)(0.5)]} = 0.0000075 \ Ω$$

The regulation percentage remains approximately the same because the beta effect of the series pass transistor is offset by the decreased value of load resistance.

The series pass transistor must be capable of a maximum power dissipation determined by maximum collector-emitter voltage and maximum load (collector) current. In the regulator shown in Figure 3–15, maximum power dissipation is 2.5 W (5 V × 0.5 A). The series pass transistor must also be capable of sustaining the expected maximum collector current. In the regulator shown in Figure 3–15, the maximum current requirement is 0.5 A. Therefore, a series pass transistor capable of constantly passing 0.5 A and dissipating 2.5 W of power must be used. Series pass transistors require a way to dissipate heat generated by current flow. Heat sinks are used, as you learned when you studied transistors.

Output current limitations in the regulator circuit of Figure 3–15 are generally set by the op amp selected to drive the series pass transistor and the β of the pass transistor. It is relatively simple to increase the current-handling capability of the pass transistor. If an op amp with greater output current capability cannot be used, a **Darlington configuration** transistor or circuit can be used. Figure 3–15 also shows how to use the additional current gain of the Darlington transistor.

Error Sources

In reality, the regulation percentage of voltage regulators does not approach the theoretical values we have calculated. A number of factors prevent achieving ideal conditions. Temperature variation is probably the major factor. As mentioned in Chapter 2, one of the errors associated with op amps is the input offset voltage V_{io}, the small output voltage that exists with both op amp inputs grounded. V_{io} is due to unbalance in the input stages of the op amp, and it may be balanced out with external components. Unfortunately, V_{io} is temperature sensitive and drifts as temperature changes. Therefore, a balance at one temperature is not true as temperature changes. The output voltage change as a result of V_{io} drift thus appears to change the percentage of regulation.

It should be pointed out that the temperature change that causes the V_{io} drift (among other problems) is the actual temperature of the IC op amp. Not only is the actual air temperature important, but anything that changes the chip temperature will have an effect. For example, as the op amp is required to supply more and more output current, more and more heat is generated internally. The resulting temperature rise, though not directly related to V_{io}, causes the V_{io} to drift. Temperature variations also cause change in V_{ref}, as mentioned earlier.

Power supply sensitivity also detracts from the theoretical low regulation percentage. The PSRR (power supply rejection ratio) is the ratio of change in V_{io} to the change in the power supply voltage producing it:

$$\text{PSRR} = \frac{\Delta V_{io}}{\Delta V}$$

If both + and − supplies are used, a PSRR + and a PSRR − are defined. The supply not being varied must be held constant when determining the PSRR of the other supply. PSRR is another characteristic dependent upon matched transistors and other components. The unit of measurement for PSRR may be either μV/V or dB. One of the major manufacturers lists the PSRR of the 741 op amp as from 30 μV/V (90 dB) to 150 μV/V (76 dB). Thus, under the best circumstances, if the power supply changed 1 V, V_{io} would change 30 μV. Under worst-case conditions, V_{io} would change 150 mV for each 1 V change in power supply voltage. As noted before, V_{io} may be balanced out, but changes in the power supply voltage will upset that balance. For high-precision voltage regulators, it is advisable to use op amps that have a very low PSRR (that is, a change of very few microvolts/volt).

It is also desirable to use an op amp with a high CMRR (common-mode rejection ratio). CMRR is a measure of the op amp's ability to reject signals that are present on both inputs at the same time. The op amp interprets a changing supply voltage as a change common to both inputs. This common-mode voltage will appear as a change in V_{io}. Op amps with high CMRR ratings (in dB) will show less V_{io} change as the power supply voltage changes.

When all of the possible error sources are combined, it is easily possible to reduce the regulation percentage of a voltage regulator by a factor of 100 to 1000. With a little care, regulation percentage on the order of 0.01% to 0.001% can be obtained. Except in the most critical of applications, such accuracy is more than adequate.

SHUNT REGULATION

Voltage regulation can also be obtained by using a regulating device across or in-shunt-with the load. Figure 3–16A will help explain the concept of **shunt regulation**. We can use the same approach as was used with the series voltage regulator. See Example 3–7 for calculations.

Example 3–7

In Figure 3–16A, $V_s = 20$ V and $R_s = 15$ Ω. V_o must remain a constant 15 V even though R_L varies between 500 and 100 Ω. Calculate the resistance variation required for R_1 to maintain V_o constant and V_o variations without the shunt resistance R_1.

Figure 3–16
Shunt Regulation

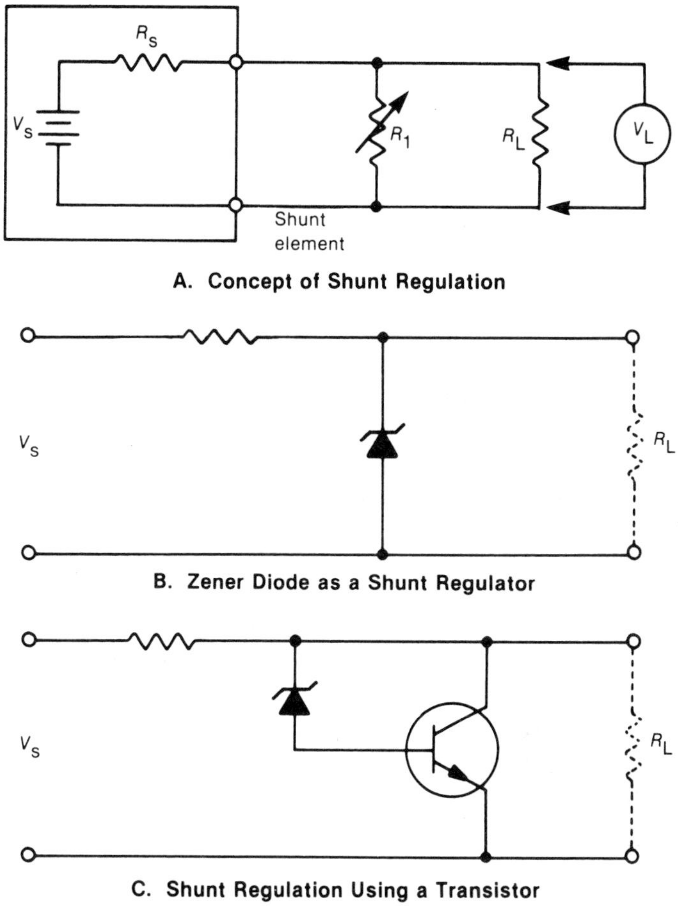

A. Concept of Shunt Regulation

B. Zener Diode as a Shunt Regulator

C. Shunt Regulation Using a Transistor

Solution

For $R_L = 500\ \Omega$,

$$I_T = \frac{V}{R_s} = \frac{5}{15} = 0.333\ \text{A}$$

$$I_L = \frac{V_L}{R_L} = \frac{15}{500} = 0.03\ \text{A}$$

$$I_{R_1} = I_T - I_L = 0.333 - 0.03 = 0.303\ \text{A}$$

$$R_1 = \frac{V_L}{I_{R_1}} = \frac{15}{0.303} = 49.5\ \Omega$$

continued

(Example 3–7 continued)

For $R_L = 100\ \Omega$,

$$I_T = \frac{V}{R_s} = \frac{5}{15} = 0.333\ \text{A}$$

$$I_L = \frac{V_L}{R_L} = \frac{15}{100} = 0.15\ \text{A}$$

$$I_{R_1} = I_T - I_L = 0.333 - 0.15 = 0.183\ \text{A}$$

$$R_1 = \frac{V_L}{I_{R_1}} = \frac{15}{0.183} = 81.97\ \Omega$$

With no shunt element (R_1) and $R_L = 500\ \Omega$,

$$V_o = \left(\frac{R_L}{R_T}\right)(V_s) = \left(\frac{500}{515}\right)(20) = 19.4\ \text{V}$$

With no shunt element (R_1) and $R_L = 100\ \Omega$,

$$V_o = \left(\frac{R_L}{R_T}\right)(V_s) = \left(\frac{100}{115}\right)(20) = 17.4\ \text{V}$$

With only R_L connected, the voltage supplied to R_L will vary between 17.4 V and 19.4 V, as shown in Example 3–7. Maintaining a constant 15 V across R_L requires that R_s have a constant 5 V drop. A constant current of 0.333 A thus provides the necessary drop across R_s. Therefore, as R_L changes, a resistor shunting R_L must be adjusted to make up for the changing load current. Ohm's law calculations in Example 3–7 show that the shunt resistor (R_1) must be 49.5 Ω to establish the required 0.333 A through R_s when R_L is 500 Ω. Changing R_L to 100 Ω requires adjusting R_1 to 82 Ω. Thus the output voltage is regulated by maintaining a constant current from the voltage source.

It is, of course, impractical to try to manually adjust the shunt resistor as load requirements change. A zener diode may be substituted as the shunt element. (See Figure 3–16B.) As a semiconductor device, the zener diode changes its internal resistance as required to maintain a constant voltage drop. Selection of the appropriate series resistor and zener diode will provide regulation percentages on the order of 3% to 5%. The regulation percentage of a zener diode can be improved by the scheme shown in Figure 3–16C. This is often known as the *amplified zener* circuit. Since the total shunt current flows through the transistor, not through the zener diode, increased power-handling capability is provided, and regulation percentages on the order of 1% are obtained.

Even better regulation may be obtained with shunt regulators by using an op amp as the sensing element. As with series regulators, the op amp compares the load voltage with a reference voltage. The op amp output causes the shunt transistor to shunt sufficient current so that the load voltage remains constant. The same type of calculations used with series regulators apply to op amp controlled shunt regulators.

Shunt regulators are becoming less popular. Although good regulation may be obtained, they are inefficient. Better regulation schemes are now available.

SWITCHED-MODE REGULATORS

Both series and shunt regulators are inefficient devices. In both cases, the power transistor(s) is operated in an active mode. That is, they are always conducting current and dissipating power. This results in an energy loss and reduced efficiency. Vastly improved efficiency may be obtained using **switched-mode regulators**.

Figure 3–17A shows the basic concepts of switch-mode, or

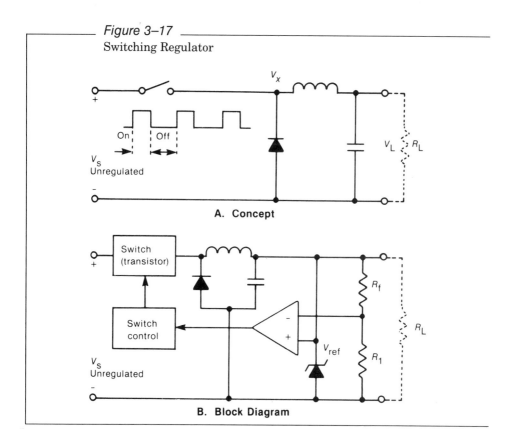

Figure 3–17

Switching Regulator

A. Concept

B. Block Diagram

switching, regulators. Three general functions are shown: a switch, a current-directing diode, and an inductor/capacitor filter. When the switch closes, the voltage applied to the filter (V_x) rises toward V_s. The voltage difference between V_x and V_L is applied across the inductor, and current through the inductor increases. This current flows to the filter capacitor and to R_L. If the instantaneous inductor current is greater than that required for the load, the excess current is used to charge the capacitor. If the inductor current is less than that required for the load, the capacitor supplies the additional requirement. With proper timing, the inductor current will continue to increase as long as the switch is closed. Note that the diode has been reverse biased during the switch-on time.

When the switch opens, energy is no longer supplied from V_s. The inductor, however, does not allow the current to return to zero instantaneously. Counter-emf generated forward biases the diode to provide a return path for current flow. Thus, the energy stored in the inductor during the switch-on time is released during the switch-off time. With proper timing, the average inductor current is equal to the load current, the average capacitor current is zero, and the output voltage remains constant. Note that the capacitor and inductor not only perform an energy storage function but also filter the pulse output of the switch.

Figure 3–17B is a block diagram of a switching regulator. A switch control block, an op amp with reference voltage, and a feedback network have been added to the conceptual diagram of Figure 3–17A. The mechanical switch has been replaced by a switching transistor to perform the off-on operation. The switching transitor is controlled by a pulse generator (switch control). The switch control operates with a variable **duty cycle** (on-off ratio). The duty cycle is controlled by an input from the op amp. When the output voltage is a multiple of the reference voltage as selected by the feedback network (R_f and R_1), the op amp output is zero. The switch control supplies on-off pulses of the proper duration to supply the desired load current. If the load current should increase, the output voltage will drop. The op amp output then causes the switch control to increase the on time and decrease the off time of the transistor switch. Output current demand is met, and the voltage returns to normal. If the load current should decrease, the output voltage will rise. The op amp output then causes the switch control to decrease the on time and increase the off time of the transistor switch. Output current demand is again met, and the voltage returns to normal.

Figure 3–18 is a simplified functional block diagram of the 5561 integrated circuit. It is a control circuit for use in switched-mode power supplies. It contains a stabilized supply for internal circuits, a sawtooth oscillator, comparators, and operational amplifiers, control logic, and an output transistor.

Figure 3–18

Switched-Mode Power Supply Control Circuit

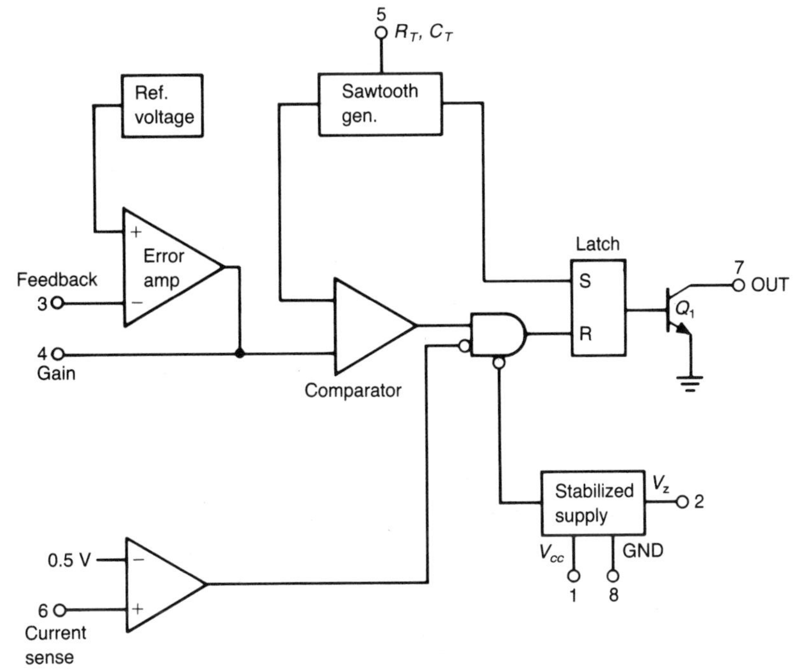

As previously discussed, switching regulators operate on the principle of varying the duty cycle of a transistor connected between a source of voltage (V_i) and the desired load voltage (V_o). Transistor Q_1 on the 5561 IC is the series transistor, which can pass up to 40 mA. The base of Q_1 receives a variable duty cycle pulse train from the latch. Let's determine how the variable duty cycle pulse is developed.

The 5561 IC contains a sawtooth generator whose frequency is set by the external R_T and C_T values. Typical operating frequencies vary from 10 kHz to 100 kHz. The sawtooth generator output is applied to one input of a comparator. The other input of the comparator is the error amplifier output. A sample of V_o is applied to the − input of the error amplifier (pin 3), and an internally generated reference voltage is applied to the + input. Note that error amplifier gain is adjustable with an external resistor between pins 3 and 4.

The latch controls output transistor on-time. When the latch is reset, the transistor is turned OFF. When the latch is set, the transistor

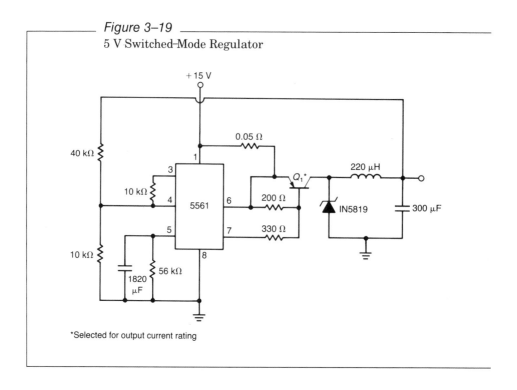

Figure 3–19

5 V Switched–Mode Regulator

*Selected for output current rating

is turned ON. A pulse is generated at the beginning of each cycle of the sawtooth generator to set the latch. The latch is reset by

1. an internal stabilized supply problem,
2. sensing excessive current flow in the load, or
3. HIGH output from the comparator.

Comparator output is LOW until the amplitude of the sawtooth signal equals the amplifier error signal. When the comparator output goes HIGH, the latch is reset and the output transistor turns OFF.

The output voltage is sampled each cycle of the sawtooth generator. If, for example, load current increases, the output voltage decreases. The error amplifier amplifies the difference between the reference voltage and the sampled output voltage. Comparator input changes, and the comparator output stays HIGH longer. The latch stays set longer, causing the output transistor to conduct longer. Thus the output voltage rises to compensate for the drop caused by increased current demands.

Figure 3–20

Switching Regulator Capabilities

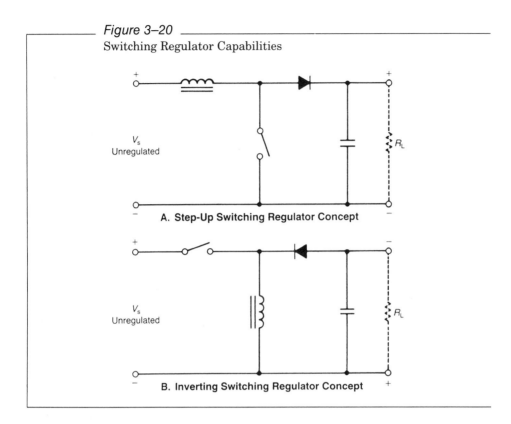

A. Step-Up Switching Regulator Concept

B. Inverting Switching Regulator Concept

Figure 3–19 is a schematic diagram of a 5 V power supply using the 5561 switched-mode regulator. The power supply of Figure 3–19 operates in the buck or step-down mode. Output voltage is less than input voltage. Boost regulators convert a low input voltage into a higher output voltage. See Figure 3–20A. Energy is stored in the inductor while the switch is ON and then transferred to the output capacitor for filtering when the switch is OFF.

Switched-mode regulators can also be used as inverting regulators. See Figure 3–20B. The input voltage may be +, but output is −. Output may be less than, equal to, or greater than the input.

Efficiencies on the order of 80% to 90% can be achieved with switching regulators. It is no wonder that they are appearing in many applications that formerly were served by series and shunt regulators with 25% to 35% efficiency.

INTEGRATED CIRCUIT VOLTAGE REGULATORS

The **IC voltage regulator** is an example of integrating op amp circuits with other circuits to form a more powerful integrated circuit, IC voltage regulators contain, as a minimum, the op amp, reference source, and pass transistor in a single package. Additional features such as overcurrent and overtemperature protection are common. Dozens of variations and features exist in modern IC voltage regulators. We will investigate the functions of a typical regulator without being specific about type. When we become familiar with the general characteristics of IC voltage regulators, we will discuss some of the specific devices in common use.

Figure 3–21 is a block diagram of a typical IC voltage regulator. Included on the IC chip is a voltage reference source, an op amp, the pass transistor, and both thermal and short-circuit protective circuits. Except for the added protective circuits, the diagram resembles a typical series regulator using an op amp to develop the pass transistor control input. One of the primary advantages of the IC voltage regulator (other than size) is that all components of the regulator are in the same temperature environment. Many of the temperature-related errors mentioned earlier are a lesser problem.

Let's examine the voltage reference source first. Depending on precision requirements, the reference may be as simple as a zener diode or as complex as an amplified zener. Figure 3–22A shows a high-preci-

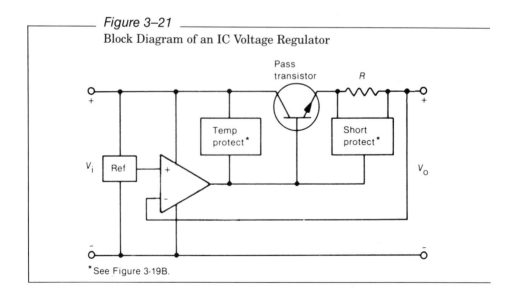

Figure 3–21

Block Diagram of an IC Voltage Regulator

*See Figure 3-19B.

Figure 3–22

Details of an IC Voltage Regulator

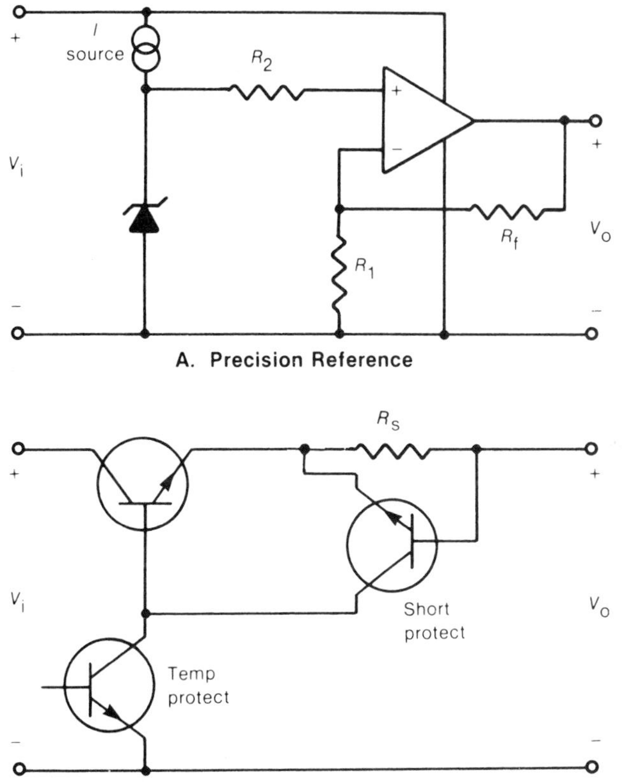

A. Precision Reference

B. Short-Circuit and Overtemp Protection

sion voltage reference source using a temperature-compensated zener diode supplied by a constant current source and a noninverting op amp. The op amp isolates the zener diode from the remainder of the regulator circuit, providing the usual high input impedance and low output impedance. References such as this are generally accurate to within 0.1% to 0.01% with similar temperature characteristics.

On the IC regulator, the op amp used to compare the reference voltage with the output voltage is connected as a voltage follower. Output voltage will be equal to the reference voltage less the base-emitter voltage drop of the pass transistor and any voltage drop occurring across the current-sensing resistor R_s. As with voltage regulators using discrete components, this configuration results in very low output resistance and excellent regulation characteristics.

Short-circuit or current-limiting protection is shown in Figure 3–22B. A transistor is all that is required. The base is connected to the output voltage side of the current sensing resistor and the emitter is connected to the opposite side. As current flows through R_s, a voltage drop is developed. A value is selected for R_s such that when excessive current flows the emitter-base junction of the sensing transistor is forward biased. At this point, the sensing transistor turns on, shorting the base-emitter junction of the pass transistor. The pass transistor now has zero bias, and can no longer conduct current. Effectively, then, the regulator is shut down when a short circuit at the output occurs or when excessive load current flows. A similar arrangement is used for over-temperature protection. A transistor is connected as shown from the base of the pass transistor to common. A small base-emitter bias is applied to the temperature-shutdown transistor. This bias is not sufficient to turn the transistor on under normal temperature conditions. However, one of the principles of transistor operation is that turn-on bias gets lower as temperature increases. When the base-emitter junction of the temperature shut-down transistor reaches the designed shutdown temperature, the transistor turns on. The base of the pass transistor is thus connected to ground, removing all drive. With no drive, the pass transistor can no longer conduct, and the power supply again shuts down. The temperature-shutdown transistor is placed very near the collector of the pass transistor, ensuring that the hottest spot on the chip will be sensed.

When regulated voltage is required, all we now need is an IC voltage regulator. Figure 3–23 shows how simple it really is. We must consider input voltage and output current maximums, of course, but a wide variety of IC regulators exist. The 309 series regulator shown in Figure 3–23 is available from many manufacturers. Both current limiting and thermal shutdown are used in the 309 regulator to make it virtually

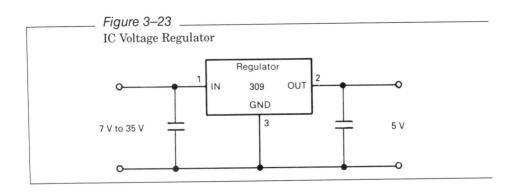

Figure 3–23
IC Voltage Regulator

blowout-proof. Output voltage is a constant 5 V, with current capability up to 2 A, depending on the type of package, the heat sinking used, and the input-output voltage differential. Input voltage may be between 7 V and 35 V.

Troubleshooting: Let's consider a typical malfunction encountered in equipment that uses the type 309 IC regulator. The equipment has quit operating, and we have isolated the difficulty to low supply voltage. Do we automatically replace the regulator? It could be the source of the problem, but let's review some troubleshooting philosophy. When your car won't start, do you replace the engine? Probably not—at least until you check to see whether you are out of gas! The same philosophy should prevail when troubleshooting electronic equipment.

Caution: Always turn off the equipment and remove the source of power (batteries or AC supply) before working on the equipment. Power must be reapplied to make any voltage or current checks.

But first, do you detect smoke or the smell of a hot component? Or is the regulator too hot to touch? If so, disconnect the regulator output from the equipment, and verify that the equipment is not presenting a higher-than-normal current requirement to the regulator. That is, make sure that a short circuit or low-resistance load is not being applied to the regulator output. If a short circuit exists, fix it before proceeding.

As long as the regulator is disconnected from the equipment, check the output voltage of the regulator. If the output voltage is OK and you have fixed the short circuit, you can reconnect the regulator to the equipment with good probability of success. If the regulator output voltage is not OK with no load, verify that the input voltage to the regulator is OK. If it is not, repair the input voltage source before proceeding. If the input voltage to the regulator is OK, then the regulator must be defective. Replace the regulator and recheck the output voltage with no load. Correct output voltage should now exist, and you can reconnect the equipment to the regulator.

Troubleshooting is easy! All it takes is knowledge of what the equipment is supposed to do, knowledge of the components' functions, and an organized approach to finding the malfunction. Many other troubleshooting problems are shown in later chapters. Apply these simple concepts to each of the situations.

IC voltage regulators are available for many purposes. Fixed voltage ratings range from 2.2 V to 36 V for both positive and negative applications. Current capability ranges from 35 mA to 4 A. Adjustable voltage regulators range from 1.2 V to 1000 V, with current ranges from 10 mA to 5 A. Both positive and negative adjustable regulators are available.

SUMMARY

Chapter 3 has shown some common applications of operational amplifiers. Each of the applications took advantage of the op amp's ability to function as a DC amplifier. Actually, many of the applications in Chapter 3 could previously have been accomplished only with great difficulty. DC amplifiers, before operational amplifiers, required extreme care in their use. The DC stability of op amps has made such devices as highly accurate electronic thermometers, high-input-impedance measuring instruments, and well-regulated power supplies the rule rather than the exception.

The DC stability of op amps even allowed simple temperature transducers such as thermistors and thermocouples to perform excellent temperature measuring functions. Solid-state temperature transducers, however, are even more effective and accurate when combined with integrated circuit technology. Additional DC applications of op amps and transducers may be seen in Chapters 10 and 11.

Conventional moving-coil meters have long provided a needed voltage and current measuring function. However, in many cases, their low resistance and sensitivity made them useless. Op amps have allowed the convenience of moving-coil meters to be applied to many new measurement situations by effectively isolating the meter from the circuit to be measured.

Op amp techniques have had an even more dramatic impact in the voltage regulation field. Starting as simple transistor amplifier regulators and advancing to complete integrated circuit assemblies with high-gain op amps, references sources, and integral pass transistors, today's regulators are a tribute to the op amp designer.

We have deviated somewhat from our main objectives in this chapter, but the side journey will serve a good purpose. The lessons learned during design and application of op amps allowed the engineers to develop such complex and useful ICs as the voltage regulator chips just discussed. As we discuss other applications of ICs, we will also have to examine the natural circuit derivations that have occurred. The world of **linear integrated circuits**, of which op amps are a small part, is growing. Many functions are appearing on a single chip, resulting in complete systems in IC form.

QUESTIONS

1. Define (a) transducer, (b) thermistor, and (c) thermocouple.

2. Explain the principles of operation of a thermistor.

3. Discuss the disadvantages of thermistors as temperature transducers.

4. Explain the principles of operation of a thermocouple.

5. Discuss the disadvantages of thermocouples as temperature transducers.

6. Explain the principles of operation of solid-state temperature sensors.

7. Discuss the advantages and disadvantages of solid-state temperature sensors.

8. Draw a diagram showing the use of an operational amplifier to isolate a moving-coil meter from a solid-state temperature sensor. Discuss the operation of the circuit.

9. Draw a diagram showing the use of operational amplifiers to scale solid-state temperature sensors to an indicating device. Explain how either degrees Fahrenheit or degrees Celsius may be indicated.

10. Discuss the trend in recent solid-state temperature transducers.

11. Why may it be necessary to increase the current sensitivity of a moving-coil indicating instrument? Show how an operational amplifier can provide this function.

12. Why may it be necessary to increase the voltage sensitivity of a moving-coil indicating instrument? Show how an operational amplifier can provide this function.

13. Explain how an operational amplifier can be inserted in series with a circuit to perform current-to-voltage conversion.

14. What is voltage regulation?

15. Show by diagram how manual voltage regulation may be accomplished. Include typical calculations to demonstrate the regulation process.

16. Draw a diagram showing how a series transistor may be used to accomplish voltage regulation. Explain circuit operation.

17. Can an operational amplifier be used as a voltage regulator? Explain.

18. Show how an operational amplifier may be used with a series transistor to improve voltage regulation. Explain circuit operation.

19. A regulated voltage supply must supply more current than originally included in the design. Show how this could be accomplished.

20. List and discuss the factors that affect the regulation percentage of a regulated power supply.

21. Define power supply sensitivity, and give an example.

22. Draw a block diagram of a shunt-type voltage regulator.

23. Discuss the principles of operation of shunt-type voltage regulators.

24. Is a series-type or shunt-type voltage regulator most efficient? Explain.

25. Draw a block diagram of a switched-mode voltage regulator.

26. Discuss the principles of operation of switched-mode regulators.

27. Is a series-type, shunt-type, or switched-mode regulator most efficient? Explain.

28. Draw a block diagram of an integrated circuit voltage regulator.

29. Discuss the principles of operation of an integrated circuit voltage regulator.

30. Explain how short-circuit protection is incorporated in integrated circuit voltage regulators.

31. Explain how over-temperature protection is incorporated in integrated circuit voltage regulators.

32. List three more DC applications of operational amplifiers. Draw at least a block diagram (a more detailed diagram if possible), and discuss circuit operation.

═══ PROBLEMS ═══

1. Using Equation 3–1 and the information in Figure 3–3, calculate V_{be} for the following temperatures: (a) $-20°C$, (b) $0°C$, (c) $+20°C$, (d) $+40°C$, (e) $+60°C$, and (f) $+80°C$.

2. In Figure 3–7, voltmeter V is changed to a 1000 Ω/V moving-coil meter with a 1 V range. What will be the indication with the new meter?

3. Microammeter M in Figure 3–8 is replaced with a 50 μA movement having a resistance of 2000 Ω. What input voltage is required to provide full-scale indication?

4. If I_i in Figure 3–9 is 100 μA, what is the indication of voltmeter V? What is the value of R_i?

5. Calculate the regulation percentage for a power supply with $V_{nl} = 20$ V and $V_{fl} = 19.5$ V.

6. Calculate the regulation percentage for a power supply with $V_{nl} = 5.05$ V and $V_{fl} = 5.01$ V.

7. In Figure 3–13 and Example 3–5, change V_{ref} to 5 V, leaving all other parameters the same. Calculate I, V_{nl}, V_{fl}, and regulation percentage. Assume a type 741 op amp with $R_o = 75$ Ω and $A_{ol} = 200,000$.

8. In Figure 3–14, change R_f to 5 kΩ, leaving all other parameters the same. Calculate A_{cl}, output resistance, and regulation percentage. Assume a type 741 op amp with $R_o = 75 \ \Omega$ and $A_{ol} = 200,000$.

4

AC Specifications
and Circuits

OBJECTIVES   After studying Chapter 4, you will be able to

1. Use logarithmic scales with graphs.
2. Explain the purpose of frequency response graphs.
3. Define cutoff frequency, unity gain frequency, roll-off characteristic, Bode plot, and slew rate.
4. Explain how to specify roll-off characteristic.
5. Explain how to determine gain-bandwidth product.
6. Explain the purpose of phase response graphs and why phase response is important.
7. Determine gain and bandwidth of an operational amplifier circuit graphically and mathematically.
8. Combine gain and phase characteristics of operational amplifiers.
9. Describe the relationship between roll-off characteristic and phase response of operational amplifiers.
10. Explain the common types of frequency and phase compensation used with operational amplifiers.

_____ INTRODUCTION _____

Although many applications of operational amplifiers can be explained using only DC characteristics, the majority of circuits must also consider AC specifications. Chapter 4 integrates AC characteristics with DC characteristics to show a complete picture of operational amplifier operation.

BASIC AC CHARACTERISTICS

In addition to the DC characteristics discussed in Chapters 2 and 3, a number of strictly AC characteristics help determine op amp operation with AC inputs. Frequency response, phase response, and slew rate all must be considered when op amps are used in AC applications. Each of these terms is described in this section.

Frequency Response (Gain versus Frequency)

As mentioned earlier, the amplification or gain of an op amp is not the same with AC input as it is with DC input. The gain reduction with AC input as frequency increases is caused by distributed capacitance and some complex characteristics of active devices such as propagation delay and switching time on the integrated circuit chip. A graph showing op amp gain versus input frequency is shown in Figure 4–1. Much information is available from this **frequency response** graph. But first let's look at *what* we are graphing. Note that the horizontal scale, frequency, is a **logarithmic scale**. Logarithmic scales compress the range of information to be graphed so that a wider band of frequencies may be shown over a given length. Figure 4–1 covers from near DC (1 Hz) to 10 MHz. Getting the same range on a linear scale and seeing any useful information would be difficult.

Note also that the amplification, or gain, is graphed on a logarithmic scale (dB). (A review of dB applications is given in Appendix B.)

Figure 4–1

Type 741 Op Amp Frequency Response

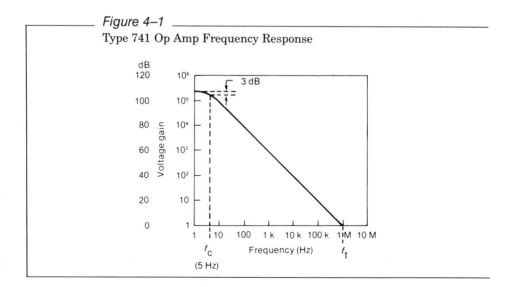

Once again, the great range of gain (from 1 to over a million) would be very difficult to graph on a linear scale.

Perhaps the most important thing that Figure 4–1 shows is how poorly the type 741 op amp functions as an AC amplifier at maximum gain. The flat portion of the response graph extends from DC to only about 5 Hz. As frequency increases from 5 Hz, the gain of the amplifier steadily decreases. There are a couple of important checkpoints on the graph. The first is labeled f_c and is the **cutoff frequency**—that is, *the frequency at which the gain has dropped 3 dB from its low-frequency or constant gain value.* (Note that the terms *cutoff* frequency and *corner* frequency may be used synonymously, but that in this text the term *cutoff* frequency is used.) The 3 dB point, or **half-power point**, is a widely recognized method of describing amplifier and filter frequency characteristics. (The implication of the term half-power point is reviewed during discussion of dB in Appendix B.) The 3 dB point is also important in terms of **phase response**, which is discussed shortly.

Another important checkpoint on the frequency response graph is f_t. The frequency at which the open-loop gain of the amplifier has dropped to 1 (or 0 dB) is called the **unity gain frequency**, or f_t. The unity gain frequency is also important in terms of phase response. Even more important is what has happened to the gain between f_c and f_t. Unity gain occurs in Figure 4–1 at 1 MHz. If we investigate the gain at 100,000 Hz, the graph shows a gain of 10, or in terms of dB, 20 dB. In fact, for every 10 times change in frequency, a change in gain of 20 dB occurs. The amplifier is said to have a **roll-off characteristic** of 20 dB per decade, or 20 dB/decade. (A **decade** is a ten-fold change in frequency.) For many applications, it is desirable that an amplifier possess this roll-off characteristic, as will be seen during discussion of phase response. The type 741 op amp is **internally compensated** so as to give a 20 dB/decade roll-off characteristic.

It should be noted that another type of roll-off characteristic specification is commonly used. A 20 dB/decade roll-off is equivalent to 6 dB/octave, where an **octave** is a two-fold change in frequency. Both terms are seen in op amp specifications. The 20 dB/decade term, however, is easier to use when logarithmic scales are employed for frequency response graphs.

For simplification, sometimes frequency response graphs are drawn as straight-line approximations, as shown in Figure 4–2. The dashed line shows the actual frequency response, while the solid line is the straight-line approximation, or **Bode plot**. Low-frequency gain is extended horizontally as a straight line. The straight portion of the roll-off characteristic is also extended. Both lines will intersect at the cutoff frequency (f_c). An error of 3 dB occurs at the cutoff frequency using the Bode plot, but that is a small amount when compared with a total gain

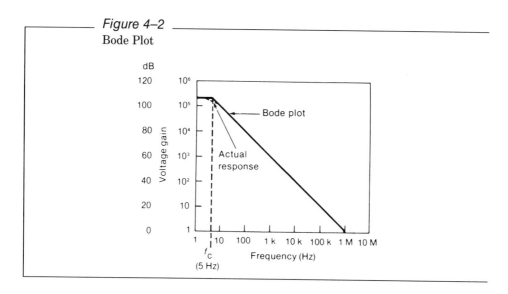

Figure 4–2
Bode Plot

of over 100 dB. The straight-line approximations are well worth the small error when ease of use is considered.

Another interesting fact can be seen in Figure 4–2. First, let's multiply gain times frequency at unity gain. The result ($1 \times 1,000,000$) is 1,000,000. Now note where the roll-off characteristic intersects the gain-of-10 line. Once again, the product of gain times frequency ($10 \times 100,000$) is 1,000,000. In fact, anywhere along the 20 dB/decade roll-off characteristic, the product of gain and frequency is the same. This constant value is called the **gain-bandwidth product** and is a measure of how much gain can be obtained at a specified maximum frequency. **Bandwidth** for op amps is defined as the number of cycles per second (hertz) from DC to the cutoff frequency f_c. For example, the open-loop bandwidth of the type 741 op amp is about 5 Hz. When gain is reduced, as is done with feedback, note that the bandwidth increases. A voltage follower, with unity gain, has a 1 MHz bandwidth. If feedback reduces gain to 10, then the bandwidth is 100,000 Hz. By extending *any* gain line horizontally to intersect the roll-off characteristic, we can find the expected bandwidth. A gain of 1000, then, allows a bandwidth of 1000 Hz. We now have the tools to determine not only gain but also amplifier circuit bandwidth.

Phase Response (Phase versus Frequency)

The next thing we need to investigate is phase response. We've considered that a typical inverting amplifier's output is 180° out of phase with its input. This is true *only* at low and medium frequencies. At some frequency, internal capacitance, circuit delays, and semiconductor characteristics start adding more delay or phase shift. It is entirely possible that at some frequency the extra phase shift may reach an *additional* 180°. Consider what this means in an amplifier with negative feedback. At low and medium frequencies, the feedback is 180° out of phase, and the desired results of negative feedback occur. The fed-back signal cancels part of the input signal, gain and output impedance are reduced, and input impedance is increased. However, at higher frequencies, with increased phase shift, that fed-back signal might be *in phase* with the input signal. Instead of canceling part of the input signal, it adds to it. The now-increased input signal results in greater output, which results in greater input, which results in greater output, and so on. Oscillation is the inevitable result, and the output is no longer dependent on the input. We have lost control of the amplifier.

Let's look at the phase response of an op amp with the frequency response of Figure 4–2. See Figure 4–3. A new scale is added on the right side of the graph to allow plotting of phase response in conjunction with frequency response. Assuming an inverting amplifier, 180° of phase shift exists between input and output at DC and low frequencies. As frequency increases, however, internal capacitance, delays, and semiconductor characteristics combine to start adding additional delay or phase shift. When f_c is reached, those factors have already added an extra 45° for a total of 225°. Further increasing the frequency of the input signal results in additional phase shift. At f_t, the total phase shift is 270°. Further increases in frequency cause more phase shift, but once f_t is

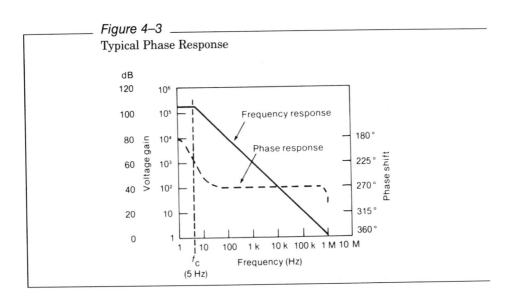

Figure 4–3

Typical Phase Response

reached, a problem no longer exists. Op amp gain is less than one beyond f_t, so even if all of the output is fed back to the input, oscillation cannot occur.

If the op amp has a 20 dB/decade roll-off characteristic, the gain will always be less than one before a full 360° of phase shift are generated. Many op amps are internally compensated so that their roll-off characteristic meets this requirement. Other op amps have roll-off characteristics greater than 20 dB/decade. If internal compensation is not provided, external components must be added. Frequency and phase compensation are discussed later in this chapter. To summarize, phase response is directly related to the rate of change of attenuation of an op amp. The greater the rate of change of attenuation (more dB/decade), the greater the phase shift. Great care must be exercised when using op amps to ensure that any roll-off characteristic greater than about 20 dB/ decade is carefully handled.

Slew Rate

The frequency response we have been discussing is primarily a measure of the small-signal characteristics of an op amp. When large signals must be processed by an op amp, a different view of frequency response is used. **Slew rate** describes the op amp's ability to supply large, rapid changes in output voltage. Another description of slew rate is that it indicates how fast the output of an op amp can change. It is defined as the *maximum voltage per unit time* that the op amp can deliver. Whereas the small-signal response of an op amp is only related to frequency, the large-signal response includes both frequency and voltage. The reasons for the op amp not being able to respond instantly to changes in input are the internal (or external) compensation capacitors and internal current limiting. It takes time to charge and discharge capacitors, so the output cannot instantaneously follow the input if the input is changing rapidly. Slew rate is usually listed in volts per microsecond (V/µs), which includes both voltage and frequency ($f = 1/T$ where T = time in seconds).

A simple op amp circuit is shown in Figure 4–4A. We can use it to demonstrate the effect of slew rate on op amp operation. As shown, we are using our old friend the type 741 op amp in an inverting configuration. If $R_f = R_1$, the gain of the circuit will be unity. According to what we have learned so far, if a 1 MHz signal is provided to the input, an exact replica of that signal should appear at the output. Let's not push the op amp, though. The input signal we will use is a 5 V amplitude, 10 kHz square wave (see Figure 4–4B). But, when the output is examined, it is no longer a square wave. The output swing is 5 V, which is correct, but the shape of the wave is more like a trapezoid (see Figure 4–4C). The time it takes to change from maximum negative to

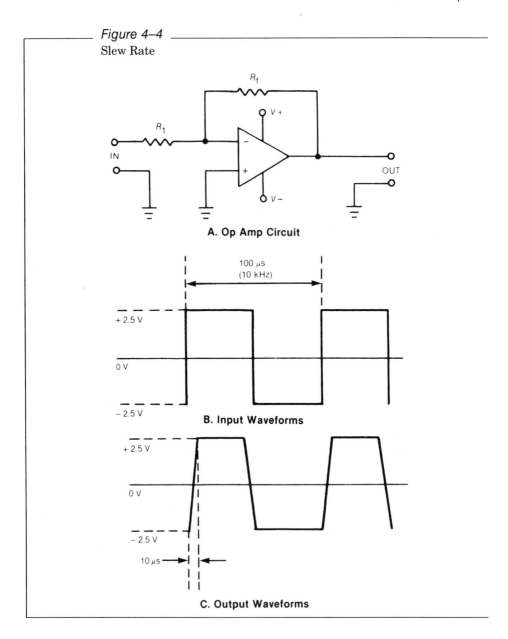

Figure 4–4
Slew Rate

A. Op Amp Circuit

B. Input Waveforms

C. Output Waveforms

maximum positive output is 10 µs. In terms of the usual slew rate ter-
minology, the slew rate is 5 volts per 10 microseconds, or 0.5 V/µs. Even
though the input square wave transition from maximum negative to
maximum positive took a very short time (nanoseconds), the output
could not follow. That, in effect, is what is meant by slew rate. Read the
complete section about slew rate and do the examples before you at-

tempt any slew rate calculations. When we check the 741 op amp data sheet in Appendix A, we will see that the published slew rate is typically 0.5 V/μs.

Once again, it should be emphasized that slew rate considers *both* frequency and amplitude. The mathematical equation that relates slew rate to frequency and amplitude is as follows:

$$S = 2\pi \times f \times V_p \times 10^{-6} \qquad \textbf{(4–1)}$$

where

S = slew rate in V/μs
f = frequency in Hz
V_p = peak volts

With a little manipulation, this equation can be used to determine maximum frequency or maximum amplitude for a given slew rate. Perhaps a simple explanation of the equation will clarify how it is used. A 100 kHz, 10 V peak-to-peak sine wave can be used as an example. See Figure 4–5. Since slew rate is concerned with the maximum change in voltage per unit time, let's see if we can find out what that is for a 100 kHz sine wave. The period for a 100 kHz sine wave is 10 μs. Examining voltage

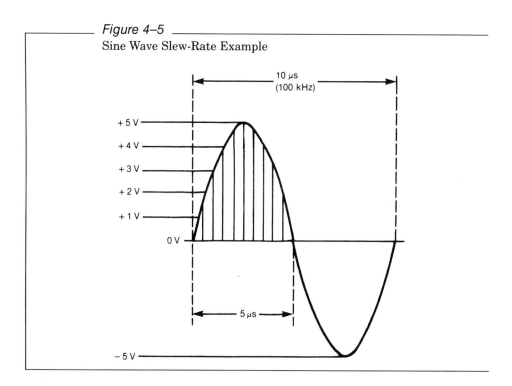

Figure 4–5

Sine Wave Slew-Rate Example

Table 4–1
Voltage Values Calculated from Sine Wave Equation

Time (μs)	Voltage (V)	Difference (V)
0	0	—
0.5	1.55	+1.55
1.0	2.94	+1.39
1.5	4.05	+1.11
2.0	4.75	+0.7
2.5	5.00	+0.25
3.0	4.75	−0.25
3.5	4.05	−0.7
4.0	2.94	−1.11
4.5	1.55	−1.39
5.0	0	−1.55

differences at 1 μs intervals provides the following information. Note that the sine wave is symmetrical, so only the positive half-cycle has been calculated. This is also in keeping with Equation 4–1, which considers *peak*, not peak-to-peak voltage.

From Table 4–1, it appears that the greatest rate of change of voltage appears as the sine wave goes through zero volts. (If you cannot read the voltage values from the sine wave graph as closely as Table 4–1 shows, don't worry. The table values were calculated from the basic equation for a sine wave.) For the 100 kHz, 10 V peak-to-peak sine wave, the rate of change is about 1.55 volts per 0.5 microseconds, or about 3.1 V/μs. The slew rate of the 100 kHz sine wave can be verified by using Equation 4–1. To properly reproduce the input signal, the op amp must have a slew rate 1.5 to 2 times the maximum rate of change of the input signal. It is likely that the 100 kHz, 10 V peak-to-peak sine wave applied to the input of the circuit in Figure 4–4 would appear at the output as shown in Figure 4–6. The type 741 op amp's slew rate of 0.5 V/μs cannot follow the higher input rate of change. Even though the unity gain bandwidth of the op amp is 1 MHz, the slew rate limits the input frequency of high-voltage input signals.

What can Equation 4–1 do for us here? In its basic form, as we first used it, it provided the maximum rate of change of voltage (slew rate) for a sine wave at a selected amplitude and frequency. Comparing the *slew rate* of a signal with the *slew rate characteristic* of an operational amplifier gives an indication of how well the amplifier will reproduce the input signal. A good designer will limit the signal amplitude and frequency to allow about a 2 to 1 margin. Example 4–1 shows the

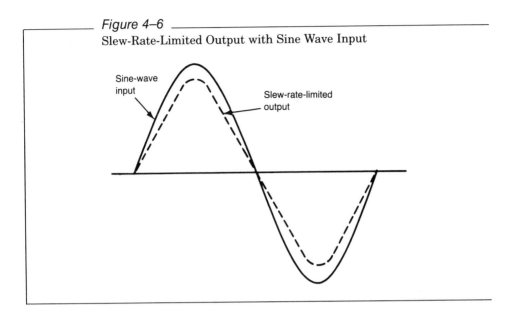

Figure 4–6

Slew-Rate-Limited Output with Sine Wave Input

use of Equation 4–1 to obtain the peak voltage at a chosen frequency that can be faithfully reproduced by an amplifier with a known slew rate. The calculated value is reduced by a factor of 2 to allow a safety margin.

Example 4–1

What is the maximum voltage that a type 741 operational amplifier can provide at 100 kHz without slew-rate limiting?

Solution

$$V_p = \frac{S}{6.28} \times f = \frac{0.5}{(6.28)(100{,}000 \times 0.000001)} = 0.796 \text{ V}$$

where the 0.000001 factor accounts for the use of microseconds in the equation rather than seconds. Providing a 2 to 1 margin, the maximum voltage is, therefore, approximately 0.4 V.

Example 4–2 provides another use of Equation 4–1. As stated, the large-signal response of an operational amplifier is related to *both* amplitude and frequency. The *frequency* at which slew-rate limiting occurs for a given amplitude of operational amplifier output can be determined as shown in Example 4–2.

───────── *Example 4–2* ─────────────────────────────

What is the maximum frequency at which a type 741 operational amplifier can provide a 1 V peak-to-peak output?

Solution

Again, transposing Equation 4–1 gives us

$$f = \frac{S}{(6.28)(V_p)}$$

Then, since a peak-to-peak voltage of 1 V means that the peak voltage (V_p) is 0.5 V, we have

$$f = \frac{0.5}{(0.000001)(6.28)(0.5)} = 0.159 \text{ MHz} = 159 \text{ kHz}$$

A safety factor of 2 shows that 1 V peak-to-peak output from a type 741 operational amplifier will be free of distortion from slew-rate limiting with a safe margin at 79.6 kHz.

We now have another tool with which to analyze and troubleshoot the circuits of operational amplifiers. As we proceed to more complex op amp applications, the knowledge of slew-rate limitations will help explain *why* circuits are designed in a particular way. Awareness of slew-rate limitations may also make it easier to locate reasons for distortion in op amp circuits.

───────── *FEEDBACK AND STABILITY* ─────────────────
     CONSIDERATIONS

Feedback affects more than gain, input resistance, and output resistance. Both frequency response and stability are closely related to the type and magnitude of feedback. Feedback and stability are considered in this section.

Frequency Response

As noted earlier, the term *frequency response* refers to the change in amplification of an op amp as the frequency of the input signal changes. (Frequency response is also used to define filter characteristics as discussed shortly.) We will continue with the logarithmic scales for frequency response graphs. Furthermore, the straight-line approximations

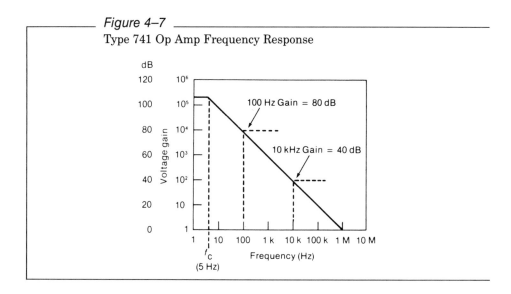

Figure 4–7

Type 741 Op Amp Frequency Response

of the Bode plot will be employed to simplify discussion. The *shape* of the frequency response graph is particularly important as far as amplifier stability is concerned.

The frequency response graph of the type 741 op amp is repeated here as Figure 4–7 so that its use may be further studied. As with any amplifier, the gain is not constant with changing frequency. The traditional droop in gain at low frequencies is not present with op amps because of the direct coupling from stage to stage. No coupling capacitors are used, so gain is achieved even at DC inputs. In fact, all of the circuits shown in Chapter 3 function as DC amplifiers of one sort or another. However, as frequency increases from DC, gain begins to drop. The cause of the high-frequency gain reduction is generally considered to be stray capacity due to IC construction and semiconductor device junction characteristics. These are usually lumped together as a single capacitor for calculation purposes.

Most op amps do not operate without some type of feedback from output to input. Frequency response is just too poor for anything but DC operation. Without feedback, the gain of the op amp is known as *open-loop* gain (A_{ol}). If the open-loop gain is known, the gain at any frequency of operation can be found by the following equation:

$$A = \frac{A_{ol}}{\left[1 + \left(\frac{f}{f_c}\right)^2\right]^{1/2}} \qquad (4\text{–}2)$$

where

A_{ol} = open-loop gain (V_o/V_i)
f = frequency of operation
f_c = cutoff frequency as defined earlier

Note that Equation 4–2 provides gain in absolute terms rather than in dB. We have already stated that it is easier to work with dB than with absolute terms, so gain Equation 4–2 becomes:

$$A_{dB} = 20 \log A_{ol} - 20 \log \left[1 + \left(\frac{f}{f_c}\right)^2 \right]^{1/2} \qquad (4\text{–}3)$$

The first term represents the numerator in the original equation; the second term is the denominator. It is subtracted from the first term because of the rules of operation for logarithms.

Fortunately, it is not necessary to perform all of the calculations if the open-loop gain graph of Figure 4–7 is available. All we need do is construct a vertical line up from the frequency of operation until it intersects the gain curve. Then move horizontally to the left to see the gain in dB. Table 4–2 shows typical calculations at 100 Hz and 10,000 Hz. The results may be compared with Figure 4–7 to verify both mathematical and graphical methods.

As frequency increases, gain drops steadily until it becomes unity, or one. The frequency at unity gain is called f_t. If the behavior of the op amp between f_c, the cutoff frequency, and f_t, the unity gain frequency, is investigated, it will be seen that gain drops at a constant rate. This rate is the *roll-off rate* and is 20 dB/decade (6 dB/octave) for the type 741 amplifier. (These terms were described earlier.) Actually, the type 741 op amp is *internally compensated* to achieve the 20 dB/decade characteristic. Without compensation, most op amps would be unstable. The reasons for instability are discussed in the following paragraphs.

We have to go back a long way to show the reason for op amp instability. Let's start with the simple *R-C* combination of Figure 4–8A, which is called a **low-pass filter**. When a constant-voltage, varying-frequency input is provided to a low-pass filter, it responds as shown in the accompanying frequency response graph. The reason for the term *low-pass* should now be evident; the filter *passes* low frequencies and reduces or attenuates high frequencies. There is even a cutoff frequency f_c that is defined in the same manner as the op amp's f_c. See Figure 4–8B. If the roll-off rate of the low-pass filter is examined, it will be found to be 20 dB/decade. The reason for the roll-off rate may be proved mathematically. For our purposes, however, it is adequate to know that the 20 dB/decade **slope** (another word for roll-off rate) is basic to electronic theory.

<hr>

_____ *Table 4–2* _____

Operational Amplifier AC Gain Calculations

$$A = \frac{A_{ol}}{\left[1 + \left(\frac{f}{f_c}\right)^2\right]^{1/2}} \qquad\qquad A = 20 \log A_{ol} - 20 \log \left[1 + \left(\frac{f}{f_c}\right)^2\right]^{1/2}$$

100 Hz:

$$A = \frac{200,000}{\left[1 + \left(\frac{100}{5}\right)^2\right]^{1/2}}$$

$$= \frac{200,000}{\sqrt{401}}$$

$$= \frac{200,000}{20.02}$$

$$= 9990 \text{ or } \approx 10,000$$

$$A = 20 \log 200,000 - 20 \log \left[1 + \left(\frac{100}{5}\right)^2\right]^{1/2}$$

$$= (20)(5.3) - (20)(1.3)$$

$$= 106 - 26$$

$$= 80 \text{ dB}$$

10 kHz:

$$A = \frac{200,000}{\left[1 + \left(\frac{10,000}{5}\right)^2\right]^{1/2}}$$

$$= \frac{200,000}{\sqrt{4,000,001}}$$

$$= \frac{200,000}{2,000}$$

$$= 100$$

$$A = 20 \log 200,000 - 20 \log \left[1 + \left(\frac{10,000}{5}\right)^2\right]^{1/2}$$

$$= (20)(5.3) - (20)(3.3)$$

$$= 106 - 66$$

$$= 40 \text{ dB}$$

Assumptions: $f_c = 5$ Hz $A_{ol} = 200,000 = 106$ dB

<hr>

Phase Response

Another concept basic to electronic theory is that of the phase response of a simple low-pass filter. In our early electronic studies, we learned that in a series *R-C* circuit the voltage across the capacitor *lagged* the voltage applied across the total circuit. Those calculations showed that the phase angle was near zero at low frequencies and near 90° at high frequencies. When resistance and capacitive reactance were equal, the phase angle was 45°. (All phase angles are lagging, or negative.) Further calculations during our early study of AC theory showed that the voltage across the capacitor was 3 dB lower than the voltage across the total circuit at this point. Thus, the definition of cutoff frequency (f_c) is the same for a low-pass filter as for op amps. Figure 4–8C is a graph of the

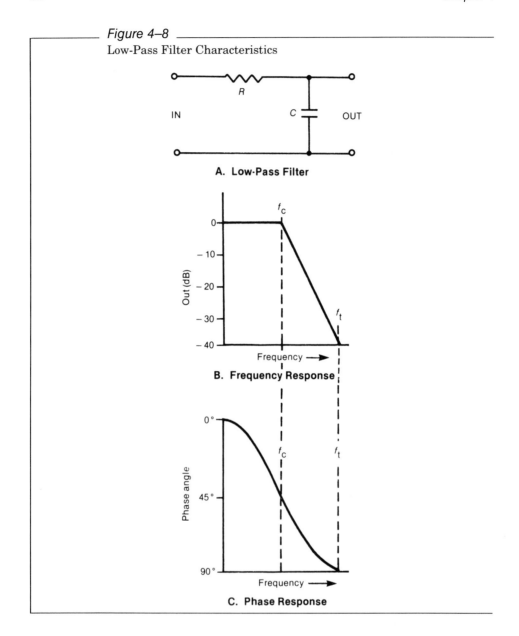

Figure 4–8

Low-Pass Filter Characteristics

A. Low-Pass Filter

B. Frequency Response

C. Phase Response

phase response of a low-pass filter correlated with the frequency response graph of Figure 4–8B.

The correlation between low-pass filters and op amps is due to the manner in which we view op amp equivalent circuits. Let's assume an imaginary single-stage op amp (noninverting). The output equivalent circuit is shown in Figure 4–9A. As usual, the op amp is considered

Figure 4–9

Operational Amplifier Characteristic

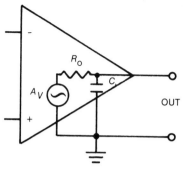

**A. Op Amp Output
as Low-Pass Filter**

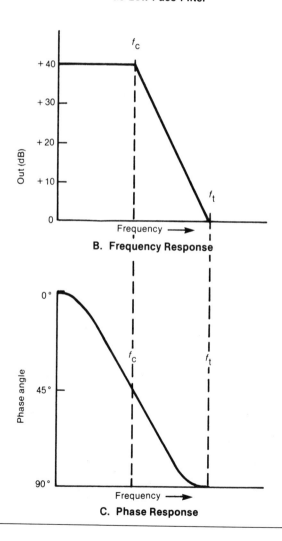

B. Frequency Response

C. Phase Response

equivalent to a voltage generator whose output is equal to the input voltage multiplied by the open-loop gain ($A_{ol} \times V_i$). The equivalent voltage generator applies its voltage to the output terminals of the op amp through an equivalent resistance (R_o). That's all we had to consider when working only with DC. However, when we use AC, any capacitance in the circuit must be taken into consideration. All capacitance internal to the op amp is lumped together into a single equivalent capacitance (C) connected in parallel with the output. Therefore, the output circuit of the op amp is actually a low-pass filter. When the equivalent voltage generator is combined with the equivalent low-pass filter, we have a device with the frequency and phase response of the low-pass filter but with amplification. In Figure 4–8, the response of the low-pass filter for a unity-gain amplifier was plotted arbitrarily starting at zero dB, and, as frequency increased, the output decreased, resulting in negative dB (less than 0) output. If the equivalent amplifier has a 40 dB gain, then the whole curve shifts upward on the scale by 40 dB (see Figure 4–9B). Note that the shape of the curve does not change, nor does the roll-off rate. The curve merely shifts upward, with the dB gain of the amplifier added to the original value of the low-pass filter. Phase response does not change as a result of amplification (Figure 4–9C).

Composite Response

When we add another section to a low-pass filter, two things happen. Both the roll-off and phase characteristics change. The roll-off characteristics are additive. That is, if each section has the basic 20 dB/decade roll-off, then the combination will have a 40 dB/decade characteristic. The phase shifts are also additive. The composite characteristics depend on the individual sections of the filter. Let's take a look at the amplifier equivalents of a two-stage op amp. The first stage (F_1) has a gain of 30 dB with a cutoff frequencey (f_c) of 400 Hz. The second stage (F_2), with a gain of 20 dB, also has a cutoff frequency of 400 Hz. Both are graphed separately in Figure 4–10. What happens when the output of the first stage is connected to the noninverting input of the second stage? Recall that, when one amplifier follows another, amplification of the first is multiplied by the amplification of the second. However, since we are using dB to describe stage gain, the dB figures are *added*. Decibels are logarithmic, and with logarithms, remember, multiplication is performed by adding. Rather than do all that mathematically, though, why not just add the values on the graph. The composite curve resulting from the combined gain characteristics of both stages is also shown in Figure 4–10. Note that both the 20 dB/decade and 40 dB/decade slopes extend *below* the 0 dB line into negative dB regions.

The phase response of each of the 400 Hz low-pass filters is plotted in Figure 4–11. Since the filters are identical, their phase responses

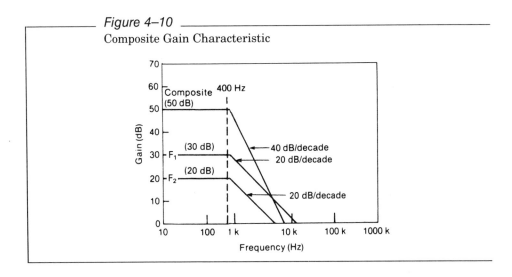

Figure 4–10

Composite Gain Characteristic

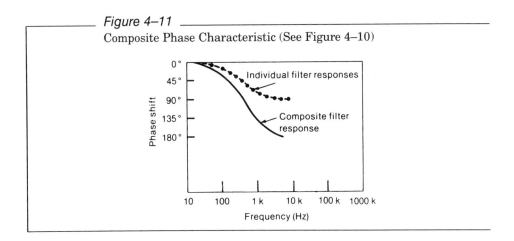

Figure 4–11

Composite Phase Characteristic (See Figure 4–10)

are identical and fall on top of each other. Logically, if the first section shifts the phase 45° at a particular frequency, then the second section will add another 45° shift. Phase shifts, therefore, are additive, as shown on the composite phase shift curve in Figure 4–11. Note that the composite gain is the sum of the individual gains and that the roll-off rate of the combination is 40 dB/decade—the sum of the individual roll-off rates.

If cutoff frequencies of two or more series-connected low-pass filter sections are not the same, strange things happen. The gain characteristics of a 30 dB gain 400 Hz section followed by a 20 dB gain 1000 Hz

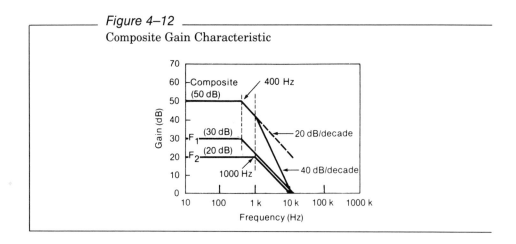

Figure 4–12
Composite Gain Characteristic

section is graphed in Figure 4–12. Table 4–3 provides some examples from the frequency response graph of Figure 4–12. Remember, the composite gain is the sum of the gains of the first stage (F_1) and the second stage (F_2).

Figure 4–12 and Table 4–3 show that although each individual stage has a roll-off rate of 20 dB/decade, the composite characteristic contains two roll-off rates. The first cutoff frequency is the cutoff frequency of F_1, 400 Hz. From 400 Hz to 1000 Hz (the cutoff frequency of F_2), the roll-off rate is 20 dB/decade. From 1000 Hz (the second cutoff frequency) to the unity gain frequency, the composite roll-off rate is 40 dB/decade. The addition of yet another stage will merely increase the roll-off rate in some part of the frequency response curve to 60 dB/decade. If we were expecting our amplifier to work as a filter, the increased roll-off rate would be desirable. However, the increased roll-off rate brings with it a lot of trouble, which brings us to the subject of real-life op amps and feedback.

Most real-life op amps have at least three separate internal amplifier stages. Each of the stages contributes a 90° maximum phase shift at its unity gain frequency. As seen from the discussion in previous paragraphs, that makes it possible to have as much as 270° of phase shift and a roll-off rate as high as 60 dB/decade at *some frequency*. Now comes the problem. As we saw in earlier chapters, negative feedback is almost universally used to stabilize op amp operation. Stabilization assumed, however, that feedback was indeed negative—that is, in opposition to the input signal of the op amp. With the input signal applied to the noninverting input, the output signal is in phase with the input. But when the fed-back output signal is applied to the inverting input, the desired result is obtained. Remember, the signal at the inverting input

Table 4–3

Frequency and Gain Values from Frequency Response Graph

Frequency (Hz)	Gain (dB)		
	F_1	F_2	Composite
50	30.0	20.0	50.0
200	30.0	20.0	50.0
400	30.0	20.0	50.0
600	26.5	20.0	46.5
1000	22.0	20.0	42.0
2000	16.0	14.0	30.0
4000	10.0	8.0	18.0
6000	6.5	4.5	11.0
10000	2.0	0.0	2.0

results in an output of opposite phase to that of a signal at the noninverting input.

Stability

Now that we're using AC input to the op amp, we need to further investigate the effects of feedback. It was determined earlier that negative feedback reduced op amp gain, and this fact was used to obtain accurate gain values with DC amplifiers. Earlier in this chapter, the term _gain-bandwidth product_ was also mentioned. Once again, bandwidth for op amps is defined as the number of cycles per second (hertz) from DC to the cutoff frequency f_c. The frequency response curve for the type 741 op amp shows that the gain is unity (one) at a frequency of 1 MHz. Such conditions occur when the voltage follower configuration is used. Therefore, the gain-bandwidth product is 1,000,000. Now assume enough feedback to increase the gain to 10 (20 dB). A noninverting amplifier configuration with a R_f/R_1 ratio of 10 will accomplish the desired results. The effect of the increased gain shows as a _reduction_ in maximum frequency, which is shown in Figure 4–7 by the intersection of the horizontal 20 dB gain scale with the frequency response curve. The intersection point is at 100,000 Hz (100 kHz). Note that the product of gain (10) times bandwidth (100,000 Hz) is 1,000,000. The gain-bandwidth product is constant, as can be seen by examining other gain settings. It should be noted, however, that the constant gain-bandwidth product factor is true _only_ when the roll-off rate is 20 dB/decade. At other roll-off rates, things get more challenging.

Now you may begin to see what one of the problems might be

when using op amps with AC input. That nice gain of 100 dB or so can only be achieved with a bandwidth of 5 Hz. Since the audio bandwidth required for relatively good reproduction of sound and music extends to 20,000 Hz, we're not going to get very good results with a bandwidth of only 5 Hz. If a 20,000 Hz bandwidth is required, the open-loop frequency response curve shows that we can only achieve a gain of between 20 and 30 dB. Negative feedback must be applied to limit the gain to that range.

But more about gain and bandwidth later. Let's investigate the effects of feedback and phase response a little more. As long as feedback is negative, the desired stabilization of operation occurs. If, however, the fed-back signal somehow manages to appear in phase with the incoming signal and is of sufficient amplitude, an unstable condition known as **oscillation** can exist. A circuit is oscillating when its output frequency no longer depends on its external input frequency. In other words, the circuit provides its own input signal. There are circuits whose primary function is oscillation, but when amplification is the desired result, oscillation is *not* desirable.

Is there any way that conditions for oscillation can exist in op amp circuits? First, any amplifier with gain develops an output signal that is larger than the input signal, which satisfies one of the criteria for oscillation. The other condition required for oscillation relates to the phase response of an op amp. Let's begin with an op amp like the 741. It is internally compensated so that its roll-off rate is 20 dB/decade, at least to its unity gain frequency. That means that at any frequency from DC to the unity gain frequency, no matter how high or how low the gain, a maximum 90° phase shift can occur (see Figure 4–9). As implied earlier, the fed-back signal from the output to inverting input must be 180° out of phase with the noninverting input signal. The inverting input signal then will cause an increasing output instead of a decreasing output, and oscillation will occur. Circuits and wiring external to the op amp may cause phase shift that adds to the op amp phase shift. It is highly unlikely, however, that enough additional phase shift could be established by the external circuit to extend the total phase shift of a 20 dB/decade op amp to 180°. Therefore, an op amp with a 20 dB/decade roll-off characteristic is **unconditionally stable**.

An op amp with a 40 dB/decade roll-off characteristic can develop up to 180° of phase shift internally, as shown in Figure 4–13. However, the full phase shift may not occur until the unity gain frequency is reached. Since the criteria for oscillation is 180° of phase shift *and* a fed-back signal greater than the original input signal, it would seem that an amplifier with a 40 dB/decade roll-off characteristic would also be **unconditionally stable**. Unfortunately, there may also be external circuit phase shift present, and the 180° phase shift criterion can be met *before* unity gain is reached. In addition, manufacturing tolerances can cause a few percentage points of variation in op amp characteristics.

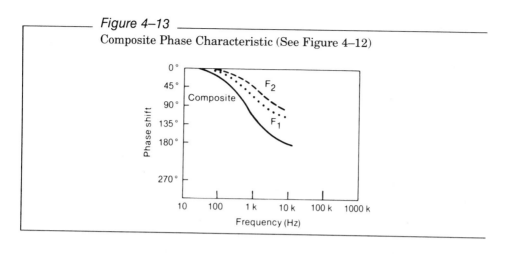

Figure 4–13

Composite Phase Characteristic (See Figure 4–12)

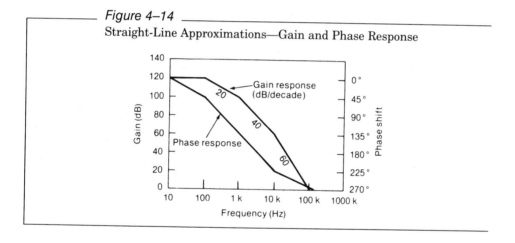

Figure 4–14

Straight-Line Approximations—Gain and Phase Response

Therefore, the 40 dB/decade roll-off characteristic is considered to be **conditionally stable**. Common practice is to leave about a 45° **phase margin** to ensure stable operation.

If a 60 dB/decade roll-off characteristic is encountered, the op amp circuit will *surely* oscillate at some frequency. Although the phase response of a 60 dB/decade characteristic was not graphed when phase response was discussed earlier, the trend was evident from the 20 dB/decade and the 40 dB/decade response. The 270° total phase shift of the 60 dB/decade roll-off characteristic will reach 180° at some gain, and oscillation will set in.

Figure 4–14 summarizes the gain/phase response information

discussed in previous paragraphs. Refer to this figure often as operational amplifier applications are discussed. Much important information is shown in the figure, and it will help in understanding circuit operation.

FREQUENCY COMPENSATION

It is relatively easy to use op amps like the 741. They are internally compensated so that the roll-off rate cannot exceed 20 dB/decade. Consequently, internal phase shift cannot reach 180° before the unity gain frequency is reached, and oscillation should not occur. When the type 741 op amp frequency response curve is used, it is no problem to determine what a circuit's gain and bandwidth characteristics are. Knowing the slew rate of the op amp even allows easy determination of large-signal response. Given the characteristics of the type 741 op amp, let's analyze and evaluate the circuit of Figure 4–15.

Example 4–3

Calculate the closed-loop gain of the inverter circuit of Figure 4–15.

Solution

$$A_{cl} \approx \frac{R_f}{R_1} \approx \frac{1,000,000}{10,000} \approx 100 \qquad \text{or 40 dB}$$

Figure 4–15
Type 741 Inverter Amplifier

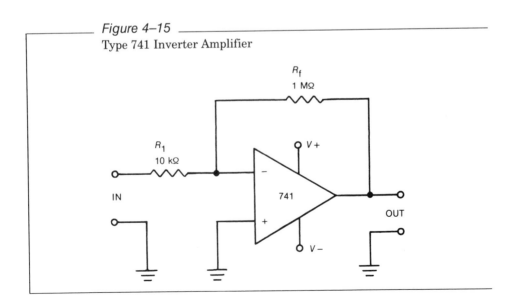

Bandwidth of the amplifier circuit is 10 kHz. By extending the 40 dB gain line to the frequency response curve (Figure 4–7), it can be seen that the two lines intersect at about 10 kHz. This point identifies the cutoff frequency of the op amp circuit with feedback. Since the 40 dB gain line intersects the frequency response curve at a 20 dB/decade slope, oscillation should not occur.

_____ *Example 4–4* _____

Calculate the maximum output amplitude possible for the circuit in Figure 4–15. The slew rate of the type 741 op amp is 0.5 V/μs.

Solution

For $f = 1$ kHz,

$$V_p = \frac{s}{2\pi f} = \frac{0.5}{(6.28)(1000)(0.000001)} = 79.6 \text{ V peak}$$

For $f = 10$ kHz,

$$V_p = \frac{s}{2\pi f} = \frac{0.5}{(6.28)(10,000)(0.000001)} = 7.96 \text{ V peak}$$

With a gain of 40 dB (100), input signal amplitude would have to be limited to less than 0.0796 V peak to ensure that slew-rate limiting would not occur.

When an op amp is internally compensated, its roll-off characteristic is controlled so that unity gain occurs before 180° of phase shift happens. Basically, the frequency response of the amplifier is controlled. If the roll-off characteristic of a typical uncompensated op amp is examined, it will be found to have three or more *different* roll-off rates. Figure 4–16 shows the frequency response curve of an uncompensated op amp. Note the 20 dB, 40 dB, and 60 dB per decade roll-off rates. Now let's connect a negative feedback network such as was used in Figure 4–15. Using an R_f/R_1 ratio of 10,000/1, circuit gain would be 10,000, or 80 dB. Remember, closed-loop gain depends primarily on the ratio of the components in the feedback path. The line for 80 dB closed-loop gain intersects the line for open-loop gain at 10 kHz. Note that the new cutoff frequency (f_c) is now higher than the open-loop gain cutoff frequency. Furthermore, the rate of closure between open-loop gain and closed-loop gain lines is a measure of stability of the closed-loop circuit. The 20 dB/decade closure rate for 80 dB gain is equivalent to a maximum open-loop phase shift of 90°. As discussed earlier, this is a stable condition. Thus, if we are willing to settle for a cutoff frequency of 10 kHz and a gain of 80 dB, the uncompensated op amp will be adequate.

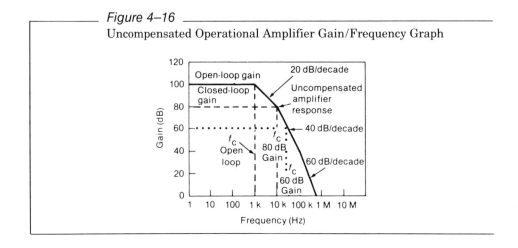

Figure 4–16

Uncompensated Operational Amplifier Gain/Frequency Graph

If the R_f/R_1 ratio is changed to 1000/1, circuit gain drops to 60 dB, or 1000. The closed-loop/open-loop intercept is now at a still higher frequency, approximately 40 kHz. Note, however, that the rate of closure of the 60 dB gain setting is 40 dB/decade. A maximum of 180° of phase shift occurs at this slope, and operation is only conditionally stable. Operation at this gain should be avoided.

Operation at 40 dB gain and below results in a closure rate of 60 dB/decade. Maximum phase shift at this slope is 270°. Instability is sure to result. Fortunately, compensation can allow operation even at unity gain, which is the worst-case condition. Let's see what compensation really is.

Each stage of an op amp behaves as an amplified low-pass filter, and a 20 dB/octave roll-off characteristic is typical. When low-pass filter sections are connected together, their roll-off characteristics become additive. That is how op amps attain 40 dB and 60 dB/decade. Most uncompensated op amps have terminals labeled "frequency compensation," "phase compensation," or "roll-off." These terminals permit connection of external components, such as capacitors and resistors, that control the phase lag of the op amp. For example, if a large-enough capacitor is connected, its phase lag will overcome the effect of the smaller stray and junction capacitances. In fact, one method of roll-off control merely connects an appropriate capacitor from the roll-off control terminal to ground. The brute-force method works but has some disadvantages. We will investigate a number of different methods for control of the roll-off characteristic and show the effect of each.

There is little need for the technician or analyst to calculate components required for compensation purposes. Each manufacturer's specification sheets supply the information necessary to compensate their

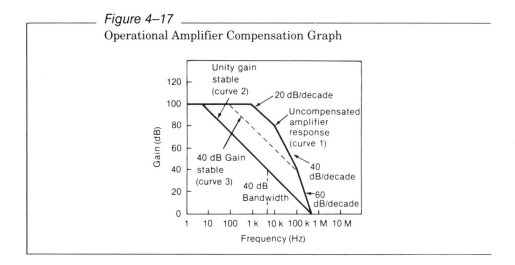

Figure 4–17

Operational Amplifier Compensation Graph

op amp for specific gain and frequency response. However, various types of compensation will be discussed here so that the purpose and common values of specific components in op amp circuits will be recognized.

One of the primary reasons for op amp compensation is to achieve stable operation at the highest required frequency and at or below a specified gain. The effects of working with increased feedback (lower gain) at higher frequencies were demonstrated in the discussion of Figure 4–16. As noted, the worst-case condition occurred at unity gain, when maximum feedback was present. If stable operation at unity gain and above is a requirement, then the roll-off characteristic must be at 20 dB/decade when it passes through the unity gain frequency point on the curve. Curve 2 on Figure 4–17 represents such a graph. Note that the cutoff frequency (f_c) of curve 2 is lower than that of curve 1. Therefore, it has been necessary to trade bandwidth for stability. The brute-force method of compensation (Figure 4–18A) is particularly notorious for large bandwidth reduction. At 40 dB gain, for example, the bandwidth has dropped from 100 kHz to well below 10 kHz.

A resistor and capacitor in series are often used to soften the effects of brute-force compensation. This generally provides better high-frequency response. Instead of forcing the *complete* roll-off characteristic to 20 dB/decade, only that portion of interest for a specific gain/bandwidth application is restricted. Once the specified high frequency is reached, the roll-off is allowed to assume a steeper slope. The amplifier is restricted to the designed gain and higher. Operation at gains less than the design value are on a roll-off characteristic greater than 20 dB/decade. Hence, instability can result. R_1 and C_1 in Figure 4–18B provide compensation that results in characteristics similar to curve 3 in Fig-

Figure 4–18

Operational Amplifier Compensation Methods

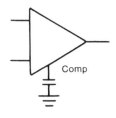

A. Brute-Force Compensation

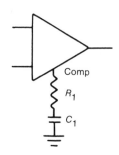

B. Lag Compensation

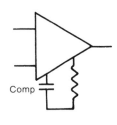

C. Improved Lag Compensation

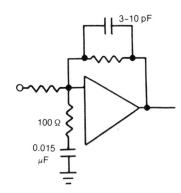

D. Input Compensation

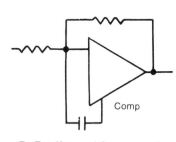

E. Feedforward Compensation

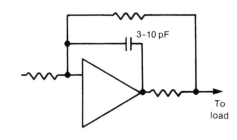

F. Capacitive Load Compensation

Note: Values shown are typical.
          Unmarked components are selected from manufacturer data.

ure 4–17. Note that the bandwidth has improved when compared with curve 2.

Many op amps connect compensating components from output to input of one of the intermediate amplifier stages instead of from output of the intermediate stage to ground. Smaller values of capacitors may be used in this configuration due to the apparent amplification of the capacitor value by the **Miller effect**. This method of compensation (Figure 4–18C) is especially useful for compensated amplifiers, where the capacitor is included as a part of the op amp IC chip. It is difficult to fabricate large-value capacitors on the tiny IC chip, so advantage is taken of the Miller effect.

When compensation is also required to optimize slew rate, the compensation network is connected to the op amp input stage as shown in Figure 4–18D. Sometimes, in stubborn cases of instability, compensation networks will even be connected directly across the differential inputs of the op amp. Except for the direct connection to the input terminals, you will probably not know what kind of compensation you are using. The manufacturer merely provides a set of gain/frequency response curves with component compensation values for each curve. The designer usually picks one of the standard curves. If component values do not agree with manufacturers' specification sheets, then it is probable that the designer has provided a custom design. The reader should be alert to this possibility, but it should not be considered overly important. Knowing the purpose of compensation is the most important factor.

Each of the compensation methods just discussed is shown in Figure 4–18. Also shown, but not discussed, are **feedforward compensation** (Figure 4–18E) and **capacitive load compensation** (Figure 4–18F). Become familiar with these circuit arrangements. They appear throughout op amp equipment.

SUMMARY

In Chapter 4, the major ideas necessary for understanding op amp applications to AC circuits have been shown. When combined with the DC information of Chapters 2 and 3, the whole world of operational amplifiers appears. The use of logarithmic scales for frequency response graphs shows such important AC characteristics as cutoff frequency, unity gain frequency, and roll-off characteristics. Simplification of frequency response graphs by using Bode plots make frequency response and gain-bandwidth product characteristics much easier to visualize. When combined with phase response information, frequency response graphs and Bode plots provide complete small-signal characteristics of operational amplifiers. (Large-signal characteristics are defined using slew-rate specifications.)

The use of feedback to extend frequency response provides a means of improving operational amplifier characteristics. It should be noted, however, that roll-off characteristics, phase response, and slew-rate are interrelated so that care must be taken when applying feedback. Unstable operation may result at specific gain and frequency combinations, and either internal or external compensation may be required.

Much remains to be said about operational amplifiers, but the fundamentals have been covered. We are now ready to take the first step into the real world of operational amplifiers. Audio applications will be examined next. We will consider how operational amplifiers contribute to audio circuits.

QUESTIONS

1. Why is it necessary to use logarithmic scales rather than linear scales for frequency response graphs?

2. Define the following terms: (a) cutoff frequency, (b) unity gain frequency, (c) roll-off characteristic, (d) Bode plot, (e) slew rate, and (f) gain-bandwidth product.

3. Explain the meaning of 20 dB/decade to describe roll-off characteristic. Is there any other way to describe roll-off characteristic? Explain.

4. Why would you use a Bode plot in preference to a conventional frequency response graph?

5. Discuss how a conventional frequency response graph and/or a Bode plot is used to determine gain and bandwidth of an operational amplifier circuit.

6. What is a phase response graph? Why is it important in operational amplifier applications?

7. Explain the difference between small-signal frequency response and slew-rate limitations for operational amplifiers.

8. What factors affect small-signal frequency response of operational amplifiers?

9. What factors affect slew rate of operational amplifiers?

10. Why is closed-loop gain in an operational amplifier less than open-loop gain?

11. Can closed-loop gain and bandwidth be determined without using mathematical formulas? How?

12. Draw a graph showing the relationship between roll-off characteristics and phase response of operational amplifiers.

13. Under what conditions will an operational amplifier circuit be unconditionally stable?

14. Under what conditions will an operational amplifier circuit be conditionally stable?

15. What is the relationship between gain and bandwidth in an operational amplifier circuit with negative feedback?

16. Why is a phase margin needed in operational amplifier circuits with feedback? What is considered an adequate phase margin?

17. Discuss the reasons for more than one roll-off rate in an uncompensated operational amplifier.

18. What must be done to an uncompensated operational amplifier to ensure unconditionally stable operation?

19. What must be done to an uncompensated operational amplifier to ensure conditionally stable operation?

20. Show an example of brute-force compensation. What type of stability would result with this type of compensation?

21. Show an example of improved lag compensation. What type of stability would result with this type of compensation?

22. What type of compensation is required to improve slew-rate limitation of an operational amplifier. Show an example.

23. Show an example of feedforward compensation. What is the primary purpose for this type of compensation?

24. Show an example of capacitive load compensation. What is the primary purpose of this type of compensation?

=== PROBLEMS ===

1. Determine the slew rate of a 10 V peak-to-peak sine wave at frequencies of (a) 5 kHz, (b) 10 kHz, (c) 15 kHz, (d) 25 kHz, (e) 75 kHz, and (f) 600 kHz.

2. Which of the above signals will be slew-rate limited in an amplifier with a slew rate of 0.5 V/µs?

3. Which of the above signals will be slew-rate limited in an amplifier with a slew rate of 10 V/µs?

4. What is the slew-rate characteristic required of an operational amplifier for each of the signals in Problem 1?

5. Assume an operational amplifier with open-loop DC gain of 100 dB, a cutoff frequency of 100 Hz, and a unity gain frequency of 10 MHz. Calculate the gain, both in absolute terms and in dB, for the following frequencies: (a) 10 Hz, (b) 500 Hz, (c) 1500 Hz, (d) 10 kHz, and (e) 500 kHz.

6. Consider that the operational amplifier of Problem 5 is connected in the conventional inverter configuration. Draw a diagram of the circuit showing component values for each of the frequencies in Problem 5.

7. If the slew rate of the operational amplifier in Problem 5 is 2 V/μs, calculate the maximum peak-to-peak input voltage allowed for each frequency.

5

Audio
Applications

OBJECTIVES   After studying Chapter 5, you will be able to

1. Recognize the important op amp characteristics that must be considered for audio frequency applications.
2. Show how to use an op amp designed for dual power supplies with a single power supply.
3. Define noise, thermal noise, shot noise, and flicker noise.
4. Define the concepts of low-frequency roll-off characteristics control.
5. Show how to improve slew-rate response of operational amplifiers used in audio frequency systems.
6. Explain the effect of frequency and phase compensation on closed-loop characteristics of audio frequency op amps.
7. Describe the characteristics of an audio frequency preamplifier and equalizer amplifier.
8. Explain why RIAA equalization is necessary.
9. Explain how passive and active tone control circuits operate.
10. Describe the differences between conventional op amps, audio frequency op amps, power op amps, and audio frequency power op amps.

INTRODUCTION

With the added knowledge of the AC characteristics of operational amplifiers, it is now possible to investigate many more electronic devices. Audio frequency applications of operational amplifiers are discussed in this chapter, where the basic slew-rate and loop-gain requirements are shown.

Common audio amplifier difficulties, such as noise, offset problems, and frequency compensation requirements, are presented in sufficient detail to aid understanding of audio amplifier circuits. Preamplifiers, equalizer amplifiers, tone controls, and power amplifiers are combined to form a typical audio amplifier system. Particular attention is paid to operational amplifiers designed specifically for audio and power applications.

_____ BASIC AUDIO AMPLIFIER CONCEPTS _____

Within the broad area classified as low-frequency amplifiers falls the region of **audio amplifiers**. Quoting from National Semiconductor's _Audio/Radio Handbook,_

> Audio is really a rather specialized area, and its requirements upon an integrated circuit may be stated quite concisely: The IC must process complex AC signals comprised of frequencies ranging from 20 Hertz to 20k Hertz, whose amplitudes vary from a few hundred microvolts to several volts, with a transient nature characterized by steep, compound wavefronts separated by unknown periods of absolute silence. This must be done without adding distortion of any sort, either harmonic, amplitude, or phase; and it must be done noiselessly—in the sun, and in the snow—forever. [National Semiconductor Corporation, _Audio/Radio Handbook,_ copyright 1980.]

Unfortunately, no such IC exists.

General Characteristics of Audio Amplifiers

In choosing op amps for audio applications, one parameter is of prime importance. Slew rate must be considered. As mentioned earlier, _slew rate_ is the maximum rate of change of the op amp's output voltage per unit time. Whereas bandwidth is usually considered in terms of small-signal input, slew rate is the important factor with large-signal input. A general rule of thumb states that a sine wave output ceases being small signal when its maximum rate of change equals the slew rate of the op amp. Bandwidth is also closely related to slew rate. Generally, wide bandwidth op amps also possess a high slew rate.

Open-loop gain is another important factor to be considered when using op amps in audio applications. Distortion, frequency response, output impedance, and input impedance are all determined by the loop gain of the circuit. _Loop gain_ is the difference (in dB) between open-loop gain and closed-loop gain. Therefore, the greater the open-loop gain the

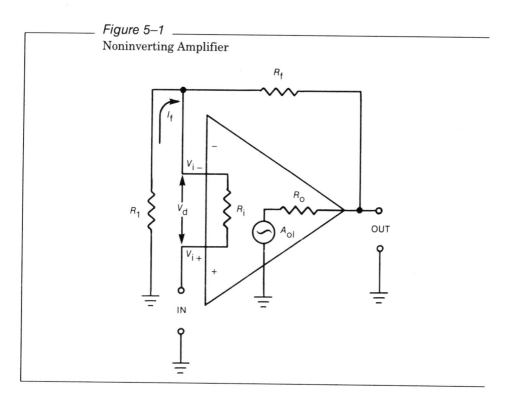

Figure 5–1

Noninverting Amplifier

better. High loop gain gives tighter control over the required circuit characteristics. We will shortly give more attention to loop gain and how to use it.

Typical Circuit Configurations

Most op amps used in audio applications employ either the noninverting or the inverting configuration. Both configurations are reproduced in Figures 5–1 and 5–2 so that we will be able to more easily analyze typical audio circuits.

Single-Supply Operation

Unless specifically designed for operation with a single power supply, most op amps require a dual ($+$ and $-$) supply. With a dual supply, the conditions of Figure 5–3A exist. Zero input results in zero output, ideally. When an AC signal is supplied to the noninverting input, for example, the output variation is an amplified version of the input. Note

Figure 5–2
Inverting Amplifier

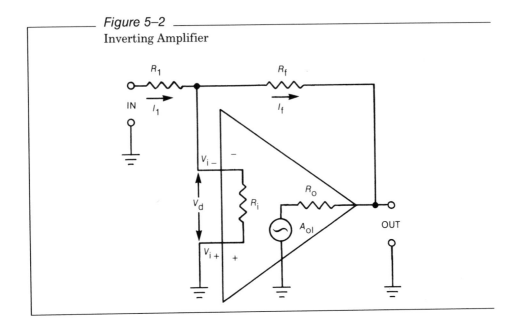

that the output varies above and below a zero reference line. The symmetrical design of the op amp and the dual power supply establish these conditions.

Let's see what happens when an op amp is operated with a single power supply. If, instead of using equal + and − supplies, only a positive supply is used (with the − supply terminal grounded), the symmetry vanishes. In this case, zero input results in a near-zero output, but since there is no − supply, the output cannot be less than zero. Therefore, only the positive-going output will be available. The circuit is no longer linear, or class A, in its operation. Something must be done to center the no-signal output half-way between the + supply voltage and zero volts. Figure 5–3C shows a possible solution. Typical component values are shown for a 741 op amp. Gain and frequency response remain the same as with previously discussed amplifier circuits. The difference is the voltage divider, composed of equal-value resistors R_a and R_b, and bypass capacitor C_a. The voltage divider provides a DC output of $V_{cc}/2$, where V_{cc} is another way of saying V_t. The capacitor C_a maintains the junction of R_a and R_b at AC ground. Symmetry is reestablished, and the output can swing in both the positive and the negative direction. The total voltage swing, however, is reduced because of the lesser supply voltage. See Figure 5–3B. Single-supply operation therefore can be identified by the presence of a voltage divider and the grounded V-terminal. Nonsymmetrical output can also be avoided by

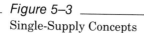

Figure 5–3

Single-Supply Concepts

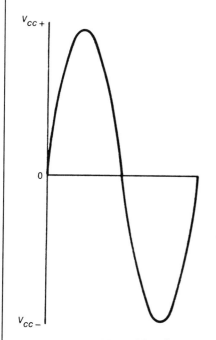

A. Output with Dual Supply

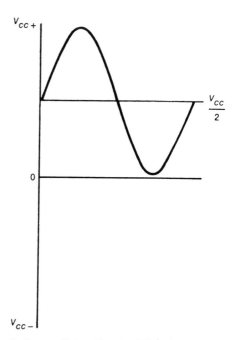

B. Output Using Circuit of Figure 5-3C

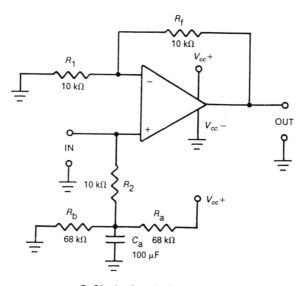

C. Single-Supply Operation

using coupling capacitors to block the DC component of the input signal. Low frequency response may suffer, however.

Noise in Audio Amplifiers

Noise is a term used to describe any unwanted random signal variations. It can be seen on a television set as the dancing black and white specks called "snow." The random hissing and crackling sounds that may come from the speakers of a stereo are caused by noise. It is definitely a problem that must be dealt with in op amp circuits because noise can completely overcome weak desired signals. From a practical standpoint, then, it is best to have lots of signal and very little noise—a high **signal-to-noise ratio** (S/N). We will first discuss the kinds of noise most often encountered and then show how noise is minimized in a well-designed circuit.

Thermal noise, sometimes called **Johnson noise**, is generated by any passive component. Carbon resistors in particular are notorious as sources of thermal noise. Entirely random in nature, thermal noise is caused by the movement of charge carriers in a circuit. Since it is random in nature, thermal noise is present from very low frequencies to extremely high frequencies. The amplitude of thermal noise is directly proportional to temperature, resistance, and circuit bandwidth. Thus, high temperatures, high resistances, and wide bandwidths tend to cause noise problems in amplifiers.

Shot noise is caused by random arrival of charge carriers crossing a potential barrier, as in diodes and transistors. It is also broadband in nature, although it does tend to be the dominant source of noise at high frequencies in op amps. The amplitude of shot noise is proportional to current flow across the potential barrier and to circuit bandwidth. Wide-band amplifiers and high-gain amplifiers with appreciable current flow in the input stages are prime sources of shot noise.

Flicker noise increases as frequency decreases. Hence, it is sometimes called $1/f$ **noise**. It seems to be caused by imperfections in materials and manufacturing techniques. Flicker noise is proportional to current flow and bandwidth.

Popcorn noise is a sudden change in DC level at the output of an op amp. The change can last from as long as seconds to as short as milliseconds. When heard on a loudspeaker, it sounds like popcorn popping. A clear explanation for the occurrence of popcorn noise is awaiting further research.

When analyzing and troubleshooting op amp audio circuits, it is not likely that knowing the intricacies of low-noise design will be necessary. However, if an op amp circuit that has been working correctly becomes "noisy," knowing what the designer considered will be helpful.

Certainly, one of the factors considered was amplifier bandwidth. Most of the noise sources supply unwanted signals over a broad range of frequencies. If the amplifier bandwidth is more than is needed, then more noise will be amplified along with the wanted signal. Therefore, a well-designed amplifier limits the bandwidth to that needed to adequately reproduce the input signal, and no more. Any attempt to change compensation and increase bandwidth will surely be accompanied by an increase in noise.

Noise generated outside the op amp can be minimized by careful design of the input circuit. Thermal noise is a function of resistance. If resistors in the input circuit can be kept to low values, less thermal noise will be generated. Don't be tempted to change feedback ratios by increasing feedback resistor values. The larger values will probably generate more thermal noise. And, while speaking of resistors, if it is necessary to replace input resistors, use special low-noise components. Regular carbon resistors are a common noise source; use instead metal-film or other low-noise resistors.

It has also been found that minimum noise is generated in input circuits if the impedance of the signal source is properly matched to the input of the op amp. A perfectly "clean" amplifier circuit often turns noisy when a different input device is used. If impedance matching is necessary, use transformers. Resistors, remember, generate thermal noise.

Another trick sometimes used to reduce noise is to operate the input stage of an op amp "single-ended." The usual input stage is composed of two (or more) transitors connected as a differential amplifier. Each of the transistors in the first stage contributes shot noise. If the circuit is designed with one of those stages disabled, don't try to change it. You will probably get twice the noise you had before. An example of single-ended operation is shown during discussion of special audio op amps. Further shot noise reduction is sometimes accomplished by *trimming*, or reducing, input current. Even though input current is very small in most op amps, it is still present and can cause noise. FET- (field effect transistor) input op amps tend to reduce the amount of shot noise to an absolute minimum because of the reduction of input current. FETs, remember, are semiconductor devices that do not depend on current flow across a junction for their operation.

Noise in amplifiers is an extremely complex subject, giving rise to volumes of mathematical formulas and theory. Such information is not required of analysts and troubleshooters. Each of the circuits discussed in this chapter will have a specific noise characteristic. That characteristic will be mentioned and explained when deemed advisable during each circuit analysis. Keep noise in mind as each circuit is presented. Failure to consider noise can result in a perfectly good op amp circuit being useless.

AUDIO CIRCUITS IN GENERAL

At a cursory glance, it would appear that the amplifier configurations and circuits already discussed would work as well with AC input as they do with DC input. This is only partially true. For example, both the inverting and noninverting configurations are used. Negative feedback is also employed so that stable operation can be achieved.

Offset Problems

In many AC applications of op amps, more than one stage is used to obtain the required gain and bandwidth. The term used to describe one stage following the other is **cascade**. When op amps are operated in cascade, the *input offset* characteristics come into play. Input offset has been sidestepped so far, and we can continue to ignore it in properly designed circuits. But let's talk about why input offset is a problem. Then the designer's solution can be shown.

Some unbalance *always* exists in an op amp. Although we assume that the voltage difference between the inverting input and the noninverting input is zero, *some* voltage will exist. Input currents will not be exactly equal and opposite, and this results in further unbalance. These nonideal characteristics result in an output voltage other than zero even with no input signal. If the output of one op amp feeds another, then the second op amp will have an input even if there is no input to the first op amp. With the tremendous gains available in modern op amps, these minute offset voltages easily become as large or larger than the actual signal. See Chapter 2 for more information about offset problems.

Most op amps provide external connections to balance the input offset voltage. A potentiometer (sometimes called null offset) is connected between the balance terminals and adjusted so that the output is minimum with no input signal. See Figure 5–4. Now we're back in business—at least until temperature or supply voltage changes. Then the balance is upset, and we're right back in trouble. Still, op amps should be balanced under normal operating conditions in order to maintain a minimum of input offset sensitivity.

Compensated Operational Amplifiers

Actually, in most audio amplifiers it is not necessary to maintain frequency response at DC. An amplifier that can respond faithfully to all frequencies from 20 Hz to 20 kHz is usually considered adequate by all but the most critical listeners. Blocking capacitors used between stages will pass AC but will prevent DC levels from interfering with following stages. Adequate capacitor size is important, of course, and that subject is discussed shortly.

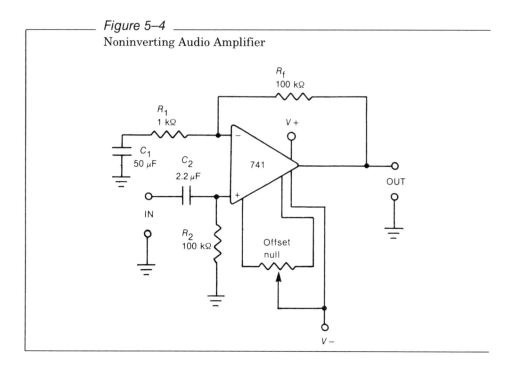

Figure 5–4

Noninverting Audio Amplifier

The use of capacitive coupling does bring with it some problems. Figure 5–4 shows a noninverting audio amplifier using the ever-present type 741 op amp. Reference will be made to this figure for discussion of both concepts and actual analysis. The first thing to examine is C_2, the blocking capacitor that passes AC from the previous stage (or signal source) but blocks any DC present. Note that it connects directly to the noninverting input. Also connected to the noninverting input is a 100 kΩ resistor to ground. This may seem like a strange thing to do, since one of the advantages of using an op amp is the extremely high input impedance it provides. But it is that high input impedance that creates problems. C_2, as any capacitor would, allows a charge to build up based on the potential difference between the two sides of the capacitor. That charge build-up would act just like a fixed DC input to the op amp, and we would be back in trouble with offset problems. R_2 keeps C_2 discharged, providing a path to ground for the charge build-up. The reduced input impedance because of R_2 usually presents no difficulty. Most audio circuits operate at relatively low impedances, and R_2 at 100 kΩ will not present an appreciable load. Therefore, although we have reduced the input impedance, we have sidestepped the input offset problem by the simple means of capacitive coupling.

If, however, any DC voltage develops across R_2 due to leakage or input offset current, the feedback to the inverting input may not be adequate to prevent output saturation. If C_1 was not in the circuit (R_1 connected directly to ground), the feedback factor (β) would be 0.01:

$$\beta = \frac{R_1}{R_1 + R_f} = \frac{1}{101} = 0.01$$

Closed-loop gain, which is $1/\beta$, is approximately 100, or 40 dB. That gives a loop gain of 66 dB:

$$A_1 = A_{ol} - A_{cl} = 106 - 40 = 66$$

In order for the feedback to control the DC output completely, a feedback factor of 1 (a voltage follower configuration) must be attained. That is, we need 100% feedback at DC but only 1% at AC. This is where C_1 comes into the picture.

As you may recall, the feedback factor is a function of both R_1 and R_f. If R_f remains constant, but R_1 increases, the feedback factor increases. In fact, the feedback factor increases as *any* opposition between the R_1-R_f junction and ground increases. The opposition (reactance) of C_1 is inversely proportional to frequency (reactance increases as frequency decreases). At DC, the reactance of C_1 is infinitely high, and R_1 is effectively disconnected from the circuit. The feedback is directly from output to inverting input via R_f. Since no input current flows in an op amp, there is no voltage drop across R_f with R_1 disconnected. The total output voltage is applied to the inverting input, and 100% feedback is achieved. Thus, at DC, the circuit of Figure 5–4 acts as a voltage follower. Any DC voltage appearing across R_2 is canceled, and a zero-volt differential between inverting and noninverting input is maintained.

As frequency increases from DC upward, the reactance of C_1 decreases. The opposition from the R_1-R_f junction point decreases, and consequently the feedback factor decreases. At 3 Hz, the reactance of C_1 is equal to R_1, and the 3 dB point (cutoff frequency) of the $R_1 C_1$ combination is reached. Equation 5–1 may be used to quickly calculate the cutoff frequency of any RC network:

$$f_c = \frac{1}{(2\pi)(R)(C)} \qquad\qquad \textbf{(5–1)}$$

where f_c = cutoff frequency (3 dB point).

────────── *Example 5–1* ──────────

Determine the cutoff frequency (f_{c1}) of the R_1C_1 combination in Figure 5–4.

Solution

$$f_{c1} = \frac{1}{(6.28)(R_1)(C_1)} = \frac{1}{(6.28)(1 \times 10^3)(50 \times 10^{-6})} = 3.18 \text{ Hz}$$

As frequency increases further, the reactance of C_1 continues to decrease and becomes effectively zero. Therefore, the feedback factor is frequency sensitive, and the actual closed-loop gain of the op amp circuit will also be frequency sensitive.

Figure 5–5 shows how to graph the feedback factor combined with the frequency response graph to form the composite frequency response. Note that the Bode-plot method is continued for ease of graphic presentation and that the vertical axis (gain) has been restructured to include negative dB. When the feedback circuitry is investigated, it is seen that the output is less than the input (except at DC). Therefore, the feedback factor is less than 1 (except at DC) and is plotted as negative at the bottom of the graph. Since closed-loop gain is the reciprocal of the feedback factor, it is plotted in the conventional manner. Now we have the feedback factor, open-loop gain, and closed-loop gain identified. The difference between open-loop gain and closed-loop gain is, of course, called "loop gain." Therefore, Figure 5–5 provides, in one graph, the relationships among open-loop gain, closed-loop gain, loop gain, and feedback factor. You may wish to refer to this figure often. It will help you relate

────────── *Figure 5–5* ──────────
Gain Graphs

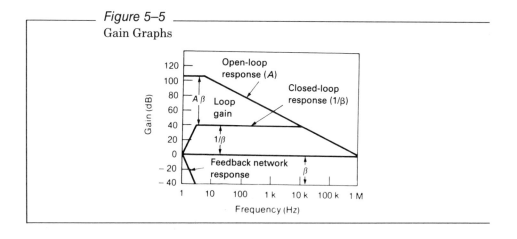

these four very important characteristics of the operational amplifier circuit.

Now for the effect of the R_2C_2 combination on the frequency response of the op amp circuit. R_2C_2 are connected as a **high-pass filter**, allowing high frequencies to pass and restricting low frequencies. Just as with low-pass filters, a cutoff frequency can be calculated.

_____ Example 5–2 _____

Determine the cutoff frequency (f_{c2}) of the R_2C_2 combination in Figure 5–4.

Solution

$$f_{c2} = \frac{1}{(6.28)(R_2)(C_2)} = \frac{1}{(6.28)(100 \times 10^3)(2.2 \times 10^{-6})}$$

$$= 0.72 \text{ Hz}$$

Thus, the lower cutoff frequency of the R_2C_2 combination is 0.72 Hz. If any frequencies below 0.72 Hz are provided at the input to the filter, they will be attenuated at a 20 dB/decade roll-off rate. (The R_2C_2 combination has the characteristics of any simple RC circuit.) Frequencies above 0.72 Hz are not attenuated. Note, however, that the cutoff frequency of the input circuit is well below the cutoff frequency of the feedback circuit. The closed-loop gain will be very low for all frequencies below 3 Hz because of the feedback circuit. Therefore, the input circuit has no appreciable effect on the overall low-frequency response of the op amp circuit.

The small-signal high-frequency cutoff frequency occurs at 10 kHz according to Figure 5–5. This is the intersection of the open-loop and closed-loop gain curves. The composite closed-loop gain curve shows that the circuit has a small-signal gain of 40 dB from 0.72 Hz to 10 kHz (within 3 dB, due to use of the Bode plot). That's not really a very good audio amplifier as far as high-frequency response is concerned. A way to improve the response is discussed as soon as we determine the maximum input amplitude that the circuit can use.

Large-signal response is generally a function of the slew-rate limit of the op amp. As calculated in Chapter 4, the peak output voltage that a type 741 op amp can supply at 10 kHz with 40 dB gain is 7.96 V. That limits the input to 0.0796 V. The combination of slew-rate limiting and poor high-frequency response makes the circuit of Figure 5–4 unsuitable for high-fidelity applications. It could be used for speech and low-to-medium-fidelity systems, but something must be done if better high-frequency response and greater input capability is needed.

One possible answer is to increase the feedback so that gain is reduced to 20 dB. The cutoff frequency at 20 dB gain is 100 kHz, which is more than adequate. Slew-rate limiting has not improved, however, and the gain reduction may be too severe. A better answer is to use an op amp with a higher gain-bandwidth product and better slew-rate characteristic. It is only necessary to have a unity gain frequency of 2 MHz to meet the 20 kHz cutoff frequency requirement at 40 dB gain. Generally, the slew rate improves as unity gain frequency improves, so the input amplitude capability increases as "better" op amps are employed. It is difficult to select a specific op amp as an example of a better device. Numerous manufacturers are almost daily introducing new op amps with bigger and better characteristics. The concepts presented herein should be adequate to select a replacement op amp that would improve the frequency and input amplitude response of the circuit in Figure 5–4. As other circuits are shown, different op amps with extended capability will be encountered. Apply what you have learned here to the new circuits, and the newer op amps will present no difficulties.

Uncompensated Operational Amplifiers

If the type 741 op amp had not been internally compensated, another alternative would have been present. Uncompensated op amps, as noted earlier, provide external connections that allow tailoring of the frequency and phase response to fit specific requirements. Figure 5–6 is an example of the type of information provided by manufacturers.

At the risk of being old fashioned, but in the interest of history, an op amp circuit using the type 709 op amp is shown in Figure 5–7 and accompanies the graphs of Figure 5–6. Complete specification sheets for the 709 op amp are available from the manufacturer. Almost as soon as integrated circuits appeared in the 1960s, operational amplifiers became a candidate for this new technique. The type 709 op amp was one of the first and has remained a useful device even in today's expanding technology. Use of *external* compensation is shown in Figure 5–7. It should be recognized that modern op amps require only a single capacitor, or are internally compensated. However, Figure 5–7 does provide some more practice in analysis and use of manufacturers' information. Chapter 4 discussed frequency compensation methods.

$R_1 C_1$ and $R_2 C_2$ combinations were discussed during examination of type 741 amplifier circuit in Figure 5–4. They perform the same functions in this circuit. Feedback establishes the AC gain at 40 dB for the major portion of the pass band of the amplifier. Very low frequency and DC gain is controlled by the capacitors C_1 and C_2 as in Figure 5–7. High-frequency response is determined as in most op amp circuits by controlling the roll-off characteristic of the op amp. As can be seen from the accompanying graphs, the type 709 op amp is quite versatile. Unity gain

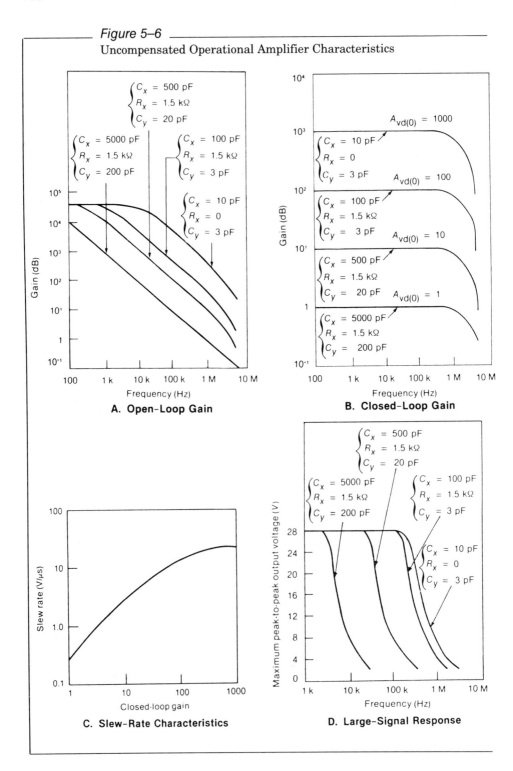

Figure 5–6
Uncompensated Operational Amplifier Characteristics

A. Open-Loop Gain

B. Closed-Loop Gain

C. Slew-Rate Characteristics

D. Large-Signal Response

_____ *Figure 5–7* _____

Using a Compensated Operational Amplifier

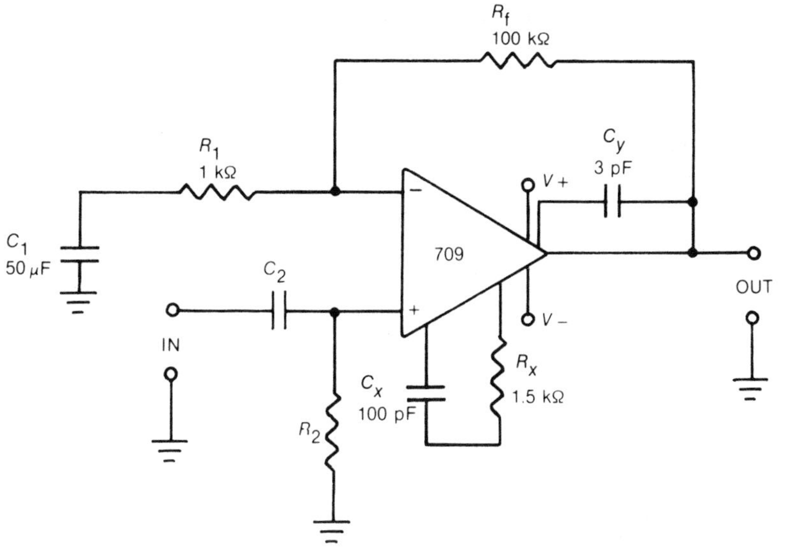

bandwidth can be controlled so that stable operation at many different gain levels is possible. Information from the open-loop frequency response (Figure 5–6A) has been replotted as frequency response for various closed-loop gains (Figure 5–6B) to establish optimum compensation values. For example, optimum response for 40 dB gain operation is R_x = 1.5 kΩ, C_x = 100 pF (picofarads), and C_y = 3 pF. Flat response (output changing no more than 3 dB) under these conditions extends well beyond 100 kHz, which is more than adequate for audio applications.

Slew rate with the selected compensation components is obtained from the graph in Figure 5–6C. The slew rate of approximately 10 V/μs is more than adequate to accommodate a 20 kHz high-frequency audio input. Calculations show that almost 80 V peak at 20 kHz can be accommodated with a slew rate of 10 V/μs:

$$V_p = \frac{SR}{2\pi f} = \left(\frac{10}{10^{-6}}\right)\left(\frac{1}{(6.28)(20 \times 10^3)}\right) = 79.5 \text{ V} \qquad \textbf{(5–2)}$$

Since the normal supply voltage of type 709 op amps is only 15 V, 20 kHz can easily be reproduced without slew-rate limiting. If the output voltage swing versus frequency or full-power bandwidth graph (Figure 5–6D) is available, slew-rate calculations may be unnecessary. A good estimate of large-signal high-frequency response may be estimated from this graph.

Adequate small-signal high-frequency response has been shown to be a matter of the unity gain frequency of the op amp. Therefore, if an op amp designed with a high unity gain frequency is used, no compensation is required. Furthermore, large-signal high-frequency response demands a high slew-rate characteristic. Op amps meeting both of these demands are available and result in the same circuit used with the type 741 op amp. Only the frequency response characteristics change. As mentioned earlier, it is only necessary to have a unity gain frequency of 2 MHz to obtain 20 kHz bandwidth at 40 dB gain. Full-power bandwidth at 20 kHz requires a slew rate of only about 1.25 V/μs for a 10 V peak output. Numerous modern op amps with internal compensation can meet these requirements.

Caution should be exercised, however, when selecting op amps for audio purposes. Specifically, do not use a bandwidth any greater than that required. Remember, from the discussion of noise, that a greater bandwidth results in greater noise output. Many internally compensated op amps have external terminals that allow connection of additional compensation. If the bandwidth of an amplifier is excessive, it is only necessary to connect external capacitors to reduce the upper cutoff frequency. Manufacturers' specification sheets contain frequency response graphs to identify correct capacitor values for specified gains and bandwidths. Examples of this technique are shown in subsequent sections of this book.

TYPICAL AUDIO AMPLIFIERS

Audio amplifiers may be treated as any other electronic system. That is, each of the major functions may be represented by a block, and the blocks combined into a functional block diagram. The block diagram of the system may then be analyzed to determine overall system operation.

Block Diagram

Figure 5–8 is a block diagram of a simple audio amplifier. Operational amplifiers may be used to perform each of the functions and will be discussed in detail in subsequent paragraphs.

Any audio amplifier is merely a control device. Its purpose is to route a controlled amount of power from a power supply to the loudspeaker(s). The amplifier inputs from either microphones, phonograph, or tape machine supply the controlling functions. To perform properly, loudspeakers require low voltage at high currents. Unfortunately, the inputs from microphones or tape machines are very low voltage at very low currents. The various stages shown in Figure 5–8 convert the low-

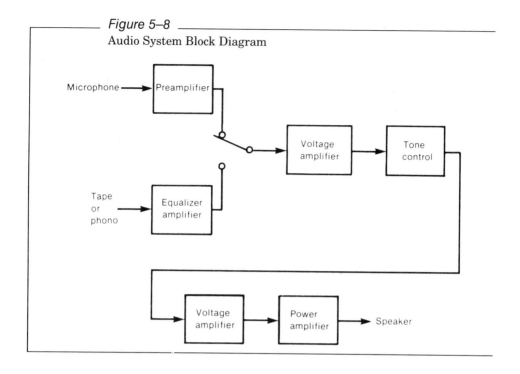

Figure 5–8

Audio System Block Diagram

voltage/low-current inputs to higher-voltage/high-current output by controlling the power supplied by the power source.

The very-low-voltage/low-current inputs from the microphones and/or tape machines must be amplified to be useful. **Preamplifiers** are used to amplify microphone signals. In general, preamplifiers must be able to accept input signals in the microvolt or low-millivolt range. Therefore, preamplifiers must be devices with low noise, so that the input is large in respect to the noise. Preamplifiers must have a frequency response compatible with the audio range and must provide gain on the order of 40 to 60 dB. As will be seen shortly, these requirements may not be compatible.

Equalizer amplifiers perform the same functions as preamplifiers with one exception. Phonograph record and tape input must be handled differently as far as frequency response is concerned. Recordings are purposely made with some frequencies weaker than others, as will be shown shortly. If the recorded material is to sound normal, the audio system must compensate for the recording discrepancies. Equalizer amplifiers have networks that make up for these discrepancies by "tailoring" the frequencies.

The *voltage amplifier* preceding the **tone control** (Figure 5–8) merely provides additional amplification. It also must have a frequency response compatible with the audio frequency range. Since some people prefer other than flat frequency response when listening to recorded material, a tone control is provided. Tone controls allow continuous adjustment of the frequency response of the audio system to best suit the listener. Most tone controls cause reduction in gain, so another voltage amplifier is required. This final voltage amplifier increases the voltage to the magnitude required to drive the power amplifier.

Generally, a *power amplifier* requires a relatively high voltage (in terms of input signal) to control the output of the power supply. The power amplifier, then, effectively is a voltage-to-current converter, with the current coming from the power supply. High voltage/low current at the input to the power amplifier becomes low voltage/high current when routed to the loudspeaker.

Operational amplifiers abound throughout an audio system. It will be seen that while general-purpose op amps may be used, the tendency is toward special-purpose audio op amps. Both are shown, however, to acquaint the reader with basic concepts of the application of operational amplifiers to audio systems.

Preamplifiers

As just noted, preamplifiers must have good frequency response, high stable gain, low noise, and an ability to operate with input signals in the microvolt region. From what we have seen so far, some of these requirements can be met using the simple op amp circuits shown in Figures 5–4 and 5–7. Rather than trying to calculate component values to obtain specific circuit characteristics, let's analyze the circuit as a technician often must do.

Often all the technician has available is the malfunctioning equipment, a schematic diagram, and some test equipment. If circuit specifications are not available, which is often the case, the technician must first determine what the circuit is supposed to do. Then troubleshooting can proceed. Let's use the circuit shown in Figure 5–7 as an example. By using the information supplied in Figure 5–6, we can determine most of the required parameters. Low-frequency response has already been determined and is well within the required range. Mid-frequency gain has been calculated as 40 dB, which is also reasonable. The graph of Figure 5–6B shows the high cutoff frequency well above 100 kHz, which more than meets the high-frequency requirement. In fact, it may be too good.

As noted earlier, when bandwidth is greater than required, noise performance may be poor. If excessive noise is one of the complaints, then it might be advisable to consider changing compensation to reduce bandwidth. Manufacturers' instructions should be consulted before taking such a drastic step. The type 709 operational amplifier is not a particularly "super"-low-noise device. It is merely used here as an example. In subsequent sections, operational amplifiers designed especially for audio applications will be shown.

Equalizer Amplifiers

In audio amplifiers, it is often necessary to use amplifiers that have other than flat frequency response. This is usually accomplished by a feedback path that is frequency sensitive. Capacitors are used in conjunction with resistors in the feedback path to tailor the frequency response of the amplifier. One simple application of frequency-sensitive feedback was shown earlier in this chapter. (See Figure 5–4.) The capacitor in series with R_1, you may recall, provided a very high reactance in series with the resistor at DC and very low frequencies. At DC, the reactance of the capacitor is infinitely high, and R_1 is effectively disconnected from the circuit. Feedback is directly from output to inverting input via R_f. Since no input current flows in an op amp, there is no voltage drop across R_f with R_1 disconnected. The total output voltage is applied to the inverting input, and 100% feedback is achieved. Thus, at DC, the circuit of Figure 5–4 acts as a voltage follower.

At a frequency of just a few hertz, however, the capacitor acts as a short circuit, and normal feedback paths are used. If other frequency-sensitive RC networks are connected in place of R_f, then the amount of feedback and the resultant op amp gain will vary as the frequency of the input signal varies. A very common audio medium, the phonograph record, makes it necessary to have an amplifier circuit whose gain is a function of frequency. This is necessary because of the manner in which phonograph records are recorded. The technical details of *why* it happens are not important. *What* happens is as follows. If a constant amplitude audio signal, whose frequency varies from 20 Hz to 20,000 Hz, is applied to the recorder, the resulting record will not have a constant amplitude when played back with a perfect record player. Figure 5–9A is the frequency response of the recorded information. Using 1 kHz as a reference level (0 dB), the lower frequencies are much weaker and the higher frequencies are much stronger. The 20 Hz signal is actually −19.3 dB, while the 20,000 Hz signal is +19.6 dB. In order to reproduce the recorded material at its original constant amplitude, the amplifier must have a frequency response opposite to that shown in Figure 5–9A. In other words, the low frequencies must be boosted and the high frequencies must be attenuated.

The idealized **RIAA** (Record Industry Association of America) **playback equalization curve** is shown as the dotted line in

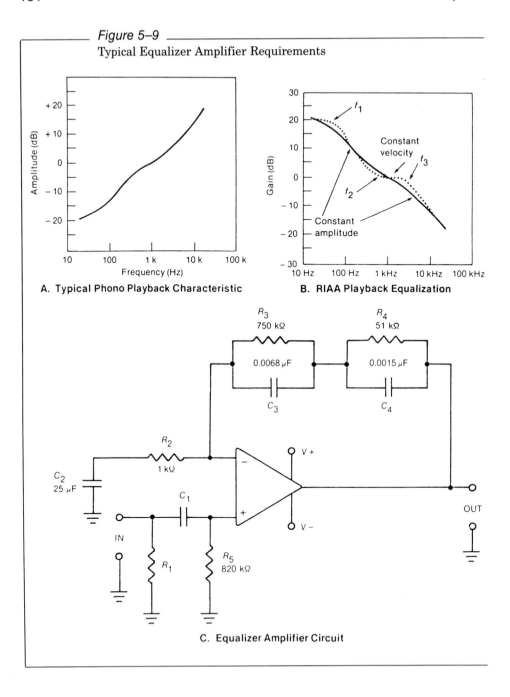

Figure 5–9

Typical Equalizer Amplifier Requirements

A. Typical Phono Playback Characteristic

B. RIAA Playback Equalization

C. Equalizer Amplifier Circuit

Figure 5–9B. Three frequencies of interest are noted. These frequencies are the cutoff frequencies at which the frequency response should change shape. The RIAA lists these frequencies as 50 Hz, 500 Hz, and 2120 Hz. Analysis of the playback equalization curve shows that response should stay relatively flat from 20 Hz to 50 Hz, then fall off at 20 dB/decade to 500 Hz. Response then should remain relatively flat to 2120 Hz, where it then assumes the 20 dB/decade slope to 20,000 Hz. The *RC* network cutoff frequencies for Figure 5–9C are shown in Examples 5–3 through 5–6.

_____ *Example 5–3* _____

Determine the cutoff frequency (f_{c1}) of the R_3C_3 combination in Figure 5–9C.

Solution

$$f_{c1} = \frac{1}{(6.28)(R_3)(C_3)} = \frac{1}{(6.28)(750 \times 10^3)(0.0068 \times 10^{-6})}$$

$$= 31 \text{ Hz}$$

_____ *Example 5–4* _____

Determine the cutoff frequency (f_{c2}) of the R_4C_4 combination in Figure 5–9C.

Solution

$$f_{c2} = \frac{1}{(6.28)(R_4)(C_4)} = \frac{1}{(6.28)(51 \times 10^3)(0.0015 \times 10^{-6})}$$

$$= 2080 \text{ Hz}$$

_____ *Example 5–5* _____

Determine the cutoff frequency (f_{c3}) of the R_4C_3 combination in Figure 5–9C.

Solution

$$f_{c3} = \frac{1}{(6.28)(R_4)(C_3)} = \frac{1}{(6.28)(51 \times 10^3)(0.0068 \times 10^{-6})}$$

$$= 459 \text{ Hz}$$

_____ Example 5–6 _____

Determine the cutoff frequency (f_{c4}) of the $R_2 C_2$ combination in Figure 5–9C.

Solution

$$f_{c4} = \frac{1}{(6.28)(R_2)(C_2)} = \frac{1}{(6.28)(1000)(25 \times 10^{-6})} = 6.4 \text{ Hz}$$

Thus, by placing frequency-sensitive components in the feedback path, the amount of feedback is related to frequency. Amplifier gain is controlled so that deficiencies in recording can be compensated.

Since the RIAA response curve is related to 1 kHz for a reference level, the gain at the reference frequency must be determined. The approximation for the equalizer amplifier of Figure 5–9C is shown in Example 5–7.

_____ Example 5–7 _____

Determine the reference frequency gain of the equalizer amplifier of Figure 5–9C.

Solution

$$A \text{ at } 1 \text{ kHz} \approx 1 + \frac{R_4}{R_2} \approx 1 + \frac{51}{1} \approx 52 \qquad (5\text{–}3)$$

$$\text{dB} = 20 \log A = 20 \log 52 = 34$$

Thus, at 20 Hz the total gain will be 34 dB + 19.3 dB, or 53.3 dB. Gain at 20,000 Hz will be 34 dB − 19.6 dB, or 14.4 dB.

R_1 is selected to properly load the pickup cartridge per manufacturers' recommendations. C_1 and R_5 couple the cartridge output to the noninverting input of the amplifier as discussed earlier.

A similar frequency response problem exists when using magnetic tape recording and playback systems. The National Association of Broadcasters (NAB) has provided a standard for tape recording similar to the RIAA phonograph record standard. Frequency-sensitive feedback networks are used with operational amplifiers to compensate recorded tapes on playback. These networks are somewhat less complex than those required for RIAA equalization.

Tone Control

In audio systems, personal preference and nonstandard program material may necessitate adjustment of the system's frequency response.

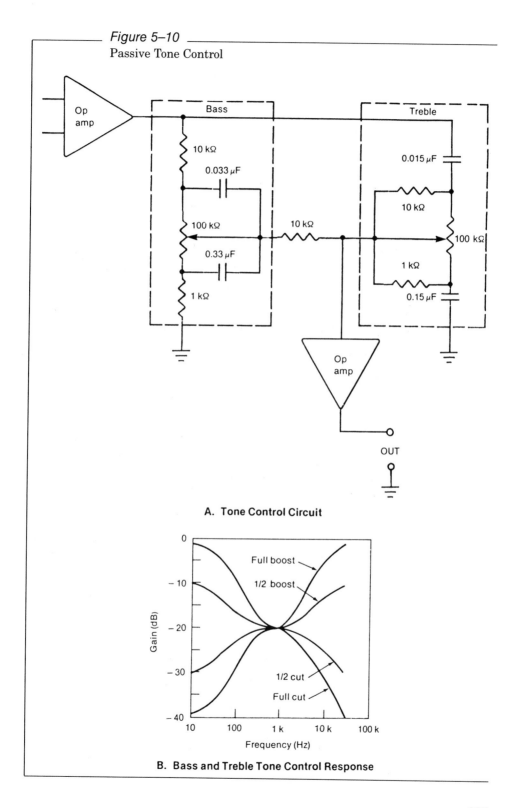

Figure 5–10
Passive Tone Control

A. Tone Control Circuit

B. Bass and Treble Tone Control Response

Circuits that perform this function are called *tone controls*. Simple tone controls that do nothing more than short out higher audio frequencies are often used in low-priced systems. If control of both high and low frequencies is needed, more complex circuits are required. Tone controls may be inserted in-line with signal flow in a system, or they may be part of a negative feedback network. Both approaches are discussed here.

Separate bass (low-frequency) and treble (high-frequency) controls provide the greatest versatility. Figure 5–10 shows passive tone control implementation. The tone control circuit is usually driven by an op amp in voltage follower or gain configuration. Filter output is also routed to an op amp for isolation purposes. The output op amp can receive an input signal from either the bass control or the treble control. Consider the route that low-frequency signals can take. (Note that 1 kHz is the reference frequency for all relative measurements.) At 50 Hz, for example, the reactance (X) of the 0.015 μF capacitor in the treble section is over 200 kΩ (see Table 5–1). The treble section is thus effectively disconnected at 50 Hz. Even the reactance of the 0.033 μF capacitor in the bass section is almost 100 kΩ. The easiest route for low-frequency signals, then, has to be through the resistive part of the bass section. How much of the bass signal gets through is a function of the ratio between the fixed and variable resistors and the capacitor ratios. The ratios in the bass section are selected to obtain the required boost or attentuation.

A similar situation exists in the treble section. The reactance of the 0.033 μF capacitor in the bass section is practically zero, so the bass section is shorted out. In the treble section, the reactance of the 0.015 μF capacitor is only about 1 kΩ at 10 kHz, so the treble signal is routed to the output op amp via the fixed and variable resistors. Note that the treble section of the tone control is just the opposite of the bass section, with capacitors replacing resistors, and vice versa. The same rationale discussed for the bass section thus holds for the treble section.

Standard tone control circuits usually boost and attenuate about 20 dB for both bass and treble. The circuit of Figure 5–10A, when using

Table 5–1

Capacitor Reactances of the Passive Tone Control in Figure 5–10

f	X_C (Ω)			
	0.033 μF	0.33 μF	0.015 μF	0.15 μF
50 Hz	96.00 k	9.60 k	212 k	21.2 k
1 kHz	4.80 k	0.48 k	10 k	1.0 k
10 kHz	0.48 k	48.00	1 k	100.0

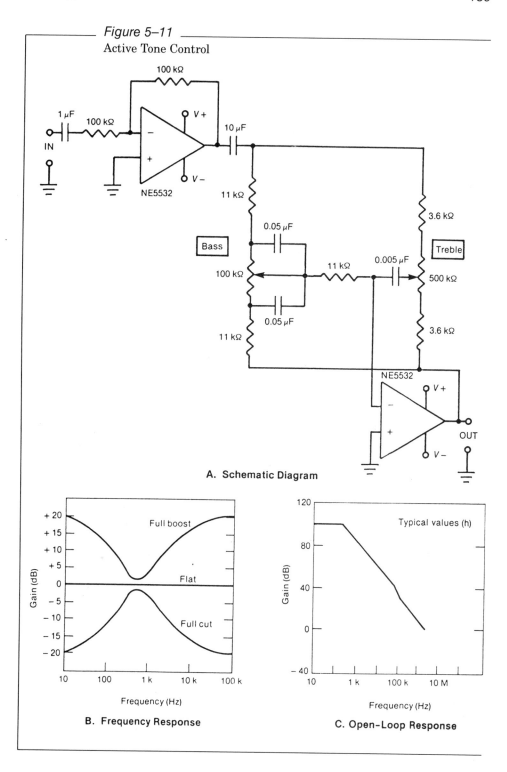

Figure 5–11
Active Tone Control

A. Schematic Diagram

B. Frequency Response

C. Open-Loop Response

Table 5–2

Capacitor Reactances of the Active Tone Control Circuit in
Figure 5–11

	X_c (Ω)	
f	0.005 μF	0.05 μF
50 Hz	636.60 k	63.60 k
1 kHz	31.80 k	3.18 k
10 kHz	3.18 k	318.00

1 kHz as a 0 dB reference point, boosts and attenuates 20 dB at 50 Hz
and 10,000 Hz. Figure 5–10B shows the response of the tone control
circuit. It can be seen from the response curves that the "insertion loss"
of the circuit is 20 dB at the reference frequency of 1 kHz. Amplifiers
must be used to make up for the tone control losses. However, a single
op amp can easily perform this function, while allowing a wide range of
control over the overall audio system's response. The relationships of
response characteristics and component values are shown in Table 5–1,
from which the reader may verify component values or calculate different values if desired.

The same type of approach used for tone control requirements
may be applied to feedback circuits with op amps. Figure 5–11 and
Table 5–2 contain the information necessary to evaluate an **active tone
control** circuit. The op amp used here (see Figure 5–11A) is a type
NE5532, which is ideally suited for audio applications. It has a gain-
bandwidth product of 10 MHz and a slew rate of 9 V/μs. Complete specification sheets for the NE5532 are available from the manufacturer. At
low frequencies, the reactance of the capacitors in the bass section is
large enough so that they may be considered as open circuits. Therefore,
the feedback from op amp output to inverting input (and consequently
the gain) is controlled by the bass control. At high frequencies, the capacitors may be considered as short circuits, and the op amp gain is
controlled by the treble control. In effect, a frequency-sensitive feedback
network has been used as the active tone control. More detail concerning
this type of operation is shown in Chapter 7.

Audio Op Amps

The use of op amps in audio applications has been widespread. However,
as more exotic input transducers such as magnetic phonograph pickups
and tape read heads appeared, some limitations of general-purpose op
amps became apparent. The extremely low signal output of the input

transducers, for example, required high gain. Op amp noise was becoming a bigger part of the total signal, and signal-to-noise ratio was poor. Many op amps had limited small signal and power bandwidth capabilities. (*Power bandwidth* is the frequency range over which the voltage gain does not fall below 0.707 of the flat-band voltage gain specified for a given load and output power.) To meet the overall requirements for audio preamplifiers, considerable compensation design was needed. Some of the op amp manufacturers decided to design an op amp specifically for audio purposes. That type of op amp, commonly found two to a package to accommodate stereo requirements, is the subject of this discussion.

The same general type of circuit already discussed will be used. Voltage gain is established at 40 dB by combination of R_f, R_1, and C_2, and the circuit operates in the noninverting mode. The LM381 audio preamplifier op amp employed has 112 dB open-loop gain and a unity gain frequency of 15 MHz (see Figure 5–12A). Not only is the op amp internally compensated, but provision also exists for additional external compensation to limit the circuit bandwidth. Power bandwidth is 75 kHz at 20 V peak-to-peak output, making the LM381 quite adequate for audio applications. In all respects but one, the LM381 appears very much like an op amp. The LM381 has inverting and noninverting inputs, feedback gain control, compensation for bandwidth control, and so on. The only characteristic that is different from an op amp is that the LM381 input impedance is not extremely high. The noninverting input impedance is about 100 kΩ, while the inverting input impedance is about 200 kΩ. Complete specification sheets for the LM381 are available from the manufacturer. Since most input transducers have much lower impedances, the amplifier input impedance is no detriment.

The input stage of the audio amplifier has been designed with special care. Although many conventional op amps use numerous active devices in the first stage, the LM381 audio preamplifier is designed with only two. In this way, some of the sources of shot noise are removed. Also, the first stage may be operated single-ended (with one transistor shut off), which effectively removes another source of noise. Excellent noise performance results from single-ended operation. An inverting input terminal that does not include the second transistor of the differential pair is provided so that normal feedback techniques may be used. If noise is not critical, the audio preamplifier may be operated as a conventional op amp. Higher input impedances result, although noise does increase.

Figure 5–12B needs only minor explanation since we have just discussed the LM381 audio preamplifier. The feedback network is identical to that used in previously discussed circuits. Another resistor has been added to bias the inverting input to the same voltage as the noninverting input. (The noninverting input terminal has an internally con-

Figure 5–12
Audio Op Amp

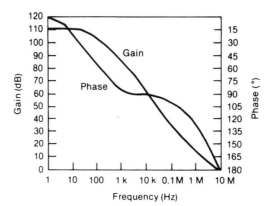

A. LM381 Gain/Phase Characteristics

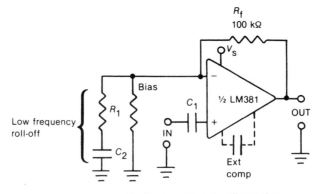

B. Noninverting Configuration

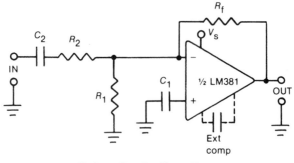

C. Inverting Configuration

nected biasing network.) Because of the internal resistor in the audio preamplifier, no ground return resistor is required to control discharge of the coupling capacitor. As shown in Figure 5–12A, the 40 dB gain amplifier has a frequency response that extends out beyond 100 kHz.

The noninverting configuration of the audio preamplifier being discussed has a maximum input signal rating of 300 mV RMS. When larger input signals must be used, the inverting circuit of Figure 5–12C may be used. As with other inverting amplifiers, the R_f/R_1 ratio determines gain. However, R_1 in conjunction with the input series RC network, reduces the input signal by voltage division. Therefore, more than 300 mV RMS of input signal may be used. The input series RC network also controls the low-frequency response of the amplifier, as discussed previously. Note that it is not necessary to provide a resistive ground return for the noninverting input. The internal resistance of the op amp is sufficient. However, capacitor C_1 grounds the noninverting input for AC signals. Finally, if bandwidth reduction is desired, an external compensation capacitor may be connected.

As just shown, all of the positive attributes of operational amplifiers have been incorporated into the audio op amp. Conventional techniques have been used to obtain low noise performance. And the input impedance of the op amp has been reduced to more adequately match audio requirements. The following section will show how operational amplifier techniques have also been included in power amplifiers.

Power Op Amps

Power op amps are basically conventional op amps with added power-handling capability. Considerable design effort has been expended to compensate for the heat generated as a result of power dissipation, but the power op amp has just about reached maturity. One of the approaches to development of op amps uses a type 741 input circuit followed by high-current output stages to obtain adequate power output. Figure 5–13 shows the characteristics of a typical power op amp and an audio amplifier circuit application. The now-familiar noninverting input configuration is used with gain controlled by the resistive feedback network R_f and R_1. Gain is set at 50 (about 34 dB). Capacitor C_1 is connected in parallel with R_f to decrease gain (increase feedback) at high frequencies. Some op amps tend to be unstable at high frequencies, and if the circuit is unity gain stable, the addition of C_c will often prevent oscillation at frequencies in the supersonic and radio range. C_c is not required when the gain of the stage is greater than 100. However, when the gain of the stage approaches 10, a 5 pF capacitor is required. Unity gain operation requires C_c to be about 100 pF. A piezoelectric or ceramic phonograph pickup cartridge provides the input to the power op amp. R_2 aids in impedance matching of the cartridge to the input circuit and

Figure 5–13

Power Op Amp Application

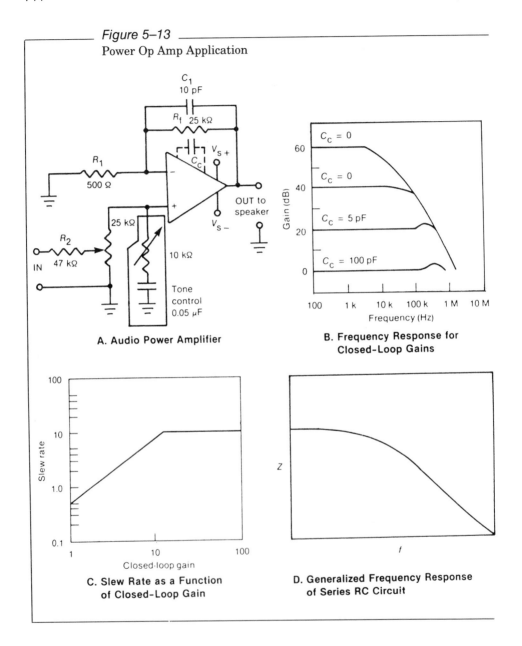

A. Audio Power Amplifier

B. Frequency Response for
Closed-Loop Gains

C. Slew Rate as a Function
of Closed-Loop Gain

D. Generalized Frequency Response
of Series RC Circuit

the volume control. The tone control adjusts the high-frequency response of the amplifier by shunting high frequencies at the input to ground. Figure 5–13D shows the general impedance characteristics of a simple series RC circuit. When such a frequency response graph is combined with the closed-loop gain response of an op amp, the net result will be a controllable decrease in high-frequency response.

Table 5–3

Amplifier Impedance Characteristics

Speaker Z (Ω)	V_o p–p	V_s	P_o (W)
4	8	14	2
8	16	22	4
16	32	38	8

The circuit of Figure 5–13A requires a dual power supply. As with other op amps, the output voltage is zero volts with zero volts input (depending on input offset voltage and current). Therefore, a low imped-ance speaker may be connected *directly* to the output of the op amp. No DC current flows through the speaker under no-input signal conditions. As shown in Table 5–3, the amplifier circuit outputs about 4 W with an 8 Ω speaker and power supplies of $+$ and $-$ 15 V. Thus, a power op amp has provided the capability to build a complete electronic phonograph with a minimum of parts. This same op amp is applicable to circuits that must operate small motors, relays, and so forth.

Many manufacturers have also developed power op amps with audio applications specifically in mind. In the region of 2 to 6 W ratings, many models (both single and dual) are in evidence. Most of them have internal compensation and are stable at relatively low gains to near 10 MHz. They have gain-bandwidth products from 5 to 20 MHz. Generally, audio power op amps use single voltage supplies, and their outputs are self-centering to $V_{cc}/2$ by methods similar to those discussed earlier. Feedback is usually set to unity gain at DC to maintain stability. AC gain is set high. Techniques explained earlier are employed to control both DC and AC feedback. There are but a few minor differences be-tween conventional op amp and power op amp applications. Let's select a simple dual-power op amp circuit and use it as an example. Both inverting and noninverting configurations are shown for purposes of comparison.

The inverting stereo amplifier of Figure 5–14 is a minimum-parts-count circuit. Both channels are identical, with gain of 50 (about 34 dB) established by R_f and R_1. The noninverting inputs are connected to an internal voltage divider on the chip that provides the $V_{cc}/2$ output centering discussed earlier. High-frequency response is determined by the op amp unity gain and roll-off characteristics. The input coupling capacitor C_i establishes the low-frequency roll-off. Two points of interest can be seen at the output. The speaker is not connected directly to the op amp output terminal but is isolated by the large (500 μF) capacitor.

Figure 5-14

Inverting Stereo Power Amplifier

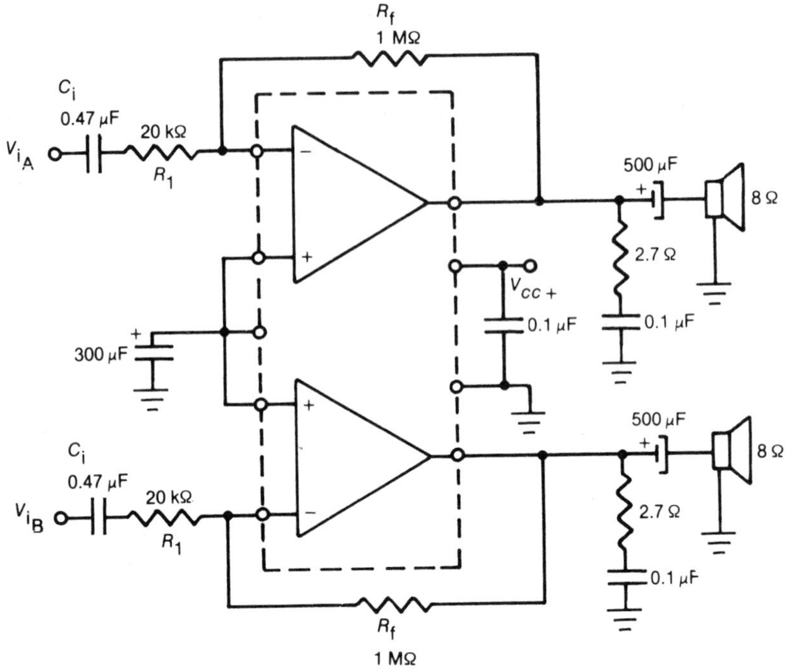

Isolation is necessary because a DC voltage ($V_{cc}/2$) is present at the output. The large capacitor prevents DC current flow through the speaker, yet allows the AC signal component to pass. Some power op amps also require the series RC network shown connected to the output terminal to reduce high-frequency instability. With a supply voltage of $+18$ V, the amplifier circuit of Figure 5-14 is capable of about 2 W output per channel. Only about 80 mV input is required to obtain this performance.

Similar performance can be achieved with the noninverting circuit of Figure 5-15. Response is controlled by the op amp characteristics at high frequencies and the input and RC networks at low frequencies. On-chip voltage division is provided for output voltage centering, as previously mentioned. The output circuit is identical to the inverting circuit. The primary advantage of the noninverting configuration is its high input impedance. When high impedance tone and volume controls precede the amplifier input, for example, the noninverting configuration should be used.

_____ *Figure 5–15* _____

Noninverting Stereo Power Amplifier

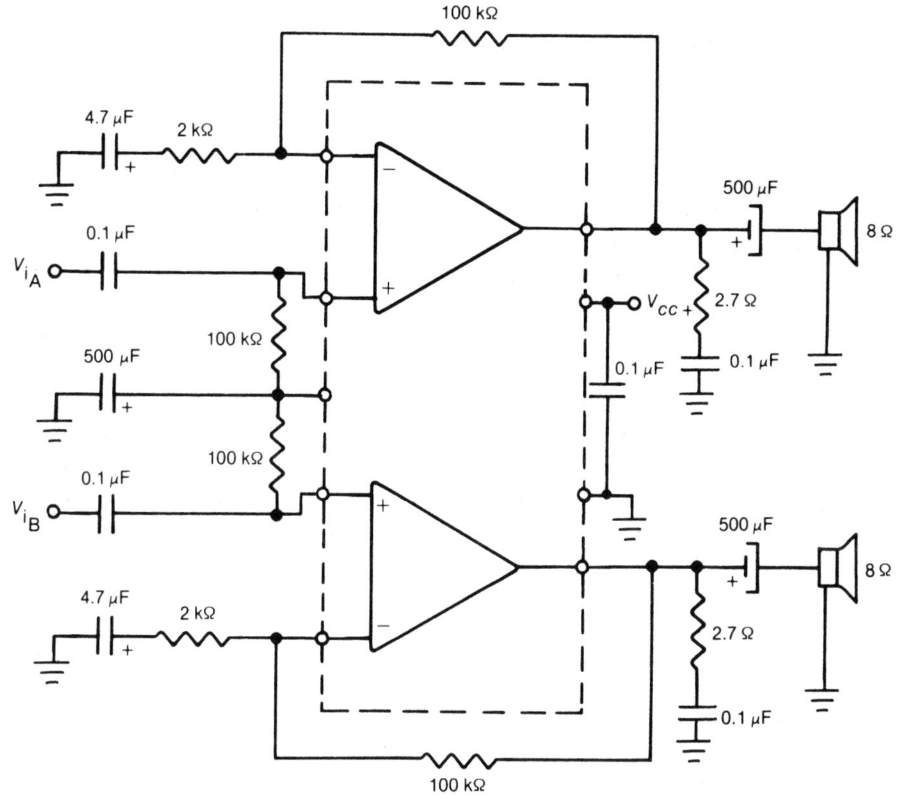

Troubleshooting: Let's practice troubleshooting on the circuit shown in Figure 5–15. Both channels of the stereo amplifier are identical, so the gain and frequency response of both channels should be the same.

The amplifier has been working properly, but now channel A is malfunctioning. Its output is weak and distorted. Let's troubleshoot with the schematic diagram first, using what we know about op amps and principles of electronics. We also should take into consideration that, from a reliability viewpoint, speakers fail first, then capacitors, followed by op amps and resistors.

First, we should verify that the input to channel A is proper. Then, we can check channel A's speaker by changing speakers from channel B to channel A. If the malfunction is still present, the next most likely failed component will be the 500 µF capacitor at the output of channel A. An easy way to check the output capacitor is to measure the DC voltage at the speaker. If no DC voltage is present, the capacitor is OK.

Assuming that both the speaker and the capacitor are not defective, what is the next troubleshooting check? Since the input to channel A is OK, what about the output? If the output is not proper, then the malfunction is caused by either the op amp or the remaining external components. From the use of reliability information, the most likely component is a capacitor, such as the 0.1 μF capacitor connected in series with the 2.7 Ω resistor at the output of channel A. If the capacitor is shorted, the amplifier output is shorted, and low output and distortion could result. An easy way to check the capacitor is to measure the DC output at channel A's amplifier output terminal. If the DC output is not $(1/2)$ V_{cc}, a good possibility for the malfunction is the shorted 0.1 μF capacitor. If the capacitor is not shorted, the op amp is the next most probable cause of the failure.

Troubleshooting time will be reduced when a plan is worked out before actually beginning troubleshooting. A little planning will always make your job easier.

SUMMARY

Chapter 5 has shown the first of the AC applications of operational amplifiers. The basic characteristics discussed in Chapters 2 and 4 have been combined to form circuits for amplification of audio frequencies. Only a few new concepts have been used. Perhaps the most important of these is the application of frequency-sensitive negative feedback to control amplifier frequency response.

Frequency-sensitive negative feedback is used to provide finite gain down to a specified low frequency, yet close to 100% feedback at DC. Control of offset problems have thus been accomplished. Equalizers and tone controls were also shown to use frequency-sensitive negative feedback to obtain desired frequency response.

Operational amplifiers were shown to be applicable to *all* parts of an audio amplifier system. From the high-gain/low-noise preamplifier to the low-gain/high-current power amplifier, the op amp was evident. Even the specialized audio voltage and power amplifiers were shown to be operational amplifiers in disguise.

Operational amplifiers are merely providing audio frequency functions that have been around for years. However, it has been the operational amplifier that has helped reduce size and cost.

═══ QUESTIONS ═══

1. What is the range of audio frequencies?

2. Explain how bandwidth is related to slew rate?

3. Discuss the relationship between closed-loop gain and loop gain.

4. What problems occur when an op amp designed for use with both positive and negative power supplies is used with only a single supply?

5. Show how an op amp designed for use with dual supplies can be used with a single supply.

6. Define the following terms: (a) noise, (b) thermal noise, (c) shot noise, (d) flicker noise, and (e) popcorn noise.

7. Discuss the source of (a) thermal noise, (b) shot noise, (c) flicker noise, and (d) popcorn noise.

8. Discuss methods that will reduce (a) thermal noise, (b) shot noise, (c) flicker noise, and (d) popcorn noise.

9. Draw a diagram showing the method(s) that can reduce input offset problems.

10. Referring to Figure 5–3, explain the purpose of (a) R_a, (b) R_b, (c) R_2, and (d) C_a.

11. Referring to Figure 5–4, explain the purpose of (a) C_1, (b) R_1, (c) R_f, (d) C_2, and (e) R_2.

12. Draw a generalized gain graph showing the relationships between β (beta), 1/β, closed-loop response, loop gain, and open-loop response.

13. Discuss the differences between small-signal response and large-signal response of operational amplifiers. What factors are common? What factors are not common?

14. Discuss the relative advantages and disadvantages of compensated and uncompensated operational amplifiers in audio frequency applications.

15. What factors affect slew rate and large-signal response in uncompensated operational amplifiers? Explain.

16. Referring to Figure 5–7, explain the purpose of (a) C_1, (b) R_1, (c) R_f, (d) C_2, (e) R_2, (f) C_x, (g) R_x, and (h) C_y.

17. Discuss desirable characteristics of an operational amplifier to be used as an audio frequency preamplifier.

18. What is the difference between a preamplifier and an equalizer amplifier?

19. Referring to Figure 5–9, state which components affect amplifier response at (a) about 30 Hz, (b) about 500 Hz, (c) about 1 kHz, and (d) about 2 kHz.

20. Explain the interaction of the resistors and capacitors of Figure 5–10 at (a) 50 Hz, (b) 1 kHz, and (c) 10 kHz.

21. Explain the operational differences between the passive tone control of Figure 5–10 and the active tone control of Figure 5–11.

22. Define power bandwidth.

23. What special factors are considered during design of audio op amps? Explain.

24. Explain the purpose of each component in Figures 5–12B and 5–12C.

25. Explain the purpose of each of the components in the diagram of Figure 5–13.

26. How does an audio operational amplifier differ from a conventional operational amplifier? How are they the same?

27. How does an audio power operational amplifier differ from a conventional power operational amplifier? How are they the same?

═══ PROBLEMS ═══

1. Using Figure 5–3, assume a type 741 op amp with $V+ = 15$ V, $R_f = 100$ kΩ, and $R_1 = 1$ kΩ. Assume also that the circuit has been operating normally, but the output has suddenly become distorted (the negative half-cycle of the AC input has "flattened"). Explain the steps you would take to locate the malfunction. Indicate the component that is most likely to have failed.

2. Assume the type 741 op amp of Problem 1. With no input signal, what DC voltage would you expect to measure at the output terminals of the op amp with R_a and R_b both equal to 47 kΩ?

3. Under the conditions of Problem 2, what would be the effect on output voltage of changing R_1 to 10 kΩ?

4. Under the conditions of Problem 2, what would be the effect on output voltage of changing R_b to 27 kΩ?

5. Graph the frequency response of the amplifier of Figure 5–4 for C_1 values of (a) 0.1 µF, (b) 1 µF, (c) 5 µF, (d) 25 µF, (e) 100 µF, and (f) 500 µF. All other components remain as shown.

6. Graph the frequency response of the amplifier of Figure 5–4 for C_2 values of (a) 0.01 µF, (b) 0.047 µF, (c) 0.1 µF, (d) 1 µF, (e) 10 µF, and (f) 100 µF. All other components remain as shown.

7. Calculate and graph the low-frequency response of the amplifier circuit of Figure 5–7 for the following component values: (a) $C_x = 10$ pF, (b) $C_x = 5000$ pF, and (c) $C_y = 200$ pF. All other components remain as shown for each of the new values. Figure 5–6 may be used for reference.

8. In Figure 5–9C, R_4 has increased from 51 kΩ to 510 kΩ. Calculate and graph the frequency response of the amplifier circuit.

9. Repeat Problem 8 for a C_2 change from 25 µF to 0.022 µF.

10. An amplifier using the active tone control of Figure 5–11 has developed poor low-frequency response. What is the component most likely to have failed? Explain your thinking, and show any calculations.

11. The amplifier shown in Figure 5–12C has developed poor low-frequency response. C_2 and R_2 test properly. What is the component most likely to have failed? Explain your thinking, and show any calculations.

12. The amplifier shown in Figure 5–13 has developed poor high-frequency response. What is the component most likely to have failed? Explain your thinking, and show any calculations.

6

High-Frequency
Amplifiers

OBJECTIVES   After studying Chapter 6, you will be able to

1. Define ultrasonic, narrow-band, wide-band, bandwidth, side-bands, and AGC.
2. Explain the difference between sound and radio waves.
3. Explain the difference between op amps used in audio, ultrasonic, video, and radio frequency applications.
4. Demonstrate how to use spectrum diagrams.
5. Explain why wide-band amplifiers are needed for pulse amplifiers.
6. Demonstrate how to use square waves to test amplifiers.
7. Discuss the relationship between unity gain frequency and pulse response.
8. Demonstrate how AGC is used.
9. Explain how and why bandwidth is restricted in intermediate frequency amplifiers.
10. Discuss why large-scale linear integrated circuits are replacing operational amplifiers.

INTRODUCTION

This chapter is the last to deal primarily with basic characteristics of operational amplifiers. When other than audio amplifiers are to be discussed, it becomes difficult to know how to classify them. Audio applications are easy—you can *hear* the results. It's all too easy to say "if you can't hear it, it's not there." But this is not really true because lots of things are done at frequencies higher than audio frequencies.

In Chapter 5, we noted that as audio frequencies get higher, it is harder to get high, stable gain from operational amplifiers. When operation is attempted *above* audio frequencies, the problem gets even worse. Strict attention must be paid to component placement, external lead length, shielding, and power supply filtering. Unwanted positive feedback and resulting oscillation is common in high-frequency amplifiers.

When audio frequency applications were discussed in Chapter 5, little attention was paid to devices that converted sound waves into electrical form and vice versa. Microphones apply principles of electromagnetism or piezoelectricity to convert sound waves into electrical form. Operational amplifiers and discrete components increase the electrical strength of the converted sound waves. Loudspeakers then change the electrical form of audio frequencies back into stronger sound waves. Similar functions are performed when ultrasonic devices are used.

ULTRASONICS

Any frequency that can cause the movement of air molecules can be classified as either an audio or an ultrasonic frequency. Frequencies above audio frequencies but below radio frequencies are classified as **ultrasonic frequencies**. There are numerous applications of ultrasonic frequencies. (We will talk about **radio frequencies** shortly.)

Applications

You might be wondering what good it does to work with "sound" waves that can't be heard. Since sound waves are merely air molecules in motion, perhaps we can find some use for the movement of air molecules. Ultrasonic applications include alarm systems, distance-measuring devices, and cleaning devices. Ultrasonic cleaning devices use op amps operating as oscillators to develop ultrasonic frequencies in electrical form. (Oscillators are discussed in Chapter 9.) Special transducers convert the electrical form of the ultrasonic frequencies into air-molecule motion. The resulting rapid motion of air molecules then agitates a cleaning solution that removes dirt from small items such as jewelry.

Ultrasonic alarm systems use both ultrasonic *transmitters* and *receivers*. The transmitter is very similar to the device used in the ultrasonic cleaner. In the ultrasonic receiver, many possible applications of operational amplifiers are found. The block diagram of Figure 6–1A shows the general concepts of an ultrasonic transmitter/receiver used as an alarm system. Ultrasonic energy radiated by the transmitter spreads throughout the room, bouncing from wall to wall, from furniture to ceiling, and so forth. The resulting complex ultrasonic information that bounces back to the receiver is used as a reference to detect motion. Any change in the reflected ultrasonic waves will result in a change in

Figure 6–1
Ultrasonic Alarm System

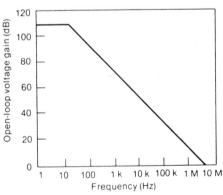

A. Alarm System

B. Schematic Diagram of Amplifier

C. Open-Loop Frequency Response of the LF353 Op Amp

amplitude (or phase) at the receiver. The change is amplified and used to sound an alarm.

The op amp circuits that are not *directly* used as amplifiers are discussed in later chapters. In this chapter, we will discuss only amplifier applications. Actually, there is little to discuss. The only difference between audio and ultrasonic amplifier applications is that the ultrasonic applications require higher frequency capability. We already know how to get that higher capability by selecting an op amp that has a high enough unity gain frequency and gain-bandwidth product and then using feedback to obtain the desired gain at the required high cutoff frequency. Some frequency tailoring, such as that used in audio equalizer amplifiers, may be necessary to reject interfering frequencies. The same techniques used in audio systems may be applied. A typical schematic diagram showing an operational amplifier in ultrasonic applications is shown in Figure 6–1B.

Op Amps for Ultrasonics

The LF353 operational amplifier is a wide-bandwidth dual-JFET-input device. As seen in the open-loop frequency response graph of Figure 6–1C, the unity gain frequency is 4 MHz. The slew rate is 13 V/μs. Let's evaluate the schematic diagram in Figure 6–1B. Note that the first op amp is structured to function with a single supply rather than the conventional dual supply. R_1 and R_2 establish the noninverting input at $V_{cc}/2$, while C_1 bypasses the junction of the voltage divider to AC ground. The ultrasonic transducer is connected directly to the noninverting input and uses R_3 for impedance matching and biasing purposes.

Feedback for A_1 is via R_5, R_4, and C_2. Note that because of C_2, A_1 operates as a voltage follower at DC, just as discussed in Chapter 5. Example 6–1 shows feedback and gain calculations at frequencies above the cutoff frequency of the R_4 and C_2 combination, where C_2 acts as a short circuit.

Example 6–1

Calculate feedback factor and gain for A_1 in Figure 6–1.

Solution

A_1 calculations assuming $X_{C_2} = 0 \ \Omega$:

$$\beta = \frac{R_4}{R_4 + R_5} = \frac{220}{220 + 1,000,000} = 0.00022$$

$$A_{cl} = \frac{1}{\beta} = \frac{1}{0.00022} = 4545$$

$$A_{dB} = 20 \log A_{cl} = 20 \log 4545 = (20)(3.66) = 73 \text{ dB}$$

Thus, the first op amp's closed-loop gain is 73 dB, rolling off at both high and low frequencies at 20 dB/decade. C_3 is included to bypass any higher frequencies that might cause unwanted oscillation. In a similar manner, A_2 characteristics are determined, as shown in Example 6–2.

Example 6–2

Calculate feedback factor and gain for A_2 in Figure 6–1.

Solution

A_2 calculations assuming $X_{C_4} = 0\ \Omega$:

$$\beta = \frac{R_7}{R_7 + R_8} = \frac{220}{220 + 22,000} = 0.0099$$

$$A_{cl} = \frac{1}{\beta} = \frac{1}{0.0099} = 101$$

$$A_{dB} = 20 \log A_{cl} = 20 \log 101 = (20)(2) = 40\ dB$$

A_2 has a closed-loop gain of 40 dB between the cutoff frequency of the R_7 and C_4 combination and the cutoff frequency of the amplifier. Therefore, except for the use of op amps with higher frequency capability, there is little difference between audio and ultrasonic applications.

NARROW-BAND AMPLIFIERS

Some applications of electronics require that a very wide band of frequencies be processed, while others use only a relatively narrow band. Wide-band electronic circuits process electrical signals ranging from DC to some defined upper frequency. Narrow-band circuits generally process some range of frequencies centered about a selected frequency and reject all other frequencies. Some of the **frequency-selective**, or **narrow-band**, applications of op amps are investigated in this section.

Spectrum Diagrams

Before we go on, however, we should define a word that is going to see a lot of use. The new word is **spectrum**, which is used to describe a *range of frequencies*. The range of frequencies that can be heard (when converted to sound waves) is called the audio spectrum. All frequencies that can exist as electromagnetic waves are lumped into the electromagnetic spectrum. Radio, light, and X ray all fall into this range. With a little change, the frequency response graphs that we have been using can be converted to **spectrum diagrams**. A spectrum diagram displays all frequencies present for a specific application on the horizontal axis. The vertical axis represents the amplitude, or strength, of each of the frequencies. Examples are shown as narrow-band applications of operational amplifiers are discussed.

The audio spectrum (range of "hearable" frequencies) was defined in Chapter 5 as including sound waves in the range of 20 Hz to 20 kHz. There are applications that require selecting only a part of the audio frequencies within the audio spectrum. All other frequencies must be rejected. In other words, a "window" is opened on a portion of the spectrum but remains closed on the remainder. Let's open a 1000 Hz window and move it around the audio spectrum diagram in Figure 6–2. (The spectrum diagram has been drawn on a linear rather than logarithmic scale to more effectively demonstrate the concept of frequency-selective operations.) Starting at the low-frequency end of the diagram, it can be seen that the window extends from DC to 1000 Hz. We already know how to amplify the frequencies from DC to 1000 Hz—use an op amp with

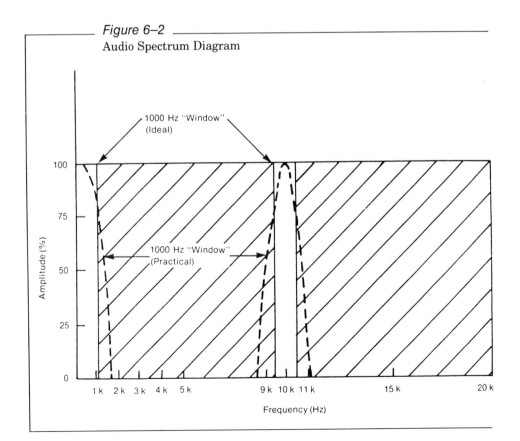

Figure 6–2

Audio Spectrum Diagram

feedback to select a gain where 1000 Hz is the upper cutoff frequency. If the range from DC to 20 Hz was not desired, a capacitor could be included in the feedback network or input/output coupling circuit, as shown in Chapter 5. It should be recognized that the window is really not as selective as it appears on the spectrum diagram. The roll-off characteristics of RC networks and op amps establish the bandwidth at the 3 dB points. In fact, **bandwidth** of a circuit is defined as the band of frequencies between the lower and upper 3 dB points on a gain versus frequency graph. It appears, then, that it is not difficult to amplify *all* frequencies from DC to some well-defined upper frequency. (That upper frequency must be within the capability of the op amp, however.) There are many applications that require better rejection of frequencies adjacent to the window. Ways to make the sides or **skirts** of the frequency-selective window steeper are investigated further in this and future chapters.

Moving the window to 10,000 Hz causes quite a change. Now the window must select only 500 Hz either side of 10,000 Hz. Instead of amplifying all frequencies, only 10% (1000/10,000) of the frequencies can be allowed through the window. The techniques for performing this function in audio frequency devices most often employ op amps and other components in *active filters*. Chapters 7 and 8 are devoted to the characteristics of active filters and their applications. It should be noted, however, that as the frequency increases while the bandwidth stays the same, the total percentage of frequencies becomes smaller. While narrow bandwidths tend to present a problem at audio frequencies, it is not difficult to handle narrow bands of frequencies in the radio frequency spectrum.

Traditionally, frequency selectivity has been obtained at radio frequencies by the use of inductors (L) and capacitors (C). The center frequency (f_0) of the window is determined by the L and C values, while the width of the **passband** (bandwidth) is a function of the Q (quality) of the circuit. Bandwidth (Δf), center frequency (f_0), and Q are related in the following manner:

$$f_0 = \frac{1}{2\pi\sqrt{LC}}$$

$$\Delta f = f_2 - f_1$$

$$Q = \frac{f_0}{\Delta f}$$

where f_2 = high-frequency 3 dB point
        f_1 = low-frequency 3 dB point

Figure 6–3 summarizes resonant circuit characteristics.

Figure 6–3

Resonant Circuit Characteristics

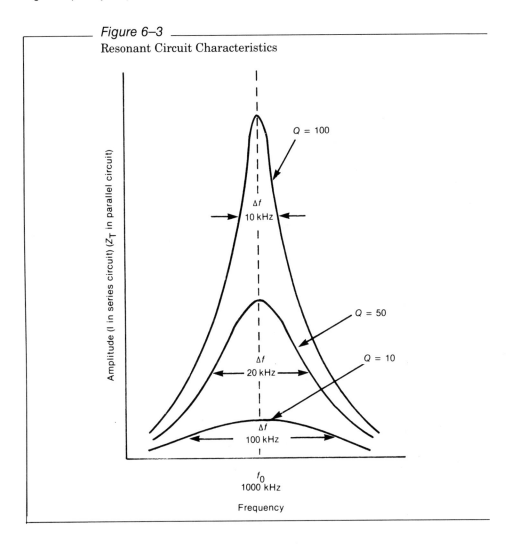

Radio Frequency Amplification

An appreciation for the high-frequency requirements of op amps used in radio frequency applications may be obtained from Table 6–1. Radio frequencies of interest for AM broadcasting, FM broadcasting, and television are listed, with indications of bandwidth requirements. AM broadcast stations, for example, operate in the range of about 550 kHz to 1600 kHz. The process of **modulation** (combining the information to be

---

Table 6–1

Frequency and Bandwidth (Δf) Requirements

	Range	Δf	% Δf*
AM broadcast			
Range	550–1600 kHz	30 kHz	3% at 1000 kHz
Intermediate frequency	455 kHz	30 kHz	6.6%
FM broadcast			
Range	88–108 MHz	250 kHz	0.25% at 100 MHz
Intermediate frequency	10.7 MHz	250 kHz	2.3%
Television			
Range	54–88 MHz ⎫ 174–216 MHz ⎬ 470–728 MHz ⎭	6 MHz	Dependent on channel used
Intermediate frequency	41–47 MHz	6 MHz	13.6%

*% $\Delta f = \dfrac{\Delta f}{f_\circ}(100)$

---

transmitted with a radio frequency carrier wave) generates additional frequencies both above and below the assigned carrier wave frequency. Audio frequencies, such as voice and music, are the information to be transmitted. The highest audio frequency determines the highest and lowest added frequency. Consider, as an example, an AM broadcast station operating at an assigned carrier frequency of 1000 kHz. With no information being transmitted, the bandwidth of the station is very narrow. As modulation occurs, however, the bandwidth expands. If a 5000 Hz audio tone modulated the 1000 kHz carrier wave, then **sidebands** would be generated 5000 Hz above and 5000 Hz below the carrier frequency. The bandwidth is thus 10 kHz centered at 1000 kHz.

Amplification at 1000 kHz (1 MHz) requires an op amp with a gain-bandwidth product high enough to provide the required gain. The universal gain bandwidth graph of Figure 6–4 shows that, for 40 dB gain, an op amp with a 100 MHz unity gain frequency is needed. Selection of the 10 kHz window centered at 1 MHz is a function of the *LC* circuit. Figure 6–5 provides the details of a 40 dB amplifier circuit that meets the 10 kHz bandwidth requirement at 1 MHz. Operation at other frequencies and bandwidths requires only changes in the *LC* components and /or R_2.

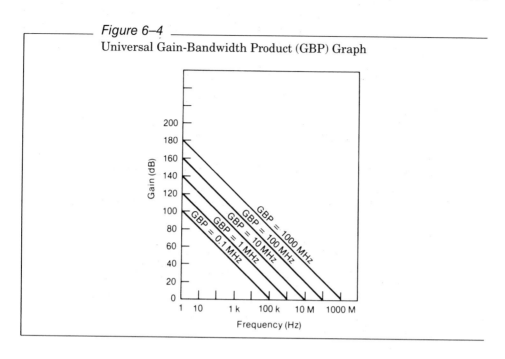

Figure 6–4

Universal Gain-Bandwidth Product (GBP) Graph

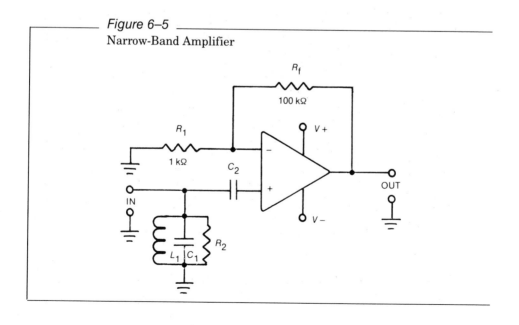

Figure 6–5

Narrow-Band Amplifier

The many advantages of op amps are often lost in simple radio frequency applications. Conventional amplifiers without the restraints of op amps can perform the required functions. When high-input-impedance/low-output-impedance and feedback characteristics are not needed, discrete component amplifiers may be the best choice. Large-scale integrated circuits that incorporate almost all of the active circuits necessary for AM / FM radios are in common use. Generally, the amplifier portion of these ICs are not operational amplifiers, but conventional circuitry.

It is possible in many op amps to tailor the frequency compensation to achieve frequency response greater than the published values. Op amps using external compensation usually operate at higher frequencies by reducing the capacitance of the external compensating capacitor. Specification sheets tend to list compensating capacitor values that provide stable unity gain. If the amplifier is to operate at some fixed gain level, less capacitance may be used. Judicious use of the frequency response curves will show how this is done. Let's use our previous example, where it was indicated that an op amp required a unity gain frequency of 100 MHz to obtain 40 dB gain at 1 MHz.

If only a narrow band of frequencies centered around 1 MHz need be amplified, then the response of the amplifier above and below 1 MHz is not important. The selectivity of the LC circuit will tend to reject other frequencies, so all we need to do is ensure that the required op amp gain is available at 1 MHz. See Figure 6–5, where L_1 and C_1 determine the resonant frequency, and R_2 determines the bandwidth. Even the old type 709 op amp is capable of 1 MHz performance, as can be seen by referring back to Figures 5–6 and 5–7. Selecting the proper compensation components (R_f and R_1) ensures 40 dB gain as required. Modernized versions, which can be identified by reference to manufacturers' specification sheets, easily accomplish this task. It should be recognized that reference to specific types or "families" of op amps is for the purpose of demonstrating the evolution of the op amp. Modern op amps usually exceed the capabilities of the early types discussed in this text. In many cases, the internal compensation of the op amp allows operation to relatively high frequencies with no difficulty. However, if the older op amps were not used as examples, we might never appreciate the problems with which early users had to cope.

_____ WIDE-BAND AMPLIFIERS _____

Wide-band amplifiers are very much like audio amplifiers, except with higher cutoff frequencies. Any amplifier that is required to operate over a range greater than 2 or 3 decades of frequency can realistically be called a wide-band amplifier. It has already been shown that very little difficulty exists when DC or very-low-frequency operation is desired. Operational amplifiers inherently operate well under these conditions because of their direct-coupled design. As with audio amplifiers, though, problems start to arise when the higher frequencies must be amplified.

The obvious answer has been to use operational amplifiers with a higher unity gain frequency (higher gain-bandwidth product). It has also been pointed out that operation at higher frequency can be accomplished by tailoring op amp frequency/phase compensation. The combination of both methods will allow wide-band operation of operational amplifier circuits into the megahertz region. It will soon be shown that operation at such high frequencies may be necessary even if the basic frequencies to be amplified are much lower. Let's see why this is true.

PULSE COMPONENTS

Any electronic circuit that processes information in nonsinusoidal form requires special attention. In particular, circuits that use pulses and square waves are particularly affected. It is generally considered that wide-band response is required of pulse and square wave circuits, even though the frequency is relatively low. Pulses and square waves are found in television, computers, remote control devices, and so forth. The reason for wide-band requirements will appear as the constituent parts of a square wave are examined.

Consider a 1000 Hz square wave as an example. A square wave has the same period as a sine wave. That is, it takes 1 ms (millisecond) to complete one cycle of any 1000 Hz wave whether it be sine, triangular, or square. Figure 6–6 shows the development of a 1000 Hz square wave from its sine wave components. A square wave is made up by combining the fundamental-frequency sine wave with the proper amplitude of each of its *odd* harmonics. (A harmonic is an integer multiple of some fundamental frequency.) The mathematicians tell us that if we start with, for example, a 1 V fundamental-frequency sine wave, we must combine with it 1/3 V of 3rd harmonic, 1/5 V of 5th harmonic, 1/7 V of 7th harmonic, and so on. By the time we get to 15th harmonic, it is difficult to really notice the effect of further additions. The general effect of combining various harmonics is now discussed.

The top diagram in Figure 6–6 shows the conventional representation of a square wave, which is symmetrical about a zero volt reference. That is, the − amplitude is the same value as the + amplitude. Theoretically, the amplitude changes instantaneously from the − value to the + value. It then remains at the + value for 1/2 the period of the square wave before changing instantaneously back to the − value, where it remains for the other half of the period. For the time that the

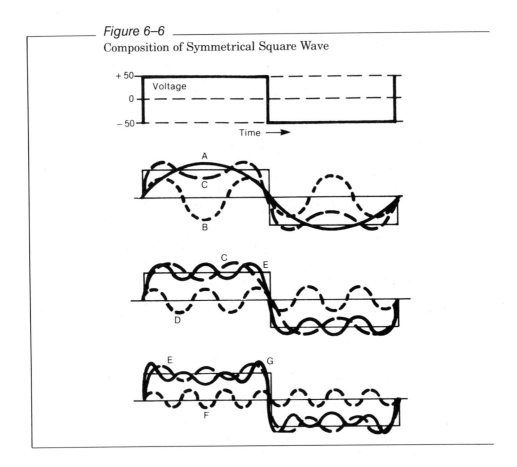

Figure 6–6

Composition of Symmetrical Square Wave

square wave is at either the + or the − value, it acts like zero frequency, or DC. During the transition from − to +, and vice versa, the frequency is infinitely high. Thus, in order to accurately reproduce a perfect square wave, an amplifier must be able to reproduce all frequencies from DC to infinity. Fortunately, the transition of square waves and pulses is not instantaneous, so the requirement for infinite frequency reduces to some finite value. It is no problem to obtain DC response with op amps, so we should be able to accurately reproduce square waves with op amps.

The second diagram in Figure 6–6 shows that waveshape formed by adding the fundamental frequency and its 3rd harmonic with an amplitude 1/3 the amplitude of the fundamental. Note that the resultant wave slightly resembles the superimposed square wave. The third diagram shows the result of adding the 5th harmonic at 1/5 the amplitude of the fundamental. Corners are much sharper, and the top and bottom are becoming flatter.

In the next diagram of Figure 6–6, the 7th harmonic is added at

1/7 the amplitude of the fundamental. The resultant curve is beginning to smooth out on the top and bottom and is becoming quite sharp at the corners. Adding additional odd harmonics at the appropriate amplitude would further sharpen the corners and flatten the top and bottom. As noted earlier, by about the 15th harmonic, the resultant waveform is relatively square.

This approach to synthesizing a square wave from sine waves provides an ideal method for analyzing circuits that contain square waves. If a reasonably good square wave is applied to the input of a circuit, the output waveform gives a clue as to circuit operation. For example, if the output transitions do not take place in the same time period as the input, the high-frequency response and/or slew rate are at fault. The corners will also appear rounded with poor high-frequency response. Low-frequency response can be evaluated by the flatness of the top and bottom of the output waveform. Any tilt is indicative of poor low-frequency characteristics.

VIDEO AMPLIFIERS

Wide-band amplifiers are often called **video amplifiers**. All video amplifiers share some basic characteristics, whether the active components are vacuum tubes, transistors, or integrated circuits.

Requirements for Video Amplifiers

A "flat" frequency response is one of the primary requirements. Video amplifiers are required to process input signals that have abrupt changes of waveshape, such as square waves and pulses. As discussed earlier, such waveforms contain a very wide band of frequencies extending from near DC to many megahertz. If the frequency response of the video amplifier is not flat, or if it has appreciable phase shift, the input waveform will not be faithfully reproduced.

A well-designed op amp is the answer to the frequency response requirements of the video amplifier. Vacuum tubes and transistors both suffer gain reduction at high frequencies because of their construction. High-frequency response improves when the output of the amplifier is loaded more heavily. However, gain is reduced, often to a value below that required. Inductive methods of compensation must be used to extend the high-frequency response, and difficulties result. The frequency response has "ripples" in it, sometimes rather large and rising to a peak near the high cutoff frequency. Phase shift can be excessive with inductive compensation, and adjustment is critical to obtain consistent operation.

Similar difficulties arise when trying to extend the low-frequency response of vacuum tube and transistor amplifiers. The ideal answer is to directly couple one stage of the amplifier to the next. Temperature and component changes, however, cause variations in DC voltages that can result in complete saturation or cutoff of the amplifier. Using large-value capacitors to couple from one amplifier stage to the next can improve low-frequency response, but such capacitors are physically large.

As has been shown many times before, both high gain and wide bandwidth do not necessarily go hand in hand. Most often gain must be traded for bandwidth, or vice versa. The op amp helps in making this trade-off because it is designed with high gain, stable operation, high input impedance, and low output impedance. It is still necessary to trade gain for bandwidth, though, even before we start. Whereas many low-frequency op amps begin with near 100 dB gain ratings, video op amps start with gains of only 30 to 60 dB. Thus, gain has already been traded for bandwidth. There are exceptions, of course, just as with low-frequency op amps. Some video op amps have gain ratings well above 50 and 60 dB, but they are the expensive, almost custom-built versions. Most of the video op amp circuits that will be encountered in everyday use are those in the 30 to 60 dB range. These are the op amps applied and discussed in detail in this chapter.

Perhaps the greatest advantage of op amps over vacuum tubes and transistors in video applications is the relatively flat gain response as frequency increases. The ripples and peaks in the passband are almost nonexistent with op amps because inductive compensation is not used. Most video op amps have terminals for external compensation. Resistors and capacitors, however, are used instead of inductors. The lack of peaks due to inductance and capacitance thus provides a flatter response.

Video Op Amps

Some op amps not specifically designed for video amplifier applications have characteristics suitable for video use. An example is the LH0032 ultra-fast FET operational amplifier manufactured by National Semiconductor. Its frequency response is shown in Figure 6–7A, along with two typical applications (see Figures 6–7B and 6–7C). Compensation is not necessary at high gains, but provision is made for lower-gain compensation as shown. The 40 dB amplifier has a bandwidth of about 5 MHz, while the 20 dB configuration extends beyond 20 MHz. Both circuits thus easily fit into the video amplifier category. Note that conventional feedback and compensation techniques are used. Gain is calculated in the usual manner. Two examples follow.

Figure 6–7

Video Amplifier

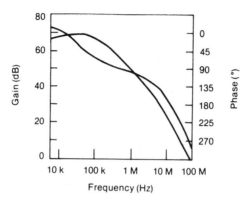

A. LH0032 Frequency/Phase Response

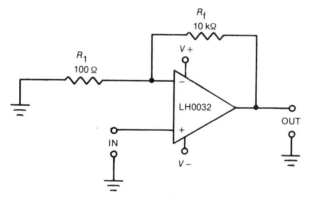

B. 40 dB Gain Video Amplifier

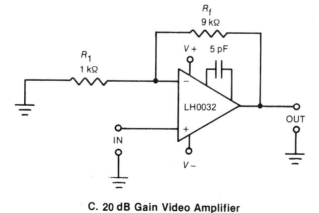

C. 20 dB Gain Video Amplifier

Example 6–3

Verify the gain of the 40 dB amplifier in Figure 6–7B.

Solution

$$A_{cl} = 20 \log \left(1 + \frac{R_f}{R_1} \right) = 20 \log \left(1 + \frac{10,000}{100} \right) = 20 \log (101)$$

$$= (20)(2) = 40 \text{ dB}$$

Example 6–4

Verify the gain of the 20 dB amplifier in Figure 6–7C.

Solution

$$A_{cl} = 20 \log \left(1 + \frac{R_f}{R_1} \right) = 20 \log \left(1 + \frac{9000}{1000} \right) = 20 \log (10)$$

$$= (20)(1) = 20 \text{ dB}$$

Although slew rate has been discussed only in relation to the large-signal characteristics of op amps, a limitation on rapid input signal changes exists even with small input signals. The pulse response of an op amp is extremely important with video amplifiers. Input signals are generally not in sine wave form but are rapidly changing waveshapes with high frequencies present. The rapid changes are indicative of high-frequency components. A general relationship exists between an op amp's pulse response and its unity gain frequency. Higher frequency op amps generally have good pulse response. That is, high-frequency op amps do not appreciably distort pulse input signals.

The frequency response of a video op amp looks much like the lower frequency op amp response curves. Figure 6–8A shows the frequency and Figure 6–8B, the pulse response of the type 733 differential video op amp. This op amp is supplied by many manufacturers and is typical of general-purpose video op amps. It is internally compensated and has a unity gain frequency of about 120 MHz. The 3 dB bandwidth (the frequency at which the frequency response curve is − 3 dB from the low-frequency gain) is approximately 30 MHz. One of the unique features of the type 733 video op amp is the ability to set the gain by merely connecting jumper wires. Gains of 10, 100, and 400 are provided. Feedback is internal, and no provision is made for conventional external feedback. This technique is common with video and wide-band amplifiers. The high frequencies present in video amplifiers make it mandatory that external connections be kept to a minimum. Intermediate gain values may also be obtained by connecting a variable resistor between

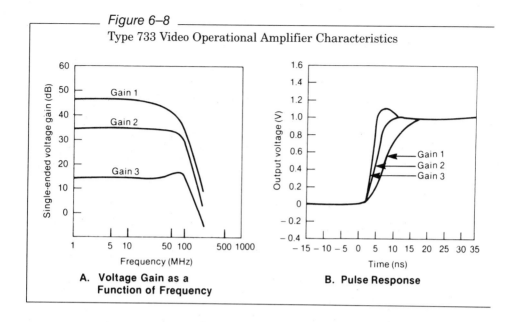

Figure 6–8

Type 733 Video Operational Amplifier Characteristics

A. **Voltage Gain as a Function of Frequency**

B. **Pulse Response**

appropriate terminals. It should be noted that frequency and phase response are related to gain, just as with lower frequency op amps.

An op amp designed to take maximum advantage of phase compensation techniques is shown in Figure 6–9. The CA3038 op amp is one of a family of ICs manufactured by RCA. From the open-loop gain curve (Figure 6–9B), it can be seen that the 3 dB bandwidth is about 320 kHz with a gain of 70 dB. Terminals are provided for conventional phase-lead and phase-lag connections in addition to the Miller effect (see Chapter 4) phase-lag terminals (Figure 6–9A). Using only **phase-lead compensation** and conventional negative feedback (Figure 6–9C), a 50 dB amplifier with a 3 dB bandwidth of 3.5 MHz is easily obtained. This is adequate for video amplifier applications such as small television receivers where maximum picture quality is not necessary. Extension to more than 6 MHz occurs by merely changing the feedback network to achieve 40 dB gain.

Figure 6–9D shows the addition of Miller effect **phase-lag networks**. Note that two identical networks are needed. Internal design of the CA3038 uses balanced differential amplifiers that require dual phase shift networks. The gain of 10 dB and 3 dB bandwidth of 42 MHz is established by the usual resistive feedback method. If the slight peaking that occurs near 20 MHz is undesirable, it may be removed by connecting a conventional phase-lag capacitor of about 15 pF from the phase-lag terminal to ground. A reduction of 3 dB bandwidth to about

Figure 6–9

Type 3038 Wide-Band Operational Amplifier

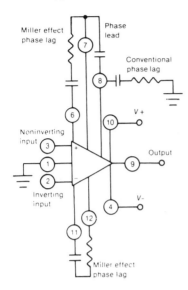

A. Terminal Connections for Phase-Lag and Phase-Lead Compensation

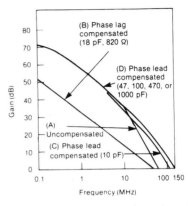

B. Open–Loop Gain as a Function of Frequency for Compensated and Uncompensated Amplifiers

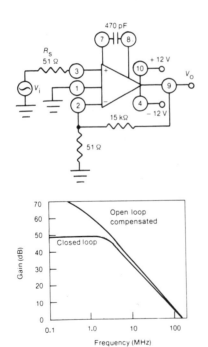

C. Circuit Diagram and Response Curve for a 50-dB Noninverting Amplifier with Phase-Lead Compensation

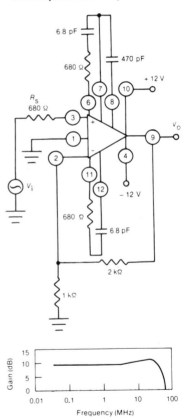

D. Circuit Diagram and Response Curve for a 10-dB Noninverting Amplifier

170

Figure 6–10
High-Slew-Rate Operational Amplifier

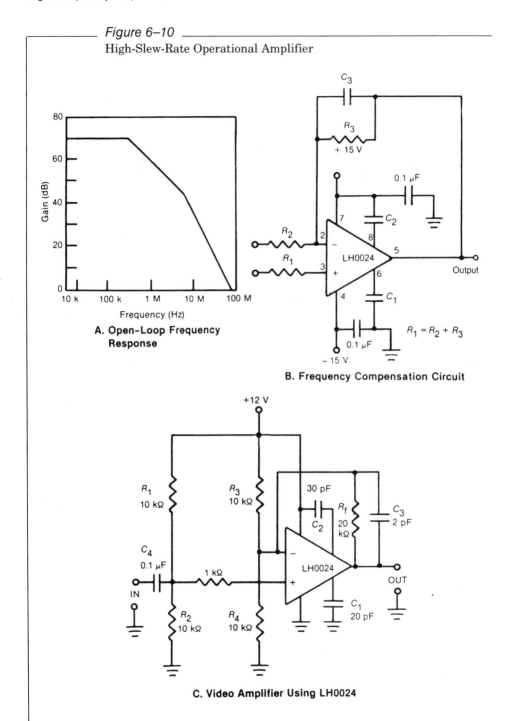

A. Open-Loop Frequency Response

$R_1 = R_2 + R_3$

B. Frequency Compensation Circuit

C. Video Amplifier Using LH0024

Table 6–2

Frequency Compensation Values

Closed-Loop Gain	C_1	C_2	C_3
100	0	0	0
20	0	0	0
10	0	20 pF	1 pF
1	30 pF	30 pF	3 pF

25 MHz will result. The amplifier of Figure 6–9D could be used quite satisfactorily in the vertical channel of a high-quality oscillosope.

Another example of the use of compensation in video amplifiers is shown in Figure 6–10. The LH0024 is a high-slew-rate operational amplifier with a unity gain frequency of about 70 MHz and a slew rate of 500 V/μs. Its combination of wide bandwidth and high slew rate makes it quite useful in video applications that require large output voltage changes. The open-loop frequency response (Figure 6–10A) shows that the LH0024 roll-off characteristic is 20 dB/decade out to about 5 MHz and 45 dB gain. Wider bandwidths and lower gain require some type of frequency compensation.

The general frequency compensation requirements are shown in Table 6–2 and Figure 6–10B. Selection of the values of capacitance listed for a specified closed-loop gain will result in optimum performance at that gain. C_1 and C_2 provide internal compensation and adjust the roll-off characteristic of 40 dB/decade to the required 20 dB/decade for stability. C_3 neutralizes the input capacitance of the op amp and often requires slight variation to obtain a perfect balance.

An example of a video amplifier circuit using the LH0024 is shown in Figure 6–10C. Let's determine the characteristics of the circuit using the information given in the figure. Note that the circuit is operating with a single +12 V supply. The op amp is designed to function with dual supplies (both + and − 12 V), so provision must be made to center the output midway between +12 V and ground. R_1 and R_2 divide the +12 V evenly to place the noninverting input at +6 V. R_3 and R_4 perform the same function for the inverting input. The combination of resistors centers the output at +6 V so that the output may change symmetrically above and below the reference 6 V.

Gain is determined in the usual manner. R_f is 20 kΩ, while the remainder of the feedback divider is made up of R_3 and R_4 in parallel. (R_3 must be considered in parallel with R_4 since it is considered that the +12 V power supply has zero output impedance. Thus, R_3 is effectively connected across R_4.) Solving the conventional voltage gain formula for a noninverting amplifier:

$$A_V = 1 + \frac{R_f}{R_3 \parallel R_4}$$

where

$$R_3 \parallel R_4 = \frac{R_3 R_4}{R_3 + R_4}$$

yields $A_V = 5$, which is approximately 14 dB (20 log 5 = 14). When the 14 dB gain line is extended to the frequency response curve, it can be seen that the roll-off rate is greater than 20 dB/decade. Therefore, frequency compensation must be used to reduce the roll-off rate to 20 dB/decade. Table 6–2 has been used as a guide to select approximate compensation capacitor values for the circuit in Figure 6–10C. Actual values used tend to become a matter of experimentation as can be seen from the circuit. If reduced bandwidth can be tolerated, the unity gain compensation values could be used, of course. In any event, the video amplifier of Figure 6–10C provides a gain of about 14 dB and a bandwidth of approximately 30 MHz (see intersection of 14 dB gain line with frequency response curve). This type of capability is needed in wide-band oscilloscopes and radar equipment.

Troubleshooting: The troubleshooting example for this chapter involves the video amplifier of Figure 6–10C. It is assumed that the video amplifier is used in a modern wide-band oscilloscope. When the oscilloscope is used to examine a 1 MHz square wave, it is noted that the leading edge of the square wave is badly "rounded" rather than vertical. The amplitude is also low. Such indications mean reduced bandwidth and gain. Troubleshooting so far has found that the input to the video amplifier is proper, but the output is not.

Let's examine the schematic diagram before proceeding. What components affect bandwidth? Specification sheet information shows that bandwidth is a function of the compensation capacitors and the op amp itself. Now what factors affect gain? Once again, specification sheet information indicates that gain is a function of the feedback resistors and the op amp itself.

Evaluating the known information indicates that the op amp is probably the malfunctioning component. Since it is not easy to desolder components from a printed circuit board, we should make certain before we proceed. Although capacitors are prone to failure, the compensation capacitors do not grossly affect gain. It is easy to check the feedback resistors, and this should be done. By eliminating everything else before desoldering the op amp, we will save time and possible damage to printed circuit boards.

When repairing high-frequency circuits, be cautious. Replace every component *exactly* where it was. Printed circuit board and component layout is often a part of the overall circuit design. Changing the relative locations of capacitors, for example, can cause undesired feedback and oscillation. Be sure to recheck your repaired circuit after the repair is completed.

NOISE

Since video and wide-band amplifiers are used in applications where a very broad band of frequencies is amplified, any noise present at the input and generated by the amplifier represents a potential source of difficulty. Fortunately, many video and wide-band amplifiers are used with low-input-impedance circuits. Since noise generated in input circuits is directly related to resistance, a low resistance generates less noise because of electron flow. Other good design techniques will ensure that minimum noise is generated by the amplifier circuit. Extreme care should be observed when troubleshooting and repairing video and wide-band amplifiers. Component location, value, type, and lead length may be very important not only for minimum noise but also for maintaing stable operation at design gain values.

Amplifier noise figure is a measure of noise performance of an op amp circuit. It should be remembered, however, that noise figure depends on the external connections to the op amp in addition to the op amp itself. As discussed earlier, signal-to-noise ratio is a better indication of circuit performance. When replacing op amps and components in wide-band and video amplifiers, don't substitute unless you really understand the full impact of the change. A replacement resistor or op amp may change a perfectly quiet wide-band amplifier into a noisy one.

AUTOMATIC GAIN CONTROL (AGC)

Tuned amplifiers using wide-band and video op amps are used throughout modern AM / FM radios, television receivers, and communications transmitters/receivers. The purpose of the tuned amplifiers is to selectively amplify only a given band of frequencies associated with a center frequency. Satisfactory reproduction of the information being transmitted by the "radio" frequencies (voice, music, picture, and so forth) generally requires that a relatively constant output be available from the amplifier stages. Such a requirement is not compatible with real-life conditions. Local radio or TV stations may have an extremely strong signal feeding into the amplifiers. Distant stations may have very weak signals. Something must be done to maintain a constant amplifier output with widely varying inputs.

Automatic gain control (AGC) has been used almost since the beginning of radio communication. (It was called automatic volume control, or AVC, then.) The need was as real with vacuum tube and transistor amplifiers as it is with IC amplifiers. Actually, the same concept is used. The amplifier output is sampled to determine its amplitude. A strong input signal provides a large amplitude output, while a weak signal results in a small output. The sample is converted to a DC control voltage and fed back to early stages of the amplifier. A large-amplitude output results in a large control voltage fed back to *reduce* the gain of the amplifier. A small-amplitude output feeds back less control voltage, and the gain increases. Thus, *negative feedback* is provided. Changing input signals cause changing AGC voltage, which maintains a relatively constant output amplitude.

Op amps designed specifically for radio frequency applications often have an AGC terminal. A control voltage applied to this terminal will change the gain over a range from 0 dB up to 60 or 70 dB, depending on design. Use of the AGC terminal allows retention of the differential input of the op amp with all of its advantages yet also allows variable gain control. An application of op amps to radio frequency circuits is shown in Figure 6–11.

Typical IF Amplifier with AGC

The circuit of Figure 6–11 represents the **intermediate frequency (IF) amplifier** stages of a superheterodyne AM radio receiver. You may be unfamiliar with the superheterodyne radio, but it is not necessary here to understand anything more than inputs and outputs. The circuit of Figure 6–11 amplifies a frequency band of about 20 to 30 kHz centered around 455 kHz. Selected frequencies are determined by the type of radio being discussed. Circuit input can have frequencies ranging from below 455 kHz up to many megahertz. Amplitudes can be from a few microvolts to tenths of a volt.

Since only a narrow band of frequencies centered around 455 kHz is desired, the op amps are *not* used as wide-band amplifiers. Selecting only the desired passband not only reduces amplification of undesired frequencies but also limits the noise that is ever present in electronic circuits. Earlier, it was pointed out that noise output from an amplifier was directly related to the bandwidth of the amplifier. If the bandwidth is limited, the noise will then be reduced. Filters FL-1 and FL-2 are responsible for establishing the bandwidth of the IF amplifier circuit.

Figure 6-11

Op Amp Intermediate Frequency Amplifier

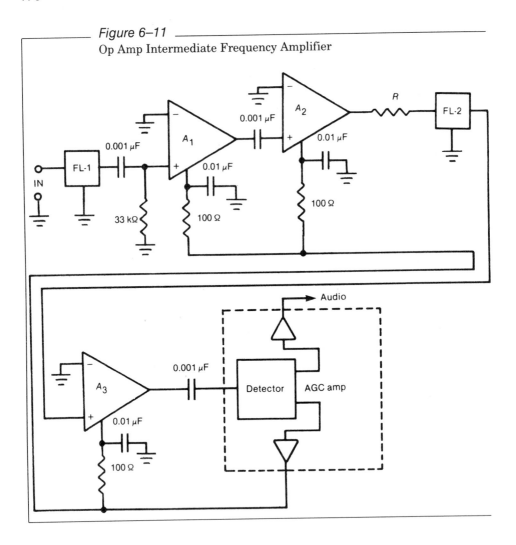

They are composed of many ceramic elements so constructed that they respond only to certain frequencies. Ceramic filters behave much like high-Q tuned circuits, but without the tuning requirement. They are quite selective, responding best to the desired band of frequencies and rejecting other frequencies quite well.

Although the input to the IF amplifier circuit contains many frequencies, FL-1 restricts the input to op amp 1 to those frequencies within the passband of the filter. The 6 dB loss of the filter is easily made up by op amps 1 and 2. FL-2 provides additional filtering before final amplification of the desired band of frequencies. The total gain of the amplifier, including the filter insertion losses, is greater than 100 dB. That kind of gain may be acceptable when very weak input signals are provided, but strong signals would definitely overload the op amps and cause distortion. That's where the rest of the circuit comes into play.

The information that is being carried by the amplified intermediate frequency signal must be recovered. In intermediate frequency form, it exists as electrical voltage and current variations at radio frequencies and cannot be heard. The **detector** (to be discussed in subsequent chapters) recovers this information and converts it into audio frequency voltage and current variations. Further audio frequency amplification then takes place so that enough power can be provided to operate a loudspeaker.

One of the by-products of the detection process is a DC voltage that is proportional to the amplitude of the IF signal coming from op amp 3. The DC voltage is amplified and used as AGC control voltage to maintain the output of op amp 3 relatively constant despite input signal variations at the input to the IF amplifier. Each op amp is isolated from the AGC control line by the 100 Ω resistor and the 0.01 μF capacitor. Capacitors used to couple between op amps are selected to pass the band of frequencies centered around 455 kHz yet restrict somewhat the lower frequencies. Further noise and unwanted signal rejection is thus provided. All the functions of the amplifier in Figure 6–11, except for the filters, are currently available on a single linear integrated circuit.

Other Applications

Similar techniques are used in other than AM radio systems. FM, television, communications, and the like employ the superheterodyne principle. The only differences are the *intermediate frequency* and the *bandwidth*. Table 6–1 provided some general information concerning these parameters. For example, FM broadcast receivers generally use 10.7 MHz as the intermediate frequency and require a bandwidth of about 250 kHz. The only change required in Figure 6–11 to make it useful for FM broadcast use, then, is to use filters with the proper center frequency and bandwidth. Operational amplifiers, of course, must be capable of operation at 10.7 MHz. Television provides a real challenge for operational amplifier circuits. Six megahertz of bandwidth must be provided, as shown by the frequency requirements diagram of Figure 6–12. The intermediate frequency is usually in the 40 MHz region (Table 6–1). Therefore, the *percentage bandwidth* is quite high. Filter requirements are stringent, and high gain in the 40 MHz region is difficult. The solution is not impossible, although it is often not provided by "true" operational amplifiers. Integrated circuit amplifiers are used, but in many cases these are not *operational* amplifiers. Linear integrated circuits are the answer.

As electronic technology advances, the functions shown in

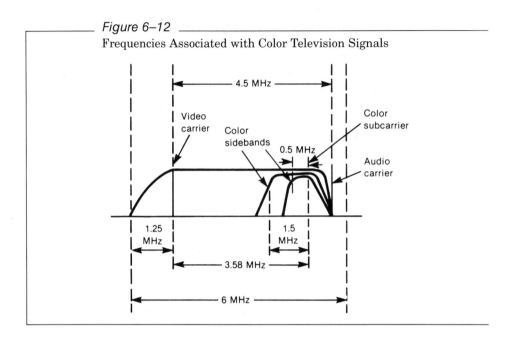

Figure 6–12

Frequencies Associated with Color Television Signals

Figure 6–11 are appearing on a single integrated circuit. Except for the filters and other discrete components, the intermediate frequency amplifier, detector, audio amplifier, and AGC amplifier are now available as a composite IC. Even the amplifiers and other functional circuits that feed the input to FL-1 are included. Op amps are not disappearing; the initial technology that allowed op amps to be developed is just expanding. Op amps will be with us for a long time, and the knowledge associated with their application just makes the use of more complex ICs easier.

SUMMARY

Chapters 5 and 6 have been devoted to operational amplifiers in strictly amplification roles. A very wide range of frequency capability has been discussed. From the low audio frequencies to the high radio frequencies, the operational amplifier has shown its versatility. A few general facts should be recalled before we discuss other applications.

First, the operational amplifier works well at DC and low frequencies because of the use of direct coupling between active devices on the chip. The lack of reactive devices (capacitors) in line with the signal path from input to output results in no degradation of low-frequency performance.

Second, the amplification capability of the operational amplifier is degraded as frequency requirements increase. Reactive components (capacitors) in parallel with (across) the signal path from input to output bypass high frequencies. Operational amplifiers either are designed for a specific high-frequency operation or may have their frequency response tailored to meet a given requirement. Both the actual high-frequency cutoff *and* the rate at which the cutoff frequency is approached must be taken into consideration to obtain stable operation. These restrictions generally result in trading gain for bandwidth, or vice versa.

Third, the frequency range of an operational amplifier may be restricted by using filters in the input and output circuits. The operational amplifiers must then only be stable within the bandpass of the filters. This technique is used in many radio applications.

Fourth, operational amplifiers should be selected to be compatible with actual frequency of operation. If the operating frequency is too high for the operational amplifier, insufficient amplification will occur. If the operating frequency is too low—that is, if the operational amplifier frequency response is too high, excessive noise will often result. Therefore, it is best to restrict selection of an operational amplifier to a frequency response no greater than the highest frequency expected.

QUESTIONS

1. How do audio and ultrasonic frequencies differ? How are they similar?

2. How do sound and radio waves differ? How are they similar?

3. Explain the principles of operation of an ultrasonic cleaning device.

4. Explain the principles of operation of an ultrasonic alarm system.

5. Discuss the differences and similarities of op amps used in audio and ultrasonic applications.

6. Draw a spectrum diagram showing the audio spectrum. Explain how you would use the spectrum diagram.

7. Why are resonant circuits used in operational amplifier applications? Show an example, and explain circuit operation.

8. Explain how you would determine the type of operational amplifier required for a specified frequency.

9. What determines the bandwidth requirements for an AM broadcast radio amplifier?

10. Why are discrete-component radio frequency amplifiers often used in place of operational amplifiers?

11. What is the difference between a narrow-band and a wide-band amplifier?

12. Is there any way that the frequency response of an operational amplifier can be extended? Explain.

13. Explain why pulse and square wave amplifiers require high frequency response.

14. Discuss the important characteristics of a video amplifier.

15. Why do some video amplifiers have no provision for external feedback control?

16. Draw a diagram showing how to operate a dual-supply operational amplifier on a single supply.

17. Discuss the factors associated with the noise response of video amplifiers.

18. Draw a block diagram showing how AGC is used to control the gain of an amplifier. Explain circuit operation.

19. Why is bandwidth restricted in some intermediate frequency amplifiers? Explain how the restriction is accomplished.

20. Discuss the use of linear integrated circuits in place of operational amplifiers in a television receiver.

═══ PROBLEMS ═══════════════════════

1. Verify the 73 dB gain of A_1 in Figure 6–1. Show your calculations.

2. Verify the 40 dB gain of A_2 in Figure 6–1. Show your calculations.

3. Estimate the low-frequency cutoff of A_1 and A_2 in Figure 6–1. Show your calculations.

4. If the Q of the LC circuit in Figure 6–3 is 60, what is the bandwidth?

5. Using Figure 6–4, determine the gain-bandwidth product required for (a) 50 dB gain at 50 kHz, (b) 80 dB gain at 100 kHz, and (c) 20 dB gain at 10 MHz.

6. If R_1 in Figure 6–7B was changed to 500 Ω, determine the operating characteristics of the circuit.

7. Predict the effect of changing the 470 pF capacitor in Figure 6–9C to 1000 pF.

8. Predict the effect of changing the 51 Ω resistor in Figure 6–9C to 510 Ω.

9. Using the data in Figure 6–10, redraw Figure 6–10C for 30 dB operation.

10. Which of the operational amplifiers in Chapter 6 would be best suited for an intermediate frequency amplifier such as that in Figure 6–11 to be used in an FM broadcast radio? Explain.

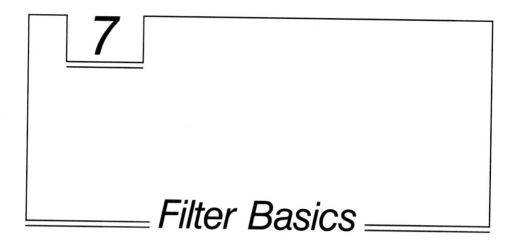

7

Filter Basics

OBJECTIVES   After studying Chapter 7, you will be able to

1. Explain what filters are and how they are used.
2. List the kinds of active and passive components used in filters.
3. Describe the various classifications for filters.
4. Identify the characteristics and applications of low-pass, high-pass, band-pass, and band-reject filters.
5. Identify Butterworth, Chebyshev, and Bessel filters.
6. Use generalized frequency response and phase graphs.
7. Explain the meaning of bandwidth and Q with band-pass and band-reject filters.
8. Recognize ways of identifying first-order filters.
9. Discuss the use of voltage followers and gain blocks with filters.
10. Describe how feedback filters operate and where they are used.

INTRODUCTION

One of the earliest and still one of the most common applications of operational amplifiers is in filter circuits. Filters may be formed without operational amplifiers, but such filters are less versatile and usually physically larger. It is important, however, to have a background in *passive* filters as well as in *active* filters. Chapter 7 develops the basic fundamentals of filters as applied to both types.

_____ FILTER FUNDAMENTALS _____

A **filter** is an electrical circuit or device that discriminates in favor of some frequencies and against certain other frequencies. In other words, _filters allow some frequencies to pass with little opposition while blocking other frequencies._ Filters are constructed using combinations of resistors (R), capacitors (C), and/or inductors (L). Certain ceramic or crystalline materials also possess electromechanical characteristics that allow them to act as filters. Discussions in this chapter are limited to _RCL_ filters.

Filters are found throughout the field of electronics. From the simple power supply that provides direct current from an alternating current source to complex communication systems and computers, filters play an important part. Many filter applications are shown in this and following chapters.

Filter Classifications

Filters are generally used in sine wave AC circuits. Direct current may also be present, but the behavior of filters with sine wave inputs/outputs is of prime importance. Filters do affect square waves and pulses, but nonsine wave behavior is not the subject of this chapter.

The common classifications of filters—_low-pass, high-pass, band-pass,_ and _band-reject_—describe filters by their function. Low-pass filters pass only frequencies _below_ a desired design frequency, blocking all other frequencies. A good example of a low-pass filter is the bass tone control on a high fidelity home entertainment system. The bass control allows the low frequencies to pass but attenuates the high frequencies. High-pass filters pass only frequencies _above_ a desired design frequency, blocking all other frequencies. The treble tone control on a high fidelity home entertainment system is an example of a high-pass filter. Only the high-frequency sounds are allowed through; the low-frequency sounds are attenuated. **Band-pass filters** pass a band of frequencies within the desired range, blocking all other frequencies both above and below the desired passband. Every time you tune an AM / FM radio or select a channel on a TV, you use a band-pass filter. Only the desired station will be allowed through; all other stations are attenuated. **Band-reject filters** reject a band of frequencies within the desired range, passing all other frequencies both above and below the desired rejection band. Perhaps you have had interference on a TV due to a local citizen's band radio. The installation of a band-reject filter stops the interfering signal but allows the desired signal through.

Although most commonly classified according to function, filters are also classified by the shape of their response. Such factors as variation in response over the flat range of the filter or the roll-off characteristic provide filters with identifying names. Thus, for example, filters with the flattest response are called **Butterworth filters**. Butterworth filters are often called flat-flat or maximally flat filters. When there are dips in the flat range of the response, the filters are called **Chebyshev filters. Bessel filters** have a very gradual roll-off characteristic and a drooping passband. Both the type and shape of response must be considered when discussing how filters operate.

Filter Graphs and Calculations

Mathematical expressions as well as frequency response curves are used to describe filter characteristics. The filter's frequency response curve is a graph where the ratio of output voltage to input voltage is on the vertical axis and frequency is on the horizontal axis. The frequency axis is plotted logarithmically so that wide ranges of frequency may be displayed adequately. Consider the audio spectrum (20 Hz to 20 kHz), for example. Figure 7–1 shows the frequency response of an audio amplifier plotted with both linear and logarithmic frequency scales. Compare the logarithmic scale in Figure 7–1A to the linear scale in Figure 7–1B, and note the additional detail that is available with the logarithmic scale. The vertical scale is often plotted in terms of dB (a logarithmic quantity) rather than the output voltage to input voltage ratios. Thus, the vertical scale of the graph is linear in terms of voltage ratios but logarithmic in terms of dB. Filter and op amp circuits that have wide ranges of attenuation and gain must be graphed in this manner in order to display

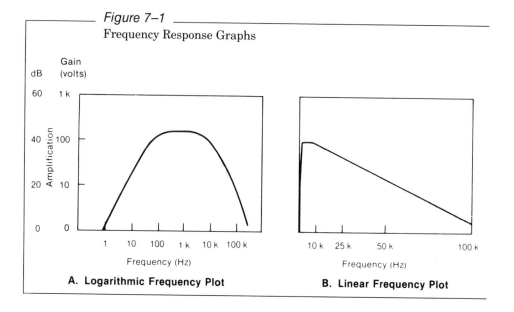

Figure 7–1

Frequency Response Graphs

A. Logarithmic Frequency Plot

B. Linear Frequency Plot

adequate detail. (See Figure 7–4B for an example of a typical filter response graph.)

It will be seen shortly that the simplifications made with the frequency response graphs for operational amplifiers can be made with frequency response graphs for filters. In the case of the audio amplifier graphs shown in Figure 7–1, note that the gain generally stays flat over most of the audio frequency range. It does, however, roll off at both low and high frequencies. Much remains to be said about roll-off, but for now let's simplify the graph in the roll-off portions. The band of frequencies passed by the amplifier (or a filter, for that matter) is defined as the range of frequencies between the frequencies at which the output is − 3 dB in relation to the flat portion of the response curve. The − 3 dB frequencies are defined as the *cutoff* frequencies of the device. (The term *corner* frequency is often used synonymously with cutoff frequency.) A simplification of the frequency response graph uses straight-line approximations instead of curves. It is called a *Bode plot* and makes calculations much easier. There is a maximum of 3 dB error with the Bode plot, but this occurs only near the cutoff frequencies. Many of the graphs of filter responses in this text use Bode plots. (See Figure 4–2 for an example of a Bode plot.)

Mathematical calculations for filter circuits can become quite complex. Although it would seem simple to merely calculate output voltage in respect to input voltage, the frequency-dependent characteristics of reactive elements make it more difficult. The minimum calculations that are necessary to understand filter operation are used in this text. Graphical methods will be employed when at all feasible.

—————— *PASSIVE FILTERS* ——————————

Before discussing active filters, which contain amplifying devices such as op amps, it is advisable to review the fundamentals of passive filters. **Passive filters** contain only resistors, capacitors, or inductors (or combinations thereof). The pi filter used in power supplies is a passive filter. They *attenuate* input signals. Thus, the frequency response graphs of passive filters will show the reference level at which minimal attenuation exists as 0 dB. When the output of the filter becomes less than the reference level, it will be shown as − dB.

Much of the work done with active filters uses only resistors and capacitors with op amps. Inductors tend to be physically large and are difficult to use in modern miniature equipment. Therefore, in preparation for discussion of active filters, in general, the passive filters discussed will be made up of resistors and capacitors. The primary advantage of passive filters is that no operating power is required. The disadvantage is that passive filters attenuate the input signal, possibly to a level that makes the output not usable.

Low-Pass Filters

A low-pass filter passes all signals from input to output, with little or no attenuation, up to a specified frequency; all frequencies above the specified frequency are rejected or greatly attenuated. The basic low-pass filter uses a resistor and a capacitor in series (see Figure 7–2A). The input signal is applied across the series combination, and the output appears across the capacitor. The general shape of the frequency response is shown in Figure 7–2B. Output remains relatively constant (that is, within 3 dB) with increasing frequency until the cutoff frequency is reached. The range of frequencies *below* the cutoff frequency of a low-pass filter is called the *passband*. At the cutoff frequency, the output voltage is − 3 dB from the flat portion of the response. Cutoff

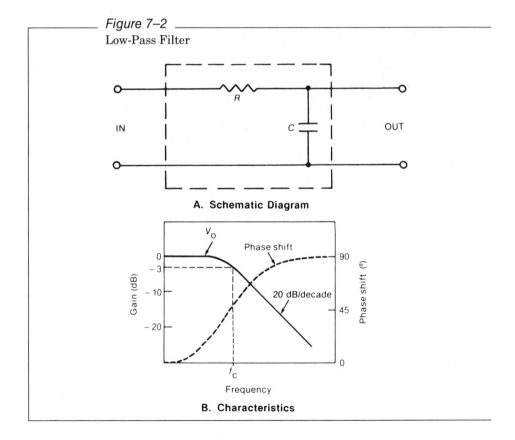

Figure 7–2

Low-Pass Filter

A. Schematic Diagram

B. Characteristics

frequency is calculated by the familiar formula $f_c = 1/2\pi RC$. The output continues to decrease at a rate of 20 dB/decade in a simple single-section, or **first-order**, RC filter. That portion of the frequency spectrum *above* the cutoff frequency of a low-pass filter is called the **stopband**. Phase shift between input and output cannot exceed 90° in a single-section RC circuit. Actual phase shift is calculated by the following equation:

$$\tan \emptyset = -\frac{X_C}{R} \tag{7–1}$$

where ∅ (phi) represents the phase angle. A phase shift diagram is also shown in Figure 7–2. Note that phase shift is near 0° at frequencies well below f_c and near 90° at frequencies well above f_c. At f_c, phase shift is 45°.

In an effort to generalize the frequency response Bode plot, the horizontal axis is sometimes scaled in terms of the ratio of some frequency f to the cutoff frequency f_c. Figure 7–3 shows the relative frequency Bode plot. Some important points on the frequency response curve can be identified. For example, f_c (the cutoff frequency) is the point where the curve breaks and starts decreasing at a rate of 20 dB/decade. Note that this occurs at the f/f_c ratio of 1. That is, the frequency in which we are interested (f) is the same as f_c. Let's pick an easy cutoff frequency (f_c) such as 1 kHz for an example. If the frequency of interest (f) is also 1 kHz, then the ratio of $f/f_c = 1000/1000 = 1$. Reading upward from the horizontal axis in Figure 7–3, we see that 1 intersects the gain curve directly at the break point. The gain, then, at 1 kHz, is 0 dB (within the 3 dB error allowed with the Bode plot).

Figure 7–3

Generalized Low-Pass Filter Bode Plot

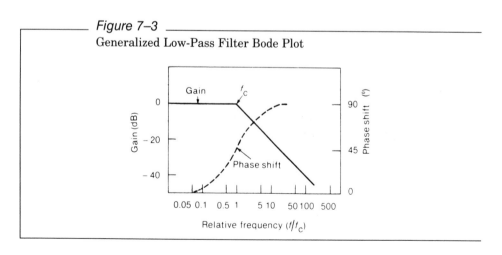

How about the gain at 3 kHz? The ratio $f/f_c = 3/1 = 3$. Intersection of the 3 point on the f/f_c axis with the gain curve is at about -10 dB. At 30 kHz, the gain is about -30 dB, since the ratio of $f/f_c = 30/1 = 30$.

_____ *Example 7–1* _____

The f_c of a low-pass filter is 5 kHz. Determine the filter gain at 15 kHz and 150 kHz using Figure 7–3.

Solution

At 15 kHz,

$$\frac{f}{f_c} = \frac{15}{5} = 3$$

From Figure 7–3,

$$\text{filter gain} = -10 \text{ dB}$$

At 150 kHz,

$$\frac{f}{f_c} = \frac{150}{5} = 30$$

From Figure 7–3,

$$\text{filter gain} = -30 \text{ dB}$$

Thus, once the cutoff frequency f_c is known, the relative response at any frequency can be determined. This technique is used throughout filter discussions to simplify calculations.

One other important fact can be obtained from the generalized frequency response graph. As mentioned earlier, the phase shift of the low-pass filter is 45° at the cutoff frequency f_c. The ratio of f/f_c may be used to determine the phase angle at any frequency related to f_c. Calculations are performed with the following equation:

$$\tan \emptyset = -\frac{f}{f_c}$$

When the frequency of interest (f) equals f_c, the ratio $f/f_c = -1$. The angle whose tangent is -1 is 45°.

_____ Example 7–2 _____

The f_c of a low-pass filter is 5 kHz. Determine the filter phase shift at 15 kHz and 150 kHz using Figure 7–3.

Solution

$$\tan \phi = -\frac{f}{f_c} = -\frac{15}{5} = -3$$

$$\phi = 71.6°$$

$$\tan \phi = -\frac{f}{f_c} = -\frac{150}{5} = -30$$

$$\phi = 88°$$

Ratios less than -1 result in angles less than 45°. The generalized phase shift graph of Figure 7–3 may be used in the same manner as the generalized frequency response graph.

The low-pass filter graphs and equations just discussed are valid as long as a substantial load is not connected across the output. If the load resistance is large compared to the series resistor in the low-pass filter, very little effect will be seen. However, if the load resistance is decreased toward the value of the series resistor, both output voltage and cutoff frequency are affected. The output voltage is reduced, and the cutoff frequency is increased. For example, when the load resistance and the series resistance are equal, the output voltage is reduced by a factor of 2, and because the effective resistance is reduced by a factor of 2, the cutoff frequency is increased by a factor of 2. In conventional low-pass filters, therefore, the load resistance must be taken into consideration during initial filter calculations. Active filters, in which op amps are often inserted between the filter output and the load, do not suffer from this decline in performance. The very high input resistance of the op amp offers very little load to the filter.

High-Pass Filters

A high-pass filter passes all signals from input to output, with little or no attenuation, down to a specified frequency; all frequencies below the specified frequency are rejected or greatly attentuated. The basic high-pass filter uses a resistor and a capacitor in series (see Figure 7–4A). The input signal is applied across the series combination, and the output appears across the resistor. Note that the only difference between the low-pass and the high-pass filter is the output connection. Output remains relatively constant with decreasing frequency until the cutoff frequency is reached. The range of frequencies *above* the cutoff fre-

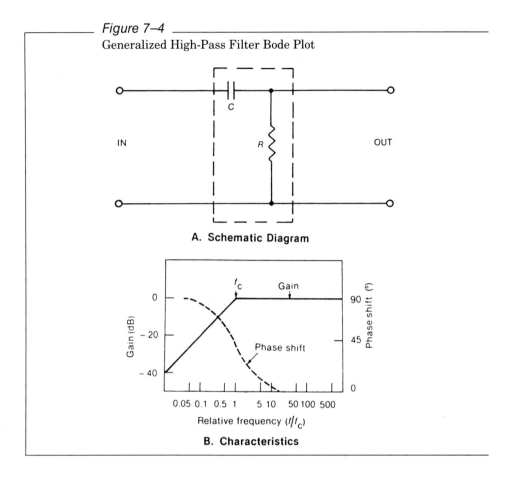

Figure 7–4

Generalized High-Pass Filter Bode Plot

A. Schematic Diagram

B. Characteristics

quency of a high-pass filter is called the *passband*. Just as with the low-pass filter, at the cutoff frequency, the output is -3 dB from the flat portion of the response. Cutoff frequency is calculated from the same formula, $f_c = 1/2\pi RC$. The roll-off characteristic of the first-order (single-section) high-pass RC filter is also 20 dB/decade. That portion of the frequency spectrum *below* the cutoff frequency of a high-pass filter is called the *stopband*. Phase shift characteristics and calculations for high-pass filters are the same as for low-pass filters, except the angle is $+$ instead of $-$.

The generalized frequency response Bode plot of Figure 7–4B is used in the same manner as the low-pass graph. Filter gain and phase shift for any frequency in respect to f_c are easily located using Figure 7–4B. The loading effect described with low-pass filters also occurs with high-pass filters and must be considered.

Band-Pass Filters

A band-pass filter passes only signals within a given range of frequencies from input to output without appreciable attenuation. Those frequencies both above and below the selected passband are rejected. A band-pass filter can be formed by using a low-pass filter combined with a high-pass filter, as shown in Figure 7–5A. The upper roll-off frequency is determined by the cutoff frequency of the low-pass filter (see Figure 7–5B). The lower roll-off frequency is determined by the cutoff frequency of the high-pass filter. When the two filter responses are combined, the result is as shown in Figure 7–5B. Frequencies below the lower cutoff frequency are rejected by the high-pass filter, while those above the upper cutoff frequency are rejected by the low-pass filter. The actual width of the passband (that is, the bandwidth) is the difference between the lower cutoff frequency and the upper cutoff frequency. The center frequency (f_0) is the frequency at which maximum amplitude would occur in a high-Q band-pass filter.

In addition to bandwidth and center frequency, the Q *factor* must also be considered. Q relates to the quality of the band-pass filter and

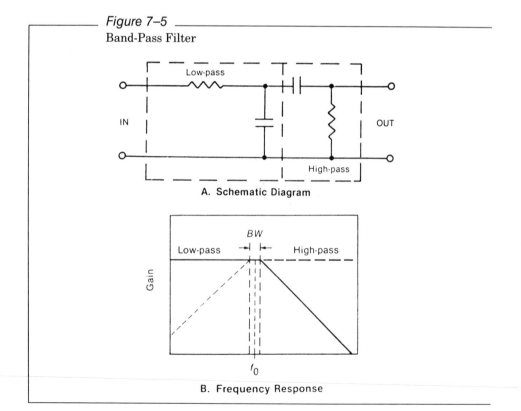

Figure 7–5
Band-Pass Filter

A. Schematic Diagram

B. Frequency Response

is an indication of its "sharpness," or selectivity. The relationship between Q, center frequency (f_0), and bandwidth (BW) is determined by the following equation:

$$Q = \frac{f_0}{BW} \tag{7-2}$$

Figure 6–3 (see page 159) related Q and bandwidth, showing that for a given center frequency, an increasing Q decreases bandwidth. Control of Q with passive RC band-pass filters is not easily obtained. It will be seen shortly that active filters are easily controllable for both center frequency and Q.

Passive band-pass filters are often constructed using inductors and capacitors. Values are selected so that the circuit is resonant at the desired center frequency. Bandwidth is controlled by selecting inductors with the desired Q or by loading the inductor with a resistor. Refer to Appendix B for graphs and formulas relating resonant circuit Q and bandwidth. Use of LC band-pass filters with active devices is not popular because of the size of the inductors. The same effect may be obtained with resistors, capacitors, and feedback in less physical space and less weight.

Band-Reject Filters

The band-reject, or notch, filter has a response opposite to that of the band-pass filter. It rejects a band of frequencies centered around the desired frequency while passing with minimal attenuation those frequencies above and below the rejected band. Definitions for bandwidth and Q are the same as for the band-pass filter.

As shown in Figure 7–6A, a low-pass filter and a high-pass filter are combined to form the band-reject filter whose response curve is shown in Figure 7–6B. The cutoff frequency of the low-pass filter is selected so that the 20 dB/decade roll-off characteristic approaches maximum attenuation at the center frequency to be rejected. Likewise, the cutoff frequency of the high-pass filter is selected so that its roll-off characteristic also approaches maximum attenuation at the center frequency to be rejected. LC resonant circuits are also used with passive band-reject filters.

Miscellaneous Filter Facts

Quite often the 20 dB/decade roll-off characteristic of a simple single-order RC filter is not steep enough to permit rejection of strong input frequencies near the desired input frequency. Figure 7–7 shows a typical

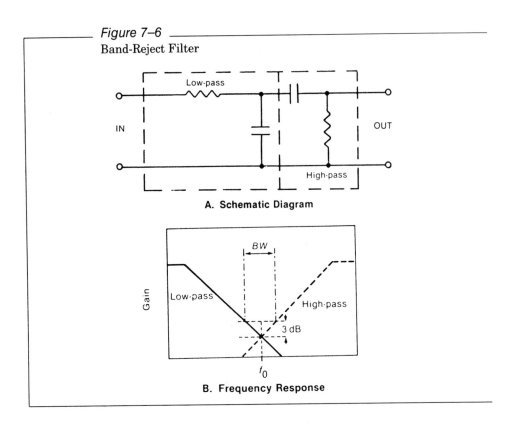

Figure 7–6

Band-Reject Filter

A. Schematic Diagram

B. Frequency Response

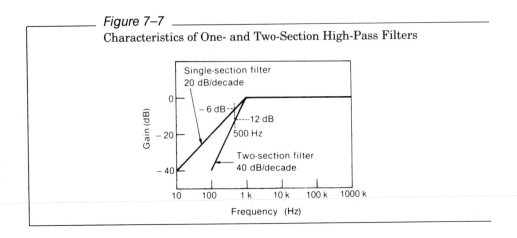

Figure 7–7

Characteristics of One- and Two-Section High-Pass Filters

case. The high-pass filter is designed with a cutoff frequency of 1000 Hz; since it is a simple single-order *RC* filter, the roll-off characteristic is 20 dB/decade. Consider a strong unwanted signal at 500 Hz. The gain of the filter is about -6 dB at 500 Hz, and if the unwanted 500 Hz signal is only 6 dB stronger than a desired signal at 1000 Hz, they will both appear at the same strength at the filter output.

When another *RC* section is added to the first section, the roll-off characteristic increases to 40 dB/decade. Now the 500 Hz gain of the filter is about -12 dB. Adding just one more filter section has doubled the rejection capability. The only problem is that adding the second section (or second-order filter) loads the first section and upsets the center frequency and voltage output. Active filters that use op amps to isolate filter sections are probably the best answer to this problem. However, if the impedance of the second section can be made quite high, it is possible to obtain the desired results without using active devices. Figure 7–8 demonstrates two *cascaded* filter sections that provide 40 dB/decade roll-off with minimal loading of the first section.

The important consideration is that both sections have a cutoff frequency of 1000 Hz. Since the determining factors are *R* and *C*, many different combinations will provide the same cutoff frequency. The first section uses a small resistor (1 kΩ) and a large capacitor (0.16 μF). Using the impedance and reactance formulas in Appendix B, $Z = 1410\ \Omega$ and $X_C = 995\ \Omega$. The second section, which connects across the 1 kΩ resistor, has a $Z = 141,000\ \Omega$. Little loading will occur, and the 40 dB/decade roll-off characteristic will provide additional rejection at frequencies near the cutoff frequency. Some overall attenuation will occur but in many cases can be countered with a simple amplifier. If a steeper

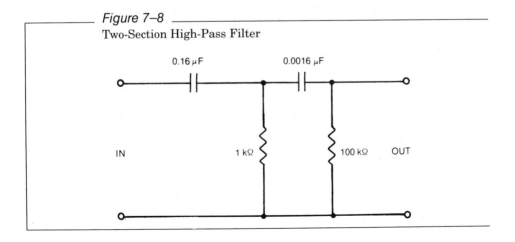

Figure 7–8
Two-Section High-Pass Filter

slope (greater attenuation) is needed, even more RC sections may be added. Loading, of course, must be considered.

The remainder of this chapter is concerned with active filters. The material just discussed is essential to understanding active filters. If, in what follows, difficulty is experienced in understanding basic filter concepts, return to this section for review. Active filters do many worthwhile things in electronics. Some of the more common applications are discussed in later sections.

SIMPLE ACTIVE FILTERS

There are many different ways to describe **active filters**: by function, by shape of passband, by designers' names, and so on. In this chapter, active filters are described first by order of complexity. Further breakdown is by function, name, passband shape, and so on. Using order of complexity as the primary description allows the simplest filters to appear first. The knowledge gained during discussion of simple filters then builds up to knowledge of more complex circuits.

First-Order Filter Fundamentals

The *order* of a filter is generally determined by the number of reactive elements in the network. In an active filter, the reactive elements are almost universally capacitors. Thus, a first-order filter will have a single capacitor in the filter network. The simple low-pass and high-pass filters described earlier are first-order filters. Only a single capacitor is used. This capacitor is in parallel with the signal path in a low-pass filter and in series with the signal path in a high-pass filter.

In first-order filters, it is possible to vary only the cutoff frequency (f_c) and the impedance (Z) of the filter. Both f_c and Z are simple functions of the resistance and capacitance in the circuit. Examples 7–1 and 7–2 demonstrate how two filter sections with the same f_c have different Z levels. Note that, for simplification, each section is calculated as though the output load was disconnected.

_____ *Example 7–3* _____

In the circuit diagram of Figure 7–2A, $C = 0.16$ μF and $R = 1$ kΩ. Determine the output impedance and cutoff frequency.

Solution

$$f_c = \frac{1}{2\pi RC} = \frac{1}{(6.28)(1000)(0.00000016)} = 994.7 \text{ Hz}$$

$$Z_o = R_o = 1 \text{ kΩ}$$

──────── *Example 7–4* ────────

In the circuit diagram of Figure 7–2A, $C = 0.0016 \, \mu F$ and $R = 100 \, k\Omega$. Determine the output impedance and cutoff frequency.

Solution

$$f_c = \frac{1}{2\pi RC} = \frac{1}{(6.28)(100000)(0.0000000016)} = 994.7 \text{ Hz}$$

$$Z_o = R_o = 100 \text{ k}\Omega$$

The filters in Examples 7–3 and 7–4 have identical characteristics as far as gain and frequency response are concerned. When their inputs are from very low impedance sources and their outputs are to very high impedance loads, both filters will have almost no **insertion loss** at frequencies well below the cutoff frequency. That is, the inputs and outputs will be almost the same. As frequency increases, the outputs start decreasing as the cutoff frequency is approached. At the cutoff frequency, the outputs are -3 dB in respect to a much lower reference frequency. As frequency continues to increase, the outputs of both filters decrease at the rate of 20 dB/decade, which is a characteristic of all first-order RC filters. Remember, the only difference between high-pass and low-pass filters is the position of the reactive element. In high-pass filters, the reactive element (capacitor) is in series with the signal path. In low-pass filters, the capacitor is in parallel with the signal path.

Active Filters without Feedback

First-order RC filters have one basic disadvantage that sometimes limits their application. Any appreciable load connected to its output changes the characteristics of the filter. Output amplitude is reduced, and cutoff frequency is changed. Again, operational amplifiers will solve the problem. Connected as a simple voltage follower (Figure 7–9), the op amp isolates the filter from its load. The voltage follower's extremely high input impedance places no load on the filter. Because of the voltage follower's very low output resistance, low resistance loads can be connected to the output of an "active" filter without changing its characteristics. Nothing has really been done to change the filter's characteristics. We have merely taken advantage of the operational amplifier to make the filter more useful.

Even with the voltage follower, simple first-order filters have insertion loss. By replacing the voltage follower with a simple noninverting operational amplifier circuit (Figure 7–10), gain may be obtained to make up for losses. The filter characteristics are not changed. Cutoff

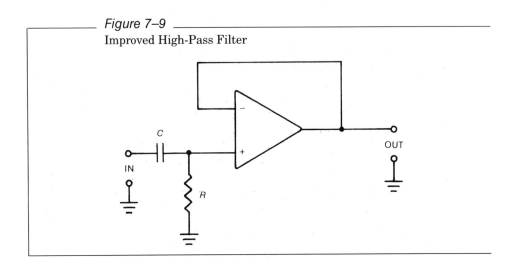

Figure 7–9
Improved High-Pass Filter

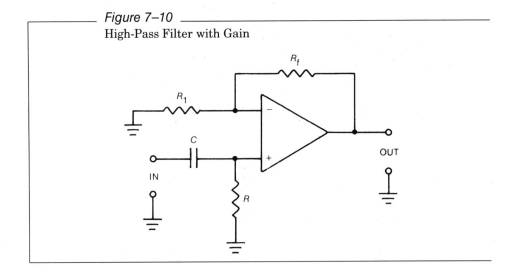

Figure 7–10
High-Pass Filter with Gain

frequency is calculated in the conventional manner—that is, $f_c = 1/2\pi RC$. Operational amplifier gain (A) is also calculated as with the conventional noninverting configuration ($A = 1 + [R_f/R_1]$).

The net effect is to shift the generalized filter response curve of Figure 7–4B from a 0 dB reference to some positive dB reference determined by the op amp gain. Gain at any frequency is also determined by use of Figure 7–4B. Let's use values of R and C that provide a 1 kHz cutoff frequency ($R = 100$ kΩ and $C = 0.0016$ μF). Without the operational amplifier, the graph of Figure 7–4B defines the filter's response.

If $R_f = 100$ kΩ and $R_1 = 10$ kΩ, then the op amp gain becomes approximately 11, or 21 dB. The reference gain on Figure 7–4B thus becomes +20 dB, and the complete graph shifts upward by 20 dB.

Active Filters with Feedback

Another approach to first-order filters is shown in the 1 kHz, low-pass active filter in Figure 7–11. The capacitor, instead of being connected *across* the input signal path, is connected *in the feedback loop* of the op amp. Operation can be explained as follows. At low frequencies, X_C is high in comparison to R_f. Feedback and gain are determined almost completely by the R_f/R_1 ratio. As frequency increases, X_C decreases. When X_C is much lower than R_f, feedback is controlled by X_C. R_f is effectively shorted out, a large amount of feedback is present, and gain is low. The cutoff frequency is determined in the usual manner—that is, $f_c = 1/2\pi R_f C$. When analyzing this type of active filter, be cautious. Don't make a hasty decision that the circuit is an active low-pass filter. Often a very small capacitor is connected across R_f for frequency compensation reasons. Always verify the cutoff frequency. If it is very high, the purpose of the capacitor is probably frequency compensation. A general rule of thumb is that if the capacitor across R_f is less than about 30 pF, its purpose is frequency compensation, not low-pass filtering.

The technique of placing the reactive element of the low-pass filter in the feedback loop is most often found in audio equalizing and tone control circuits (see Chapter 5). It is also used as a part of the overall

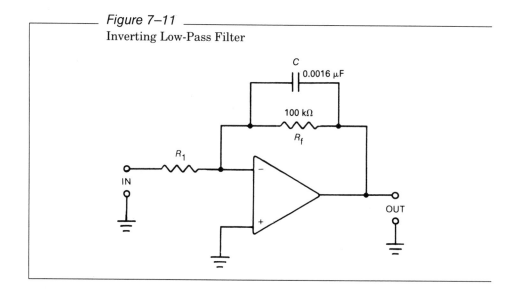

Figure 7–11
Inverting Low-Pass Filter

feedback in more complex second-order filters. Most commonly, first-order filters will be the conventional low- or high-pass filter followed by an op amp connected as a voltage follower or a *gain block*—that is, a functional block providing voltage or power gain. Identification of low- or high-pass filters, therefore, is first a matter of recognizing the filter circuit. Then it is necessary to perform simple calculations to verify that what looks like a low- or high-pass filter really is what it looks like. Once the first-order filter is identified and verified, measurements may be taken to ensure that it is operating as expected. Gain of the filter is determined by op amp feedback and can usually be easily estimated. Roll-off, if the filter is a first-order device, will be 20 dB/decade.

Active First-Order Band-Pass Filters

Band-pass filters were discussed earlier in this chapter. Although not pointed out at that time, one of the problems with passive RC band-pass filters is loading of one section of the filter by the other section. Operational amplifiers can alleviate this effect. A further problem still is present, however. The roll-off characteristic of any first-order filter is only 20 dB/decade, which may not be sharp enough for many applications. Improving the roll-off characteristic is discussed in Chapter 8.

Figure 7–12 shows how an active first-order band-pass filter may be implemented. Once again, it should be recognized that this configu-

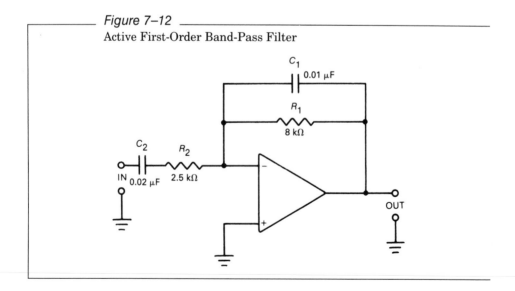

Figure 7–12

Active First-Order Band-Pass Filter

ration is merely shown for explanatory purposes, since it does have only a 20 dB/decade roll-off characteristic. The high-pass portion of the band-pass filter's characteristic is determined by C_2 and R_2. C_1 and R_1 determine the low-pass cutoff frequency. Pass-band gain is set in the conventional manner by the ratio R_1/R_2. Example 7–5 shows how to analyze the performance of the band-pass filter of Figure 7–12.

Example 7–5

In the band-pass filter of Figure 7–12, the following component values will be used:

$$C_1 = 0.01 \ \mu F \qquad R_2 = 2.5 \ k\Omega$$
$$C_2 = 0.02 \ \mu F \qquad R_1 = 8 \ k\Omega$$

Determine the midband gain (A), low-frequency cutoff frequency (f_l), and the high-frequency cutoff frequency (f_h).

Solution

$$f_l = \frac{1}{2\pi R_1 C_1} = \frac{1}{(6.28)(8000)(0.00000001)} = 1989 \ Hz$$

$$f_h = \frac{1}{2\pi R_2 C_2} = \frac{1}{(6.28)(2500)(0.00000002)} = 3183 \ Hz$$

$$A = \frac{R_1}{R_2} = \frac{8000}{2500} = 3.2 \qquad \text{or 10 dB}$$

Thus, with just a few simple calculations, it is possible to determine what the filter's characteristics should be. Troubleshooting with a variable-frequency input source and an output voltmeter or oscilloscope will quickly allow verification of correct circuit operation.

Troubleshooting: Our troubleshooting example for this chapter uses the active first-order band-pass filter of Figure 7–12. Your company has purchased 1000 of these filter assemblies, and your job is to test each assembly for low-frequency cutoff frequency, high-frequency cutoff frequency, and midband gain. If a defective assembly is detected, you must troubleshoot and identify the defective component.

You have constructed a test circuit to automatically generate the necessary frequencies, apply them to the filter assembly, and measure midband gain. Each of the assemblies is connected to the test circuit, and indicator lights show which, if any, of the tests is not satisfactorily completed.

Your supplier's quality control is good, because you detected only one defective filter assembly. Now, let's troubleshoot and decide which component is defective.

Using a variable-frequency signal generator, you find that the low-frequency cutoff frequency is approximately 200 Hz, the high-frequency cutoff frequency is approximately 3200 Hz, and the midband gain is approximately 30. The equations for the active first-order filter (Example 7–5) show that only one component will affect both low-frequency cutoff frequency and midband gain. That component is R_1. If you are to obtain a low-frequency cutoff frequency of approximately 200 Hz, calculations show that R_1 must be approximately 80 kΩ. When the new value for R_1 is inserted into the gain equation, the new gain is approximately 30. R_1 is the most probable defective component.

When visually checked, the color code on R_1 is correct. Measurement with an ohmmeter shows a resistance of approximately 80 kΩ. The resistor has been improperly marked! Replacement of R_1 with an 8 kΩ resistor will return the filter to proper operation.

_____ SUMMARY _____

Chapter 7 has provided a short introduction to the subject of filters and their applications. It is generally true that simple active filters are merely adaptations of passive filters; thus, no really new ideas have been presented. Most of the configurations and applications of high-pass, low-pass, and band-pass filters have seen use in the past either as passive filters or with vacuum tubes or transistors as active filters and are reviewed in this chapter. The basic concepts of filters, however, are of great importance since more complex filters are discussed in Chapter 8. The generalized graphs and simple formulas provided here were used generously because both passive and active filters were discussed.

As the deficiencies of passive filters were shown, operational amplifiers were applied to make high-pass, low-pass, band-pass, and band-reject filters more efficient. The addition of the operational amplifier to passive filters thus improved filter operation in both conventional and feedback configurations.

=== QUESTIONS ==

1. Define the following terms: (a) filter, (b) low-pass filter, (c) high-pass filter, (d) band-pass filter, (e) band-reject filter, (f) Butterworth filter, (g) Chebyshev filter, and (h) Bessel filter.

2. List the components used in conventional passive filters, and explain the function of each.

3. List the components used in conventional active filters, and explain the function of each.

4. Discuss the advantages and disadvantages of using logarithmic scales on filter frequency response graphs.

5. Discuss the advantages and disadvantages of using Bode plots for filter frequency response graphs.

6. Why are generalized frequency response and phase graphs used to determine filter characteristics in preference to mathematical methods?

7. What factors affect the bandwidth and shape of band-pass filter characteristics?

8. Explain what a first-order filter is.

9. What factors determine the order of a filter?

10. What characteristics are adjustable in first-order filters?

11. Discuss what factors affect the cutoff frequency of a first-order filter.

12. Discuss what factors affect the output impedance of a first-order filter.

13. What is a gain block? How does it affect operation of simple active filters?

14. Draw a diagram showing an active high-pass filter with a passband gain of 10. Explain the circuit's operation.

15. Draw a diagram showing an active low-pass filter with the reactive element in the feedback path. The filter should have a passband gain of 10. Explain the circuit's operation.

16. List four applications for simple first-order active filters. Draw a diagram if applicable, and explain circuit operation.

=== PROBLEMS ===

1. Using Figures 7–2 and 7–3, assume that $R = 16$ kΩ and $C = 0.047$ μF. Determine the output level in dB for the following frequencies: (a) 100 Hz, (b) 212 Hz, (c) 1000 Hz, (d) 2120 Hz, and (e) 6360 Hz.

2. Using the same values as in Problem 1, determine the output impedance of the filter of Figure 7–2A for the following frequencies: (a) 100 Hz, (b) 212 Hz, (c) 1000 Hz, (d) 2120 Hz, and (e) 6360 Hz.

3. Assume that, in Figure 7–4, $R = 22$ kΩ and $C = 0.022$ μF. Determine the output level in dB for the following frequencies: (a) 16.5 Hz, (b) 33 Hz, (c) 330 Hz, (d) 1650 Hz, and (e) 3000 Hz.

4. Using the same values as in Problem 3, determine the output impedance of the filter of Figure 7–4A for the following frequencies: (a) 16.5 Hz, (b) 33 Hz, (c) 330 Hz, (d) 1650 Hz, and (e) 3000 Hz.

5. Repeat Problem 3 using the diagram shown in Figure 7–10. Assume that $R_f =$ 100 kΩ and $R_1 = 1$ kΩ.

6. Repeat Problem 1 using the diagram shown in Figure 7–11. $R_f = 16$ kΩ, $C =$ 0.047 µF, and $R_1 = 1.6$ kΩ.

7. Refer to Figure 7–12. $R_1 = 20$ kΩ, $R_2 = 1$ kΩ, $C_1 = 0.0039$ µF, and $C_2 = 0.16$ µF. Determine the frequency response of the filter, indicating midband gain and lower and upper cutoff frequencies. Draw a frequency response curve of the filter.

8

Advanced
Filter Circuits

OBJECTIVES After studying Chapter 8, you will be able to

1. Identify characteristics of second-order filters.
2. Discuss the reason for using both DC and AC feedback in active filters.
3. Identify characteristics of Sallen-Key (VCVS), multiple-feedback second-order, multiple-feedback band-pass, state-variable, bi-quadratic, twin-T, all-pass, constant-time-delay, and elliptical filters.
4. Describe the purpose of the feedback capacitor in a VCVS filter.
5. Discuss the factors that control the shape of a filter's response.
6. Recognize the differences between unity gain VCVS filters and equal-component-value VCVS filters.
7. Determine and adjust the damping factor in an equal-component-value VCVS filter.
8. Obtain band-pass characteristics with low-pass and high-pass filters.
9. Determine the overall gain of a band-pass filter constructed from low-pass and high-pass filter segments.
10. Form high-order filters from first- and second-order sections.
11. Explain the concept of switched-capacitor filters.

INTRODUCTION

Now that we have worked with simple filters, we can go on to look at some more advanced circuits. Actually, the advanced circuits discussed in this chapter are merely different applications of the fundamentals of Chapter 7.

SECOND-ORDER FILTERS

The existence of *two* reactive components usually identifies a **second-order filter.** The roll-off characteristic of second-order filters is 40 dB/decade. As with first-order filters, both cutoff frequency and impedance levels are a function of resistance and capacitance values. Second-order filters are found in low-pass, high-pass, and band-pass configurations. Passive second-order filters were shown in an earlier discussion (see Miscellaneous Filter Facts, Chapter 7) to be somewhat impractical without special design techniques to minimize interaction between filter sections. That discussion should be reviewed in preparation for more advanced filter applications.

The same technique used to isolate first-order filters from external loads may be used with second-order filters. Voltage followers can be inserted between filter sections without affecting the roll-off characteristic. In addition, the op amps may be connected as amplifiers with gain to make up for circuit losses. Although this type of application is usable, there are more efficient methods. Second-order filters most commonly use a single op amp.

Low-pass and high-pass filters are generally reciprocal in nature. That is, interchanging the position of the reactive and resistive filter elements will change the filter from one form to the other. This was shown during initial discussion of passive filters. Second-order active filters are, in most cases, also reciprocal. If a low-pass second-order active filter has a specified cutoff frequency and roll-off characteristic, exchanging the capacitors and resistors will usually convert it to a high-pass filter with the same cutoff frequency and roll-off characteristic.

Improved second-order low- and high-pass filters use both DC and AC feedback. DC feedback sets the gain below the cutoff frequency for low-pass filters and the gain above the cutoff frequency for high-pass filters. Stability is also a function of the DC feedback. The AC feedback establishes the frequency dependence—that is, the roll-off characteristics. Second-order filters are used as building blocks in forming both higher-order active filters and band-pass filters. The **Sallen-Key,** or **voltage-controlled-voltage source (VCVS),** configuration is most often found in higher-order filters combined with first-order filters. *Multiple-feedback* configurations are commonly used in band-pass filters. Both types are discussed in this chapter.

In addition to control of cutoff frequency and impedence levels in improved second-order active filters, the factor called Q, or quality factor, enters the picture. Q, you may remember, was used to control the sharpness, or bandwidth of an LC tuned circuit. When band-pass filters are discussed later, Q will be used for that same purpose. However, even in low-pass and high-pass filters, Q has an effect. The reciprocal of Q ($1/Q$), called damping factor (D), is often used to describe filter response shape. But let's get on with some practical filter circuits to better explain damping factor and other new concepts.

Sallen-Key (VCVS) Filters

The voltage-controlled-voltage-source (VCVS), or Sallen-Key, second-order filter is a good place to start. Figure 8–1 shows one of the simplest versions, the **unity gain VCVS filter.** The R_2-C_1 combination is that of the typical passive low-pass filter. Its cutoff frequency is determined by the usual formula,

$$f_c = \frac{1}{2\pi RC} \qquad\qquad \text{(8–1)}$$

The op amp connected as a unity gain voltage follower serves to isolate the R_2 and C_1 low-pass filter from the output load.

Input to the unity gain second-order VCVS filter must also consider the effect of R_1 and C_2. Note that C_2 is not connected to ground as it would be in a two-section passive filter. Instead, it is connected to the *output* of the op amp, which is being used as a non-inverting voltage follower. Thus, the op amp is being used with *positive* feedback. What effect will this have on circuit operation? We have to go back to basics for an explanation.

Do you remember what happens when an inductor and a capacitor are connected in series as shown in Figure 8–2? A low-pass filter is formed when the output is taken across the capacitor. The reactance of the inductor increases with increasing frequency, while the capacitive

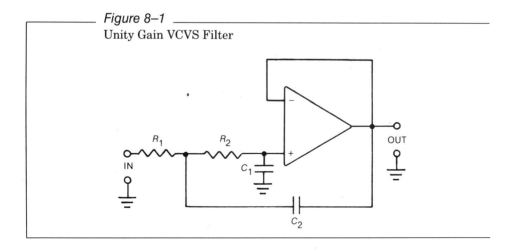

Figure 8–1

Unity Gain VCVS Filter

Figure 8–2
LC Low-Pass Filter

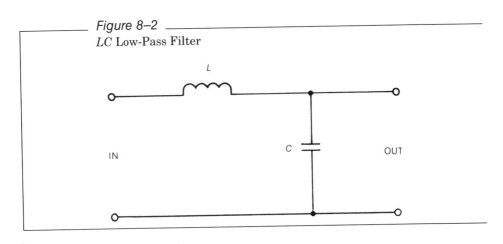

reactance decreases. Thus, as frequency increases, what little of the input gets through the inductor is shorted to ground by the capacitor. Since two reactive elements comprise the filter, it acts as a second-order filter, with a roll-off of 40 dB/decade. Sometimes filters are viewed as devices that store energy and then supply it to the load at a rate determined by component values. The low-pass filter can be considered in this manner. For example, the capacitor stores energy during part of the input signal cycle. While that energy is being provided to the load, the inductor stores energy that later is transferred to the capacitor. This is where the two-step action of the LC filter comes from.

There is a problem, though, if you want to consider it as a problem. Cutoff frequency is a function of the product of L and C, just as the RC filter's cutoff frequency is a function of the product of R and C. The typical roll-off characteristic that has been shown for RC filters is not present with LC filters except when a *specific ratio* of L and C exists. If the capacitor is very large and the inductor is small, the load will have very little effect on the response. In fact, the circuit will act very much like a resonant circuit, and a peak will appear on the response curve. The filter is said to be **underdamped,** which is typical of a high-Q LC circuit. Proper selection of L, C, and load resistance gives a **critically damped** filter, or response curve similar to an RC circuit. If L is large and C is small, the load resistance will grossly affect the response. A droopy roll-off characteristic results. The filter is said to be **highly damped,** which equates to a low-Q circuit. Although the LC ratio does not affect the roll-off characteristic or the passband gain, it does change the shape of the curve near the cutoff frequency. Thus, the designer can exercise control not only over the cutoff frequency of a filter but also over the shape of the response curve. More will be mentioned about response curve shapes shortly.

Now back to Figure 8–1 and the subject of active second-order filters. Without an inductor, something must be done to supply the energy normally stored by the inductor. It must be added to the input energy in (1) the correct amount, (2) the correct phase, and at (3) the proper frequency. C_2 performs this function. All three of the requirements are met by selection of the proper value of C_2. Since C_2 is a reactive element, two reactive elements are present to form the second-order response curve. The shape of the response curve is a function of the ratio of the two reactive elements C_2 and C_1, just as it was with L and C in the LC filter. A C_2/C_1 ratio may be used that allows the response curve to be underdamped, flat, or overdamped. The formula used to calculate the **damping factor** D is

$$D = \frac{1}{Q} \qquad (8\text{–}2)$$

Because of the reciprocal relationship, the larger C_2 is with respect to C_1, the *lower* the damping will be

$$Q = \frac{\sqrt{C_2/C_1}}{2} \qquad (8\text{–}3)$$

A damping factor near zero (underdamped) gives a peaked response. (If $D = 0$ is ever reached, oscillation can occur.) Highly damped circuits ($D = 2$) have a response that is the same as two cascaded RC sections isolated from each other. In between lie many different response shapes. For example, $D = 1.73$ gives the best response to pulse and transient inputs. $D = 1.414$ provides the best possible flat amplitude response and a cutoff frequency exactly -3 dB from the normal passband. Below $D = 1.414$, peaking starts to occur. One dB ripple occurs when $D = 1.045$; two dB ripple, at $D = 0.895$; and three dB ripple, at $D = 0.767$. Thus, the shape of the frequency response may be selected by control of the damping factor. It depends entirely on how much energy is fed back to the input via C_2.

Actually, there are names for the common filter response shapes. A filter with a flat response is called a *Butterworth* filter. It has the flattest passband shape and most closely approximates the curves that have been used to describe RC filter sections. Since the shape of the response has been shown to be related to the damping factor, each filter configuration has a critical damping factor for the desired shape. For example, a damping factor of 1.414 is required for a second-order Butterworth response. A damping factor (for second-order filters) near zero gives a highly peaked, or *Chebyshev,* response. Such filters also contain ripples in the normal passband but have sharper cutoff characteristics.

If a second-order filter has a damping factor near 2, the resulting response is droopy. This is called a *Bessel*, or all-pass, filter. Review of the literature shows that Butterworth response shapes occur most often in low- and high-pass filters. Therefore, the examples used in low- and high-pass filter discussion will be of the Butterworth type. Applications for other shape responses are discussed as they are encountered.

The mathematics of filters place restrictions on some of the active filter values and ratios. For the Sallen-Key unity gain VCVS filter with Butterworth characteristics, the feedback capacitor must have twice the capacitance of the passive section capacitor. It is assumed that the resistors are of equal value. Any change in the **shape option** (damping) or gain of the circuit requires changes in the capacitor and/or resistor values. If other than equal values of the input resistors are used, then the capacitor ratio must change. Rather than include the complex mathematical derivations, the most common configuration of equal resistors is used here. Figure 8–3 is a Sallen-Key unity gain VCVS filter with flat (Butterworth) response. $R_1 = R_2$ and $C_2 = 2C_1$. Let's analyze the circuit and be sure that we can determine the necessary information.

The equal values of R_1 and R_2, the 2 to 1 ratio of C_2 to C_1, and a unity gain op amp give a clue as to the type of filter. R_f, which is equal to $R_1 + R_2 + R_s$, has been included to minimize DC offset current errors. If the DC offset error is not important, R_f may be shorted. Calculation of the damping factor, in Table 8–1, shows that the circuit has the maximally flat, or Butterworth, response curve. Remember, when $D = 1.414$ for a second-order filter, the response curve is as close as possible to the theoretical curve. The sample frequency calculation in Table 8–1 shows that the -3 dB cutoff frequency is approximately 1 kHz. Similar cal-

Figure 8–3
Sallen-Key VCVS Filter (Butterworth Response)

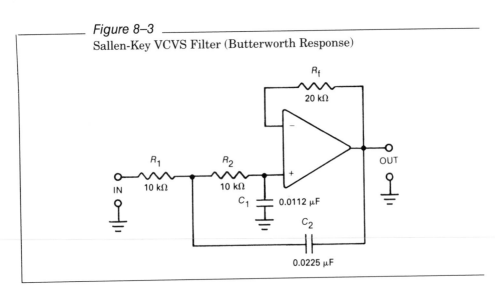

_____ Table 8–1 _____

Sallen-Key VCVS Filter Calculations (Butterworth Response)

Typical Values

	R_1	R_2	R_f	C_1	C_2
1 kHz	10 kΩ	10 kΩ	20 kΩ	0.0112 μF	0.0225 μF
10 kHz	1 kΩ	1 kΩ	2 kΩ	0.0112 μF	0.0225 μF
10 kHz	24 kΩ	24 kΩ	48 kΩ	470 pF	940 pF

Calculations (1 kHz):

$$f_c = \frac{1}{2\pi(R_1 R_2 C_1 C_2)^{1/2}}$$

$$= \frac{1}{6.28[(10 \times 10 \times 10^6)(0.0112 \times 10^{-6})(0.0225 \times 10^{-6})]^{1/2}} = 1003 \text{ Hz}$$

$$Q = \frac{\sqrt{C_2/C_1}}{2} = 0.708 \qquad D = \frac{1}{Q} = 1.411$$

culations made with the other two sets of values in Table 8–1 would show that reducing both R_1 and R_2 by a factor of 10 increases the cutoff frequency by a factor of 10. But no change in damping factor would occur since the capacitor ratios were not changed. (These statements should be checked by performing the calculations, using the formulas in Table 8–1.) Likewise, if different values are selected for R_1 and R_2, different capacitor values must be calculated to maintain f_c at the desired value. Note that R_1, R_2, C_1, and C_2 are all included in cutoff frequency calculations, while only C_1 and C_2 are used in damping factor calculations.

Some disadvantages of the unity gain VCVS Sallen-Key filter are apparent as more facts are discovered. Consider what is required if a slight change in the shape of the response curve is needed. Such a change requires changing the damping factor, which means changing the capacitor ratio. Even a small change will affect the cutoff frequency as well as the shape of the response curve. Furthermore, maintaining a given ratio with standard-value capacitors is difficult. If the filter must be switched from low-pass to high-pass configuration, the switching becomes quite complex. Fortunately, the mathematics of the Sallen-Key filter give us a simple answer.

There exists a combination of R and C values that places the damping factor under control of the op amp gain, not the capacitor ratio. It is called the **equal-component-value Sallen-Key filter.** See Figure 8–4. Not only are R_1 and R_2 equal in value, but so are C_1 and C_2. In order for this circuit to operate properly, gain must be set to a value equal to $3 - D$. Gain is set in the conventional manner by the feedback ratio using R_f and R_x. For the Butterworth response shape, op amp gain must

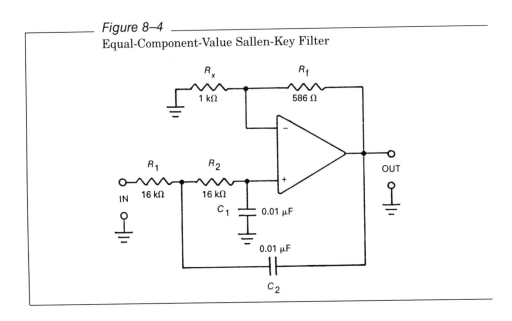

Figure 8–4

Equal-Component-Value Sallen-Key Filter

be 3 − 1.414, or 1.586. This is easily obtained by making $R_f = 0.586R_x$. The actual values are unimportant as long as the correct ratio is maintained. DC offset current error is minimized, however, when the inverting input and the noninverting input are terminated with the same resistance.

Although two more components are required than for the unity gain VCVS filter, the equal-component-value Sallen-Key filter is very popular. Calculations are simpler, as shown in Table 8–2. Changing from a low-pass to a high-pass configuration requires only interchanging the position of the capacitors and resistors. Adjustment of the damping to tailor the response shape to a specific circuit requires only the variation of a resistor. Let's evaluate Table 8–2 to see how much simpler it is than Table 8–1.

Using the values for a 10 kHz equal-component-value Sallen-Key filter, note that R_1 and R_2 are equal, as are C_1 and C_2. If the damping factor D is then 1.414, the filter should be a Butterworth-shape low-pass filter. The mathematicians tell us that $D = 3 − A_V$ for the equal-component-value Sallen-Key filter. Voltage gain A_V is determined entirely by the R_f and R_x voltage divider. The op amp is in the noninverting mode, so $A_V = 1 + R_f/R_x$. As shown in Table 8–2, $A_V = 1.586$. Subtracting A_V from 3 yields $D = 1.414$. Thus, the circuit should respond with a Butterworth maximally flat frequency response. Calculating the cutoff frequency from the simplified formula in Table 8–2 shows that the cutoff frequency is very near 10 kHz. The data for other resistor and capacitor values in Table 8–2 should be verified.

_____ Table 8–2 _____

Equal-Component-Value Sallen-Key Filter Calculations

Typical Values

	R_1	R_2	C_1	C_2	R_f	R_x
10 kHz	1.6 kΩ	1.6 kΩ	0.01 μF	0.01 μF	586 Ω	1 kΩ
10 kHz	3.386 kΩ	3.386 kΩ	0.0047 μF	0.0047 μF	5.86 kΩ	10 kΩ
1 kHz	16 kΩ	16 kΩ	0.01 μF	0.01 μF	586 Ω	1 kΩ

Calculations (10 kHz):

$$f_c = \frac{1}{2\pi R_1 C_2} = \frac{1}{(6.28)(1600)(0.01 \times 10^{-6})} = 9947 \text{ Hz}$$

$$A_V = 1 + \frac{R_f}{R_x} = 1 + \frac{586}{1000} = 1.586 \qquad D = 3 - A_V = 3 - 1.586 = 1.414$$

Generally, the equal-component-value Sallen-Key filter will be designed with equal standard capacitor values as a starting point. It is much easier to obtain odd-value resistors than nonstandard capacitors. The resistor values that result from calculations are then used for R_1 and R_2. Gain requirements for the frequency response shape desired are then fixed by high-precision resistors in the feedback voltage divider. Caution should be exercised when changing any component in an active filter. A small change in the feedback network of the equal-component-value Sallen-Key filter, for example, could drastically alter the shape of the frequency response. Many applications of this filter configuration will be shown as higher-order filters are discussed.

Troubleshooting: The troubleshooting example for this chapter uses the equal-component-value Sallen-Key filter of Figure 8–4. As in the troubleshooting example of Chapter 7, your company has purchased 1000 of these filter assemblies. Your job is to test each assembly for gain and frequency response characteristics. If a defective assembly is detected, you must troubleshoot and identify the defective component.

You have constructed a test circuit to automatically apply a variable frequency to the filter assembly and to show the output response on an oscilloscope. In other words, the test circuit "draws" the frequency response curve for you. Your supplier's quality control is good, because you detected only one defective filter assembly. Now, let's troubleshoot and decide which component is defective.

The defective filter assembly has out-of-tolerance gain and wide variations in gain as the input frequency changes. In other words, it does not meet the Butterworth response shape. However, the cutoff frequency is correct.

Information regarding the equal-component-value Sallen-Key filter indicates that only one factor affects the filter response shape but not the cutoff frequency. That factor is the feedback network. Therefore, it should only be necessary to measure the values of the feedback network resistors. One will be out of tolerance. Replace the out-of-tolerance resistor with the correct value so that the voltage gain once again becomes 1.586 and the resulting damping factor becomes 1.414. The filter assembly will function as designed.

Multiple-Feedback Second-Order Filters

Another type of second-order filter building block is shown in Figure 8–5. It is called a **multiple-feedback filter** because of the added feedback path. Note that the low-pass multiple-feedback filter of Figure 8–5 contains both resistive and capacitive feedback. The multiple-feedback filter also operates in the inverting mode as compared with the VCVS filter, which operates in the noninverting mode. Gain is difficult to control because it depends on component ratios. Therefore, the multiple-feedback filter is more often found in applications where adjustment of frequency, gain, or Q is not required. Because this configuration is used occasionally for low- and high-pass filters, and very often in band-pass applications, its operation should be understood.

The multiple-feedback filter is most often operated at unity gain and has the usual second-order 40 dB/decade roll-off characteristic. In fact, the response curve of the second-order multiple-feedback filter and the equivalent VCVS filter are the same. Let's examine the 10 kHz But-

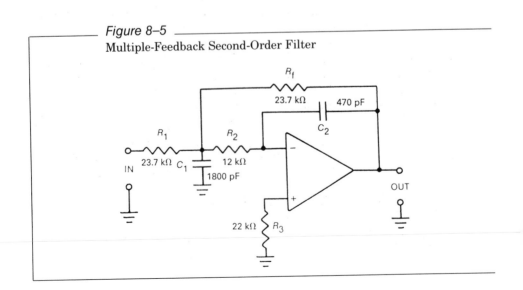

Figure 8–5
Multiple-Feedback Second-Order Filter

terworth multiple-feedback filter of Figure 8–5. It can be identified as a second-order filter by the presence of the two reactive elements C_1 and C_2. The 40 dB/decade roll-off characteristic can thus be assumed. Cutoff frequency calculations using the formula for f_c verify the 10 kHz -3 dB point. As with other types of active filters, the damping factor D is of prime concern in establishing the shape of the frequency response curve. With multiple-feedback filters and their common application to band-pass filters, however, Q is used in place of D. Q, remember, is the reciprocal of D.

Since the circuit has been identified as a Butterworth filter, D will be 1.414, which equates to $Q = 0.707$. Gain is established by the R_f/R_1 ratio. The resistors are equal, so op amp gain is 1. Enough information is now available to verify the other component values. The clues to identification of the multiple-feedback Butterworth filter are the dual feedback path and the inverting unity gain configuration. When these identifying characteristics are noted, the multiple-feedback filter can be assumed. Example 8–1 shows typical multiple-feedback Butterworth filter calculations.

Example 8–1

Calculate gain, cutoff frequency, and Q for a multiple-feedback second-order filter with the following typical values:

$$R_1 = 23.7 \text{ k}\Omega \quad R_2 = 12 \text{ k}\Omega \quad C_1 = 1800 \text{ pF}$$
$$R_f = 23.7 \text{ k}\Omega \quad R_3 = 22 \text{ k}\Omega \quad C_2 = 470 \text{ pF}$$

Solution

$$A_V = \frac{R_f}{R_1} = \frac{23.7}{23.7} = 1$$

$$f_c = \frac{1}{2\pi\sqrt{R_2 R_f C_1 C_2}}$$

$$= \frac{1}{6.28\sqrt{12 \times 10^3 \times 23.7 \times 10^3 \times 1800 \times 10^{-12} \times 470 \times 10^{-12}}}$$

$$= 10{,}266 \text{ Hz}$$

$$Q = \frac{1}{4\pi f_c R_f C_2} = \frac{1}{(4)(3.14)(10{,}266)(23.7 \times 10^3)(470 \times 10^{-12})} = 0.696$$

BAND-PASS FILTERS

A band-pass filter passes only a band of frequencies within the desired range, blocking all other frequencies both above and below the

desired passband. The general concepts of band-pass filters were discussed earlier. As with low- and high-pass filters, the addition of active
components can materially improve filter characteristics. In this section, various configurations of band-pass filters are explained. Their
basic characteristics are shown so that it will be easy to identify a circuit
as a band-pass filter and to analyze its operation.

Wide-Band Filters

There are some applications of band-pass filters that require passing a
wide band of frequencies rather than a narrow band. In voice communications, for example, a 2700 Hz band of frequencies ranging from 300
Hz to 3000 Hz is considered necessary. The **center frequency**, which
is the geometric mean of the two extremes, is about 950 Hz—that is,

$$f_0 = \sqrt{(f_1)(f_h)} = \sqrt{(300)(3000)} = 948.6 \text{ Hz}$$

The Q required to obtain the necessary bandwidth centered around 950
Hz is only 0.35. Because of the low Q, use of multiple-feedback filters is
not appropriate here. One possible approach is to cascade a high-pass
VCVS and a low-pass VCVS filter.

   A high-pass filter with a cutoff frequency of 300 Hz provides the
low-frequency cutoff. The low-pass filter with a cutoff frequency of 3000
Hz prevents all frequencies above the cutoff frequency from passing.
Theoretically, then, only frequencies between 300 Hz and 3000 Hz
should pass. Let's evaluate the filter circuit in Figure 8–6 to determine
its characteristics. Figure 8–6A shows that the first section is a high-
pass filter; the capacitors are in series with the input signal path. The
second section is a low-pass filter because the capacitors are in parallel
with the input signal path.

   In both the high-pass and the low-pass filters, the frequency-determining resistors are equal, as are the capacitors. (See Figure 8–6C.)
This identifies the circuits as equal-component-value VCVS filters. A
further identification can be made by determining the voltage gain of
each section. The voltage gain is $A_V = 1 + (R_f/R_x)$, or $1 + (27/47) =$
1.57. The result is very close to the gain required of the equal-component-value VCVS filter with Butterworth-shaped frequency response.
Cutoff frequency calculations using $f_c = 1/2\pi RC$ yield $f_c = 284$ Hz for
the low-pass filter and 2840 Hz for the high-pass filter. To obtain the
actual 300 Hz to 3000 Hz response would require selection of other than
standard-value resistors and capacitors. However, the circuit shown
does have a frequency response very close to that required.

   One more point remains. What is the overall gain of the circuit of
Figure 8–6? What happens when two or more active filters are operated
in cascade? Just as with amplifier stages in cascade, the total gain is
the product of the individual gains. Each filter section has a fixed gain

Figure 8–6

Wide-Band Band-Pass Filter

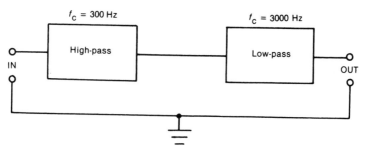

A. Block Diagram

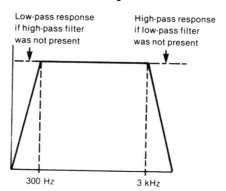

Low-pass response
if high-pass filter
was not present

High-pass response
if low-pass filter
was not present

300 Hz   3 kHz

B. Ideal Response Curve (Bode Plot)

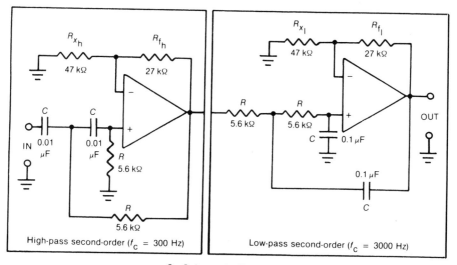

High-pass second-order (f_c = 300 Hz)

Low-pass second-order (f_c = 3000 Hz)

C. Schematic Diagram

of 1.586, so the total gain of the band-pass filter is $1.586 \times 1.586 = 3.17$, or about $+8$ dB. The Butterworth response makes the filter maximally flat. An idealized Bode plot of the filter response is shown in Figure 8–6B.

Multiple-Feedback Band-Pass Filters

The multiple-feedback low-pass and high-pass active filter circuits can be modified to perform the band-pass function. One of the simplest of band-pass filters, this second-order circuit is adequate for Q values up to about 10. The mathematics of the multiple-feedback filter show that it tends to be unstable at Qs above 10, and other circuits should be used. Figure 8–7 shows the general multiple-feedback band-pass filter configuration. The equations used during circuit analysis are as follows:

$$f_0 = \frac{1}{2\pi C} \sqrt{\frac{R_1 + R_2}{R_1 R_2 R_3}}$$

$$A_V = \frac{R_3}{2R_1}$$

$$Q = \pi f_0 C R_3$$

$$BW = \frac{f_0}{Q}$$

Notice that as circuits become more advanced, so do the equations describing circuit operation. Analysis and troubleshooting of active filter

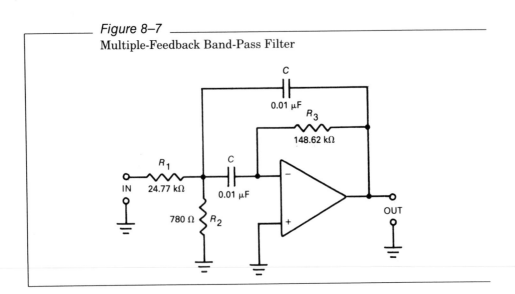

Figure 8–7
Multiple-Feedback Band-Pass Filter

circuits require a certain amount of calculation when technical data do not include the necessary information. Simplifications have been employed here so that the reader is not subjected to the complex mathematics usually associated with filters. Even if the calculations are not required, an understanding of the interaction of components may be obtained from the equations.

A good demonstration of how equations may be used to help understand filter operation is to consider what effect a change of R_2 would have on filter operation. In the equations for center frequency (f_0), voltage gain (A_V), and quality factor (Q), R_2 appears only in the center frequency formula. Thus, a change in R_2 should affect only center frequency. If the center frequency changes and bandwidth remains constant, an attendant Q change will occur. However, gain remains constant with changes in R_2. In most active filter circuits, a change in frequency usually is accompanied by a change in many of the other parameters. The multiple-feedback band-pass filter is superior in this respect, even though its maximum Q is limited.

Analysis of the multiple-feedback band-pass filter is demonstrated in Example 8–2.

Example 8–2

For the following component values, calculate the gain, Q, center frequency, and bandwidth for the multiple-feedback band-pass filter shown in Figure 8–7.

$$R_1 = 24.77 \text{ k}\Omega \qquad R_3 = 148.62 \text{ k}\Omega$$
$$R_2 = 780 \ \Omega \qquad C = 0.01 \ \mu\text{F}$$

Solution

$$A_V = \frac{R_3}{2R_1} = \frac{148.62}{(2)(24.77)} = 3$$

$$f_0 = \frac{\left[\left(\dfrac{1}{R_3 C}\right)\left(\dfrac{1}{R_1} + \dfrac{1}{R_2}\right)\right]^{1/2}}{2\pi}$$

$$= \frac{\left[\left(\dfrac{1}{(148.62 \times 10^3)(0.01 \times 10^{-6})^2}\right)\left(\dfrac{1}{24.77 \times 10^3} + \dfrac{1}{780}\right)\right]^{1/2}}{6.28}$$

$$= 1489 \text{ Hz}$$

$$Q = \pi f_0 C R_3 = (3.14)(1489)(0.01 \times 10^{-6})(148.62 \times 10^3) = 6.95$$

$$BW = \frac{f_0}{Q} = \frac{1489}{6.95} = 214 \text{ Hz}$$

The equations can be solved using a hand calculator and some algebra. If a computer (either personal or full size) is available, there are programs for solution of filter circuits that speed the calculation process. Most computer programs also allow modification of component values to evaluate the effect of such changes. If you have access to a computer and filter programs, try some variations. This will quickly show the relationships that exist between component values and filter characteristics. The same relationships can be shown using a hand calculator. It takes a bit more time, but the time is well spent.

The only remaining point for discussion of the multiple-feedback band-pass filter is its frequency response. As with LC resonant circuits, the response is maximum at the center frequency, falling off on both sides. The rate of roll-off is determined by the Q of the filter. A low-Q filter rolls off gradually, while a high-Q filter rolls off rapidly. Figure 8–8 is the generalized response of a second-order band-pass filter such as an LC resonant circuit or a single op amp multiple-feedback circuit. Note that changes in Q cause the response curve to initially fall off faster, but that eventually all curves approach the same roll-off. The roll-off rate of 20 dB/decade is characteristic of second-order, one-pole band-pass filters. (**Pole** is a mathematical term that can be equated to an equivalent resonant circuit in a band-pass filter.) Thus, a second-order band-pass filter, which synthesizes an LC resonant circuit, is a one-pole filter. If a sharper roll-off characteristic is desired, it is necessary to use higher-order filters. For the circuit under discussion, the bandwidth is 214 Hz, as determined by the equation $BW = f_0/Q$. The

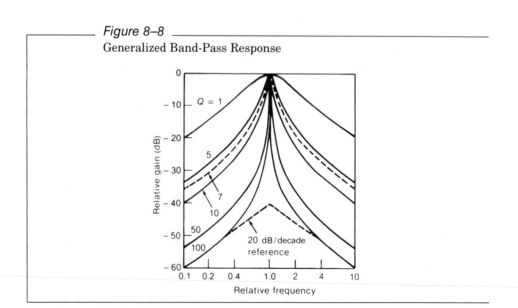

Figure 8–8

Generalized Band-Pass Response

dashed line represents the $Q = 7$ response of the multiple-feedback band-pass filter of Figure 8–7.

Single op amp second-order VCVS band-pass filters may also be used. While it does offer a noninverting configuration, it may require more components than does the multiple-feedback filter. It is not as stable as the multiple-feedback filter, having a noticeable interaction between frequency and Q. The multiple-feedback band-pass filter appears more often than the VCVS band-pass filter in modern electronic devices.

STATE-VARIABLE FILTERS

The **state-variable filter** is a multiple-feedback *universal* filter. It uses at least three op amps, but it has high-pass, low-pass, and band-pass outputs available simultaneously. (All three outputs may not be optimum simultaneously, but they are available.) Addition of another op amp provides the band-reject, or notch, capability.

General Characteristics of State-Variable Filters

The state-variable filter is generally less sensitive to component variations. Q, gain, and feedback may be adjusted independently. Adjustment is fairly easy. When adjusted for a specific frequency, all three outputs will be related to that frequency. For example, if adjusted for 1 kHz band-pass frequency, the high- and low-pass outputs will both have cut-off frequencies of 1 kHz.

As the state-variable filter is analyzed, note that particular care must be taken in selecting the Q of the filter. Since the selected Q is the same for all three sections, the requirements may not be compatible. For example, a high- or low-pass filter requires a Q of 0.707 for Butterworth-type second-order response. A band-pass filter with a Q of 0.707, however, has a very poor roll-off characteristic. Typical responses with different damping factors $(1/Q)$ for the low-pass filter section of the state-variable filter are shown in Figure 8–9. If the state-variable filter is to be used for more than one of its functions, it is advisable to provide means of Q adjustment.

Typical State-Variable Filter

A number of different configurations of the state-variable filter exist, each with its own advantages and disadvantages. Only one of the configurations is shown here (see Figure 8–10). The mathematics associated with detailed analysis of state-variable filters are beyond the scope

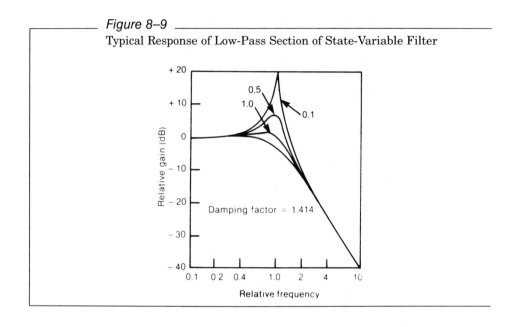

Figure 8–9

Typical Response of Low-Pass Section of State-Variable Filter

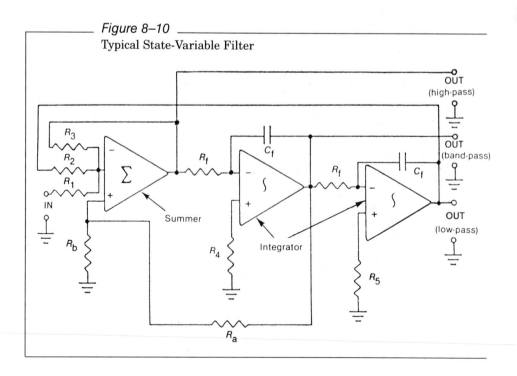

Figure 8–10

Typical State-Variable Filter

of this book. Simplifications have been made so that the user can recognize a state-variable filter and can determine its approximate characteristics. The center frequency of the state-variable filter in Figure 8–10 is controlled by the two R_f and C_f pairs—that is,

$$f_0 = \frac{1}{2\pi R_f C_f}$$

Setting both R_f and C_f pairs equal greatly simplifies both design and understanding without grossly affecting filter performance. Q is determined by feedback supplied by R_a and R_b—that is,

$$Q = \frac{R_b + R_a}{3R_1}$$

where $R_1 = R_2 = R_3$. If input offset current is disregarded, R_b may be any convenient value. R_a is then selected to fit requirements for damping (Q). If input offset current is considered, then R_a in parallel with R_b is made equal to the resistance met by the inverting input (parallel combination of R_1, R_2, and R_3). R_1 establishes the input resistance of the filter, and R_2 and R_3 are made equal to R_1 to sum the inputs. R_4 and R_5 control DC offset. Gain is set at unity for high- and low-pass outputs and is equal to Q for the band-pass output. If the high- and low-pass outputs are added simultaneously with a fourth op amp, a notch output is formed.

The state-variable filter is actually an electronic analog computer that solves an equation for a device (electrical or mechanical) that generates a sine wave. Calculation of the equation is performed by the last two op amps connected as **integrators** (to be discussed in Chapter 10). The integrator is symbolized by the mathematical symbol for integration ($\int$). The first op amp (a summer) combines positive and negative feedback and an input signal. The summer is symbolized by the Greek letter sigma (Σ). Feedbacks are controlled so that oscillation does not occur. The input signal is processed by the filter according to the mathematical formula implemented by the circuit. Implementation is such that low-pass, high-pass, and band-pass outputs are available.

A number of manufacturers supply a single integrated circuit for state-variable filters. This IC consists of three op amps with associated resistors and capacitors to implement the filter. Provisions for connecting four external resistors to set Q, frequency, and gain make this IC an extremely versatile package. A fourth op amp is also available on the chip so that notch filters may be implemented.

Figure 8–11 will give you some practice in identifying and analyzing a state-variable filter. Although it is not drawn like Figure 8–10,

Figure 8–11

Filter Circuit for Analysis

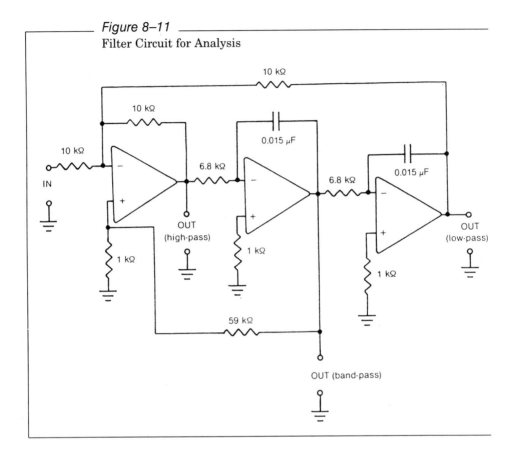

there are some characteristics that identify the diagram of Figure 8–11 as a state-variable filter. Separate high-pass, low-pass, and band-pass outputs are indicative of a state-variable filter. The capacitive feedback over the last two op amps and the resistive feedback from the last op amp to the first op amp are also typical. Using the center frequency formula used for Figure 8–10 shows that f_0 is about 1.5 kHz. The low-pass and high-pass filters thus will have a cutoff frequency of 1.5 kHz, which is also the center frequency of the band-pass filter section. The Q is 20, as determined by the formula $Q = (R_b + R_a)/3R_1$. This results in a bandwidth of 75 Hz for the band-pass filter. Both the low-pass and the high-pass filters will have a peaked response near the calculated cutoff frequency due to the high Q.

BIQUADRATIC FILTERS

The equation for a second-order function has what the mathematicians call *quadratic* terms in both the numerator and denominator. Such an expression is said to be **biquadratic,** or *biquad.*

General Characteristics of Biquadratic Filters

Techniques borrowed from analog computers allow electronic solution of the biquadratic equation. The electronic implementation of the solution uses two integrators (to be discussed in Chapter 10) and an inverting amplifier. Figure 8–12 shows a generalized diagram of the biquadratic circuit. Each integrator has 90° of phase shift. This 90° plus the 180° of phase shift from the inverting amplifier adds up to 360°. When the 360° phase-shifted output is fed back to the input, enough gain exists in the circuit to allow oscillation. The circuit acts like a theoretically perfect resonant *LC* tuned circuit. Once initially excited, it will continue to oscillate. But, just like the *LC* tuned circuit, the electronic implementation of the second-order function can be damped.

Placing a resistor across an *LC* tuned circuit will damp out the oscillation. Thus, if a resistor is placed across one of the capacitors in the generalized circuit of Figure 8–12, it will damp the oscillation. This

Figure 8–12
Generalized Biquadratic Filter

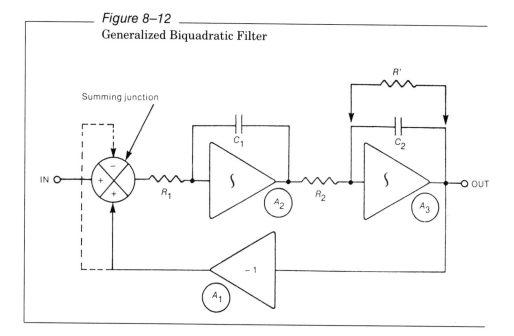

Figure 8–13
Functional Diagram of Biquad Filters

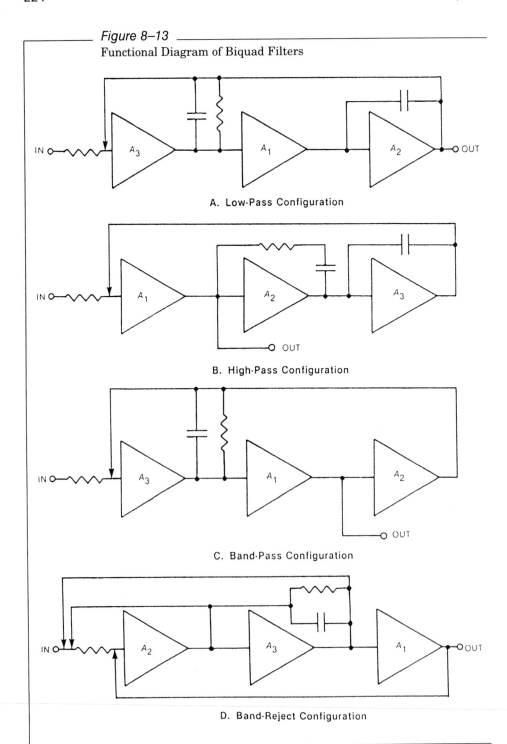

A. Low-Pass Configuration

B. High-Pass Configuration

C. Band-Pass Configuration

D. Band-Reject Configuration

method results in what is commonly called a *biquad* filter. If oscillation is damped by using negative feedback, the circuit is called a *state-variable* filter.

Biquad filters may be used in low-pass, high-pass, band-pass, and band-reject configurations. It is merely a matter of where the input is applied and where the output is removed. Figure 8–13 shows simplified functional diagrams of the four common biquad filter configurations. As related to Figure 8–12, A_1 in Figure 8–13 is the inverting amplifier, A_2 in Figure 8–13 is the first integrator, and A_3 in Figure 8–13 is the second integrator. Both the low-pass configuration (Figure 8–13A) and the band-pass configuration (Figure 8–13C) have the input applied to A_3. Note also that A_3, the second integrator, is the location of the damping resistor. Low-pass filter output is from the first integrator (A_2), while band-pass output is from the inverter (A_1) output. Therefore, either low-pass or band-pass output is available from this configuration.

The high-pass biquad filter input (Figure 8–13B) is to A_1, and its output is from A_1. Note also that the damping network is a series RC rather than a parallel RC configuration. The band-reject configuration (Figure 8–13D) is a very complex circuit, with input to A_2 and output from A_1. Three separate feedback paths are present in the band-reject biquad filter.

Typical Biquadratic Filter

Figure 8–14 shows a biquad filter to be analyzed. It can be identified as a biquad filter by the dual integrator connection with damping provided by a resistor across the integrating capacitor. Input is to A_3, while output is from A_2. By referring to the simplified diagrams of Figure 8–13, the diagram in Figure 8–14 can be identified as a low-pass biquad filter.

The equations used for analysis of the biquadratic filter of Figure 8–14 are as follows:

$$f_0 = \frac{1}{2\pi RC}$$

$$Q = \frac{R_1}{R}$$

$$A_V = \frac{R_5}{R_6}$$

where $R = R_4 = R_5$ and $C = C_1 = C_2$. Example 8–3 shows typical calculations for the biquadratic filter.

Figure 8–14

Biquad Filter for Analysis

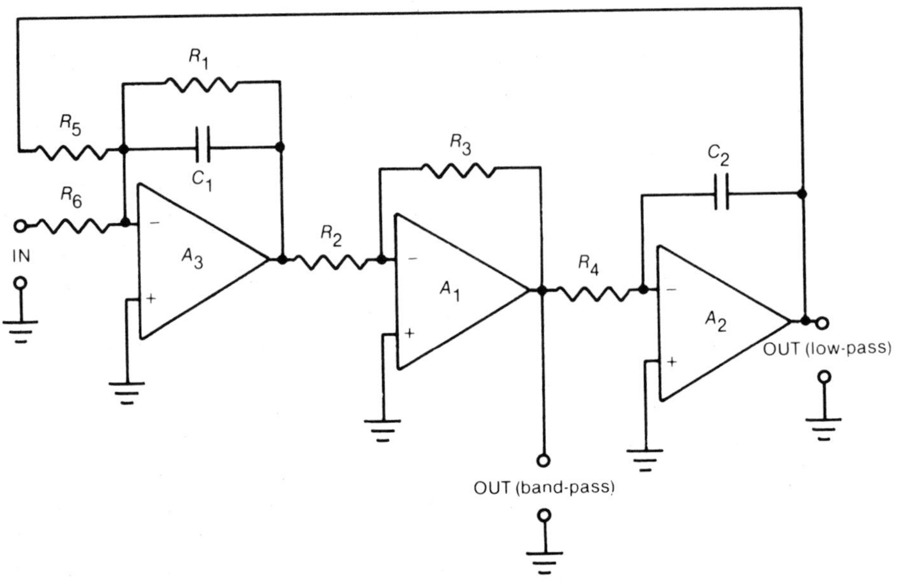

Example 8–3

Calculate f_0, Q, and A_V for the circuit of Figure 8–14 when the following component values are used:

$$R_1 = 113 \text{ k}\Omega \qquad R_4 = 160 \text{ k}\Omega \qquad C_1 = 1000 \text{ pF}$$
$$R_2 = 100 \text{ k}\Omega \qquad R_5 = 160 \text{ k}\Omega \qquad C_2 = 1000 \text{ pF}$$
$$R_3 = 100 \text{ k}\Omega \qquad R_6 = 10 \text{ k}\Omega$$

Solution

$$f_0 = \frac{1}{2\pi RC} = \frac{1}{(6.28)(160 \times 10^3)(1000 \times 10^{-12})} = 995 \text{ Hz}$$

$$Q = \frac{R_1}{R} = \frac{113 \times 10^3}{160 \times 10^3} = 0.706$$

$$A_V = \frac{R_5}{R_6} = \frac{160 \times 10^3}{10 \times 10^3} = 16$$

$$A_V \text{ (dB)} = 20 \log A_V = (20)(\log 16) = 24 \text{ dB}$$

Now let's make a couple of changes. Output will be taken from A_1, and R_1 will be changed to 2 MΩ. Reference to the simplified biquad filter information in Figure 8–13 shows that band-pass operation results from using the A_1 output. Changing R_1 should affect only the Q of the circuit, since R_1 does not appear in any of the other formulas. The Q now becomes 12.5 (R_1/R_5, or 2,000,000/160,000 = 12.5). The cutoff frequency and the voltage gain do not change. Bandwidth (f_c/Q) is 80 Hz.

The biquad filter has a number of advantages. It is possible to obtain Q values of 100 or above with reasonable stability. Most other active filters do not allow stable operation at such high Q values. Tuning is not a major undertaking—it requires only variation of the two-frequency-determining resistors or capacitors. Best of all, absolute bandwidth is constant with changing frequency. That does not mean that the percentage bandwidth stays the same, because it is a function of Q. However, if a biquad band-pass filter has a bandwidth of 100 Hz at 1000 Hz, it will have that same bandwidth at 3000 Hz. Most other filters do not have this capability.

———— *BAND-REJECT, OR NOTCH, FILTERS* ————

Band-reject filters, or notch filters, do just the opposite of band-pass filters. Only the desired band of frequencies is rejected—all other frequencies are passed without attenuation. Many of the filters already discussed can be modified and/or combined to form notch filters.

Multiple-Feedback Notch Filter

Figure 8–15 shows a multiple-feedback band-pass filter combined with an inverting amplifier to form a notch filter. The mathematicians tell us that when we subtract the output of a band-pass filter from its input we get a notch filter. Analysis is a matter of using what we already know about multiple-feedback band-pass filters and learning a bit about summing, or adder, circuits.

The notch, or null, frequency of the multiple-feedback filter will be the same as the center frequency of the band-pass section. The filter in Figure 8–15 uses approximately the same component values as the band-pass filter of Figure 8–7, so the null frequency will be the same—that is, about 1500 Hz. The slight change in some component values stems from the gain of the inverting amplifier following the filter in Figure 8–15. The computer program that has calculated the actual values for the filter takes these factors into consideration. Q and bandwidth remain the same for both the band-pass and band-reject (notch) filters.

Figure 8–15

Multiple-Feedback Notch Filter

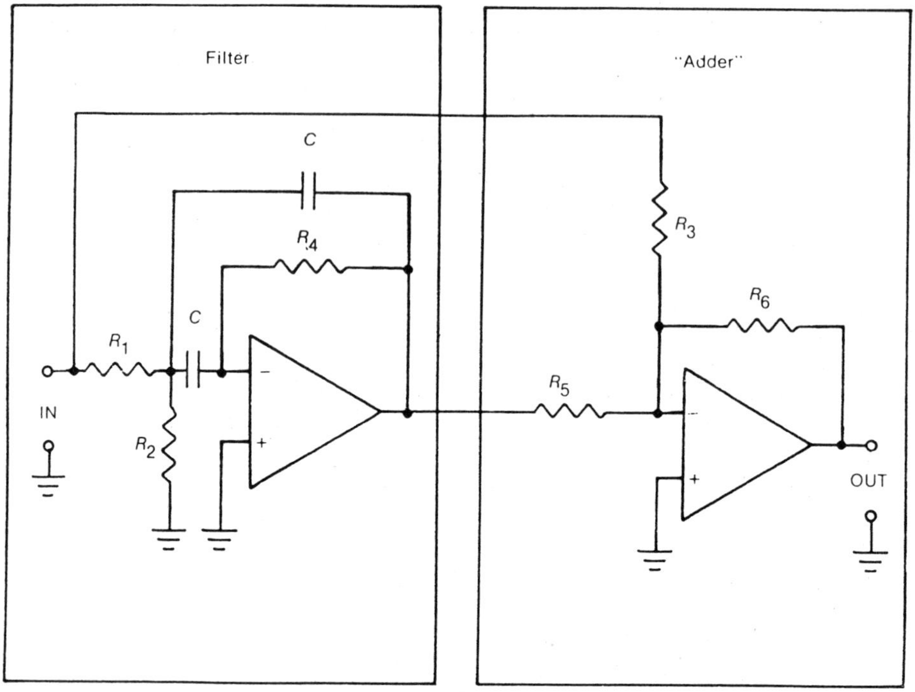

The remainder of the changes are concerned with the second op amp and its function as a summing circuit. Actually, this is merely an inverting amplifier with two inputs. One input comes from the filter input, while the other is the filter output. To obtain maximum null with this type of filter, both inputs must be of the same magnitude. The gain of the band-pass filter section requires, then, a larger series resistor to the inverting amplifier input than does the input from the filter input. On the basis of earlier discussions, we know that here the gain of the multiple-feedback band-pass filter section is equal to $R_4/2R_1$, or approximately 2 in this case. Thus, in order to have equal inputs at the **summing point** (junction of R_3 and R_5), R_5 must be twice the value of R_3. The inputs arriving at the summing point are algebraically added, and the inverting amplifier further amplifies the results. Gain of the inverting amplifier is determined in the usual manner (R_6/R_5), or $20/13.3 = 1.5$. Total gain from filter input to inverting amplifier output is the product of the two gains—that is, $2 \times 1.5 = 3$, or about 9.5 dB. With perfectly matched components, the null will be quite deep—in this case, about -77 dB. The steepness of the sides, or skirts, of the null curve is a function of the circuit Q, just as in the band-pass filter from which the notch filter originated.

Biquad Notch Filter

It may be recalled from the discussion of biquad filters that a biquad band-reject configuration existed. Figure 8–13, in fact, showed a block diagram of a biquad notch filter. It is a highly complex circuit and will not be discussed in this text. With a little practice, it may be recognized. The same basic concepts of frequency-, gain-, and Q-determining components carry over from the other biquad filters. At the technician level, analysis and troubleshooting are best limited to removal and replacement of components suspected to be defective.

State-Variable Notch Filter

State-variable filters perform the band-reject function very easily. Much earlier in this chapter it was pointed out that a band-reject filter could be formed by combining a low-pass and a high-pass filter. Since the state-variable filter has both functions, it is only necessary to sum the low-pass and high-pass outputs. In block diagram form, the state-variable notch filter looks like Figure 8–16. The state-variable filter portion of the notch filter is identical to the 1500 Hz state-variable filter of Figure 8–10. It has a Q of 20 and unity gain for both the low-pass and the high-pass outputs. Separate 10 kΩ resistors isolate the two outputs and provide a summing point at their junction. Note that the summing amplifier has unity gain as established by the 10 kΩ feedback resistor. By the addition of a single op amp, then, the state-variable filter has all four of the primary filter functions. While the available notch is not as

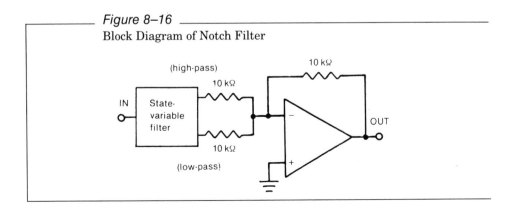

Figure 8–16

Block Diagram of Notch Filter

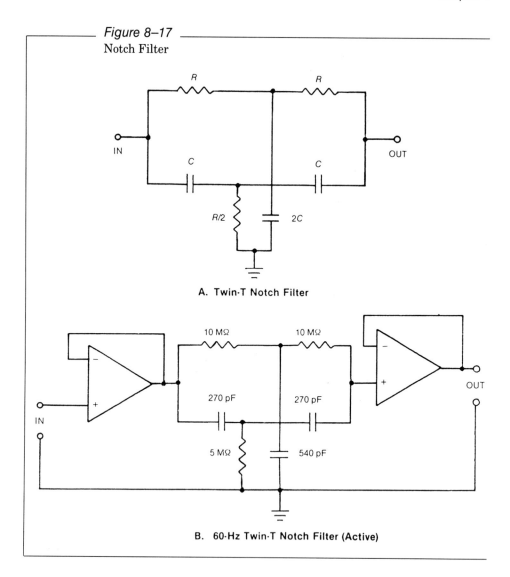

Figure 8-17
Notch Filter

A. Twin-T Notch Filter

B. 60-Hz Twin-T Notch Filter (Active)

deep (only about 30 dB) as with some of the other configurations, the state-variable notch filter is a simple, stable multipurpose filter.

One of the most common notch filters is the twin-T configuration. It has been used for many years in the passive form shown in Figure 8–17A, but operational amplifiers have made it even more popular. The **twin-T filter** likes to work from low source impedances and into high load impedances. When inserted between two voltage followers, the twin-T is right at home. The low output impedance of the input voltage follower supplies the desired source impedance to drive the filter. The high input impedance of the output voltage follower isolates the twin-T from any external load influences. Figure 8–17B shows a typical twin-T active filter. Combined with an easily obtainable 35 dB to 40 dB notch, the twin-T performs quite well. Actually, if all components are properly matched, an infinitely deep notch can be obtained.

In order to obtain deep-notch characteristics, the resistor and capacitor ratios must be maintained very closely. The Q of the circuit increases as the percentage of mismatch increases. A degradation of notch depth occurs, however. Between 10% and 20% capacitor mismatch, for example, the twin-T circuit behaves as a high-gain tuned amplifier, with voltage gains up to 400. Further increase in mismatch will cause the circuit to oscillate, with clipped sine wave output.

As long as the ratios shown in Figure 8–17 are maintained, the null frequency of the twin-T filter is calculated by the conventional formula $f_c = 1/2\pi RC$. Values shown in Figure 8–17 provide a notch at about 60 Hz. Notch depth can be as much as -60 dB if adequate precision (within 1%) is maintained with the frequency-determining components. The twin-T filter is easy to recognize. With the information supplied here concerning maintenance of component ratios, malfunction of twin-T filters should be easy to locate.

——— *MISCELLANEOUS FILTERS* ———

Many other types of active filters exist. Specialized requirements generate new designs daily. A few of the important but not so commonly encountered active filters are mentioned here in passing. No attempt is made to provide detailed explanations or analysis. Only general characteristics and applications are mentioned.

One class of filters that are hardly filters at all is the **all-pass filter.** It passes *all* frequencies at a relatively constant amplitude. The primary purpose of an all-pass filter is to provide the desired phase shift at a specific frequency. An all-pass filter can be formed by summing the outputs of a low-pass, high-pass, and a band-pass filter. All-pass filters are commonly found in audio-frequency equalizers and in specialized compensation networks.

Constant-time-delay filters are used when the delay of the filter must remain relatively constant over a given range of input frequencies. The Bessel configuration can provide this capability. Most of the filters already discussed can have the Bessel-shape response if the proper damping ratio is selected. Constant-time-delay filters find application in audio and pulse devices where a variation in delay with frequency change would result in distortion.

A variation of the notch filter formed by summing the high-pass and low-pass outputs of a state-variable filter is the **elliptical,** or

Cauer filter. During discussion of the state-variable notch filter, it was mentioned that both the high-pass and low-pass outputs must be identical to obtain the desired notch characteristic. An interesting effect can be obtained by reducing, for example, the magnitude of the high-pass input to the summing amplifier. This is easily done by increasing the value of the summing resistor in the high-pass leg of the summing network. As the high-pass magnitude decreases (series resistor increases), the filter approaches the response of a low-pass filter with very steep roll-off characteristic. In fact, that is one application of the elliptical, or Cauer, filter. Unfortunately, even though the notch is present and the roll-off characteristic is steep, the attenuation does not stay constant on the high-pass side. It bounces back up from the notch value, giving an unsymmetrical response. Proper selection of the ratio of high-pass magnitude to low-pass magnitude can establish the best filter shape for a specific application.

HIGH-ORDER FILTERS

When filters are required that have better roll-off characteristics than the first- and second-order filters already discussed, it is necessary to cascade first- and second-order sections. It has already been shown that first-order low-pass and high-pass filters have a roll-off characteristic of 20 dB/decade. Second-order low-pass and high-pass filters have a 40 dB/decade roll-off characteristic. As the order is increased, the roll-off characteristic gets steeper. A third-order low-pass or high-pass filter has a 60 dB/decade roll-off, a fourth-order filter has an 80 dB/decade roll-off, and so on.

General Characteristics of High-Order Filters

Third-order low-pass and high-pass filters are formed by combining a first-order and a second-order filter. The roll-off characteristic becomes 60 dB/decade, and greater control of the response is provided. In the first-order filter, for example, only the cutoff frequency was within design control. The second-order filter provided control of both cutoff frequency and damping factor. By the time the third-order filter is reached, the combination gives design control of damping factor and the ratio of both cutoff frequencies. As higher-order filters are used, it will be seen that damping factors and cutoff frequencies are not necessarily the same as would be expected if the filter sections were individually designed. The interaction of damping factors, gains, and cutoff frequencies presents a very complex mathematical picture.

High-order filters are definitely the subject of separate books. Designers use many tables of factors to determine the relationship of

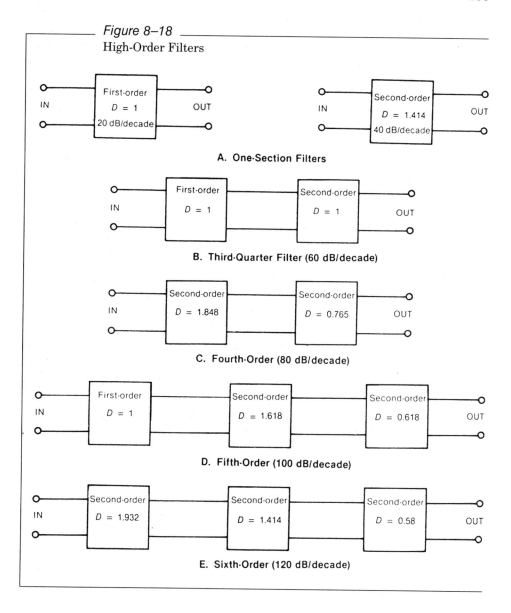

Figure 8–18
High-Order Filters

A. One-Section Filters

B. Third-Quarter Filter (60 dB/decade)

C. Fourth-Order (80 dB/decade)

D. Fifth-Order (100 dB/decade)

E. Sixth-Order (120 dB/decade)

the various filter parameters. Pages and pages of formulas and tables are required for such design efforts. Samples of existing designs are shown in this book so that some of the major high-order filter characteristics can be recognized. More detailed information can be found by consulting the books listed in the Bibliography.

Figure 8–18 (A through E) shows the general characteristics of some high-order Butterworth-shape filters. For the sake of simplicity, first-order sections are considered to be passive RC filters isolated by a voltage follower with unity gain. The second-order sections are equal-component VCVS filters. Cutoff frequencies are the same in all sections when using these building blocks. If other building blocks such as state-variable or multiple-feedback filters are used, cutoff frequencies may or may not be identical. Damping factors, however, are different, as can be noted in the individual section blocks. Selection of some other response shape will, as with individual first- and second-order sections, result in changes to both cutoff frequency and damping factor. Consult appropriate references for the necessary tables and formulas.

Third-Order High-Pass Filter

A third-order high-pass filter is shown in Figure 8–19. It consists of a passive RC section followed by a second-order equal-component VCVS section. According to the block diagram of Figure 8–18B, both sections should have a damping factor of 1. A voltage follower has a damping factor of 1, and the R_4-R_5 combination in the second section also provides

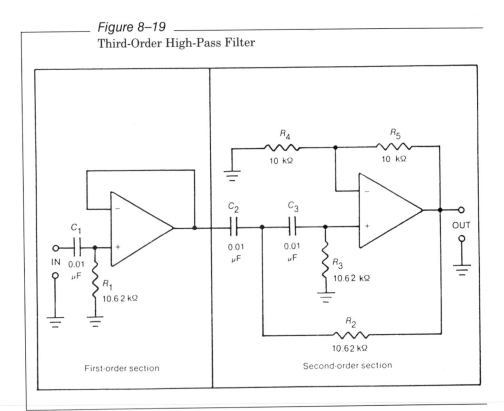

Figure 8–19

Third-Order High-Pass Filter

a unity damping factor. The frequency-determining components (R_1 and C_1) of the single-order section provide a cutoff frequency of approximately 1500 Hz. Likewise, the R_2-C_2 and R_3-C_3 components equate to a cutoff frequency of 1500 Hz. (Use $f_c = 1/2\pi RC$ to calculate cutoff frequency.) The third-order filter roll-off characteristic is the sum of the roll-off characteristics of the first- and second-order sections, or 60 dB/decade. Overall gain is the product of the voltage gains (sum of the dB gains). The first section with its voltage follower has a voltage gain of 1, while the second section with its inverting amplifier has a voltage gain of 2 ($A_V = 1 + R_5/R_4$). Total gain is 2, or 6 dB. Using this type of analysis, even the more complex high-order filters may be understood.

Fourth-Order Low-Pass Filter

A fourth-order low-pass filter consisting of two second-order sections is shown in Figure 8–20. Note that the frequency-determining components are identical in both sections. Applying the common formula for cutoff frequency shows that the filter has a cutoff frequency of approximately 3000 Hz. The roll-off characteristic is the sum of the roll-off characteristics of the individual sections, or 80 dB/decade. As with the third-order

Figure 8–20

Fourth-Order Low-Pass Filter

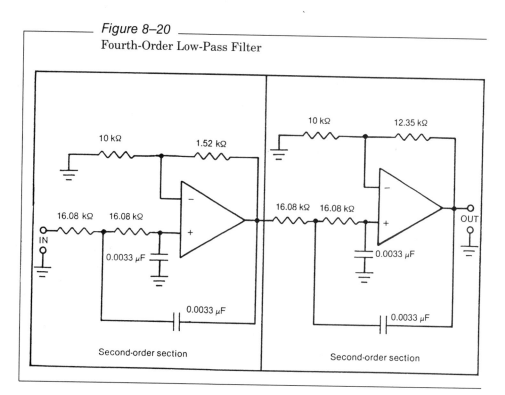

filter, total gain is the sum of individual section gains in dB. Calculations with the values of Figure 8–20 show that the first section has a gain of 1.2 dB, while the second section has a gain of 7 dB. Total filter gain is thus approximately 8.2 dB. When high-order filters are constructed from other than equal-component VCVS sections, more complex circuits result. VCVS filters are shown here only to demonstrate that it is possible to obtain sharper roll-off characteristics and gain by cascading lower-order sections.

High-order band-pass filters may also be formed by cascading lower-order sections. The ultimate roll-off characteristic also improves, just as with high-pass and low-pass high-order filters. The Qs of individual sections must be carefully controlled when cascading band-pass filters. Tables and formulas exist in the referenced material in the Bibliography. If additional information concerning high-order band-pass filters is required, it is suggested that these references be consulted.

──────── SWITCHED-CAPACITOR FILTER ────────

All of the active operational amplifier filter circuits previously discussed required precision resistors, capacitors, or inductors. Precision components are expensive; however, there is a linear integrated circuit answer to the precision component problem. It is the switched-capacitor active filter (SCF). Let's investigate how it operates.

The key element in an SCF is an operational amplifier circuit called an **integrator** (Figure 8–21). An operational amplifier integrator is a conventional inverting op amp with capacitive rather than resistive feedback. As the frequency of the input signal of Figure 8–21A increases, X_C decreases. More feedback results, gain decreases, and the output signal amplitude decreases. Figure 8–21A thus performs as a low-pass filter. Combining the integrator with a summing amplifier (Figure 8–21B) produces a high-pass filter. See the discussion of state-variable filters earlier in this chapter. Both of the integrator-based filters of Figure 8–21 require no precision components.

SCFs replace the external precision input resistor and capacitor with on-chip capacitors. How can a capacitor replace a resistor? Figure 8–22 may help explain the principles of operation of the SCF. C_1 and C_2 are matched on-chip capacitors. S_1 and S_2 are on-chip electronic switches and are controlled by an externally supplied clock. S_1 is closed when the clock is HIGH and open when the clock is LOW. S_2 is closed when the clock is LOW and open when the clock is HIGH. Consider that the input signal is a constant positive voltage supplied from a low-impedance source. When the clock becomes HIGH, S_1 closes and C_1 quickly charges to V_i. The clock then goes LOW, S_1 opens, and S_2 closes. The charge on C_1, $V_s \times C_1$, quickly transfers to C_2, and the charge on C_1

Figure 8–21

Integrators as Filters

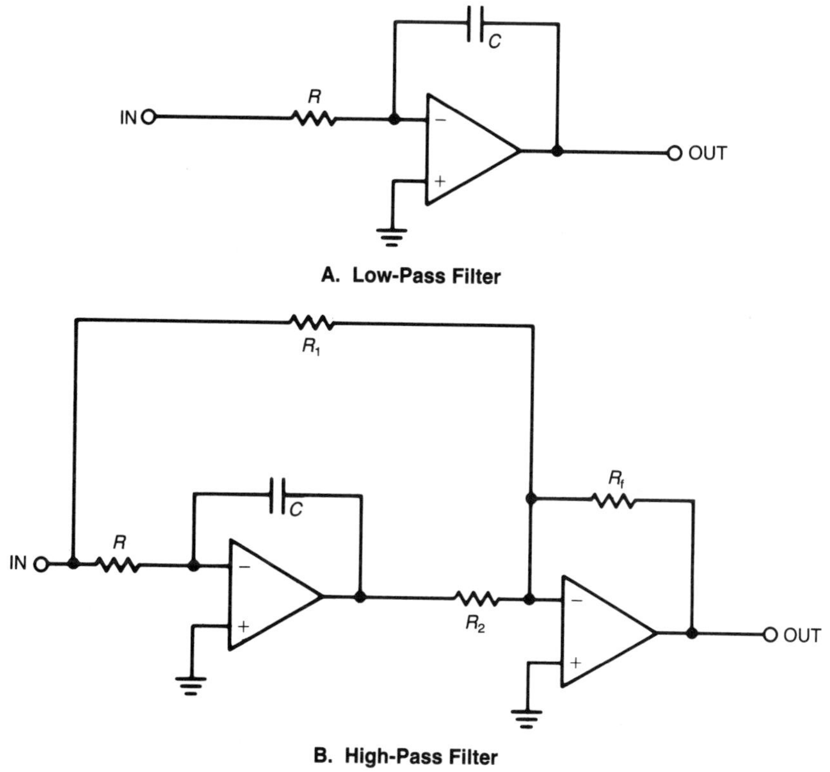

A. Low-Pass Filter

B. High-Pass Filter

---

goes to zero. Each clock cycle adds to the charge stored on C_2, and a stepped output (Figure 8–22) results.

You may recall from your study of basic electronic fundamentals that the average current flow in a capacitor is

$$I = \frac{q}{t}$$

$$= \frac{V_s \times C_1}{T}$$

$$= V_s \times C_1 \times f_{clk}$$

where

T = clock period

$f_{clk} = \dfrac{1}{T}$ = clock frequency

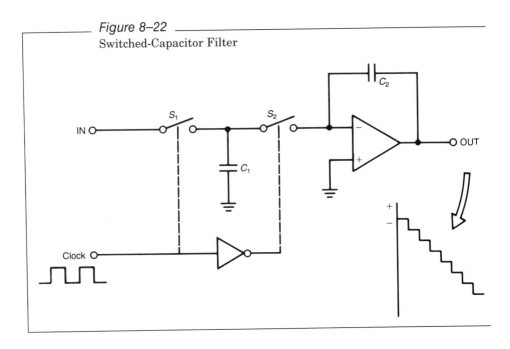

Figure 8-22
Switched-Capacitor Filter

The current flow could be considered as resulting from an imaginary resistor such that

$$R = \frac{V_s}{I}$$

$$= \frac{1}{C_1} \times f_{clk}$$

Thus the imaginary resistor's value, which controls the charging and discharging of C_1, is a function of C_1 and the clock frequency. C_1 is fixed, so R is primarily determined by the clock frequency. Our previous discussions of filters showed that filter response is a function of both R and C. Thus, if the imaginary R value changes, the SCF response changes. The filter response is controlled by the clock frequency!

A block diagram of a typical SCF filter (Figure 8-23) shows that selection of the type of filter implemented is much like the state-variable filter technique. The primary difference is the way the integrators are constructed. Dotted lines show how a typical connection that provides notch, band-pass, and low-pass outputs.

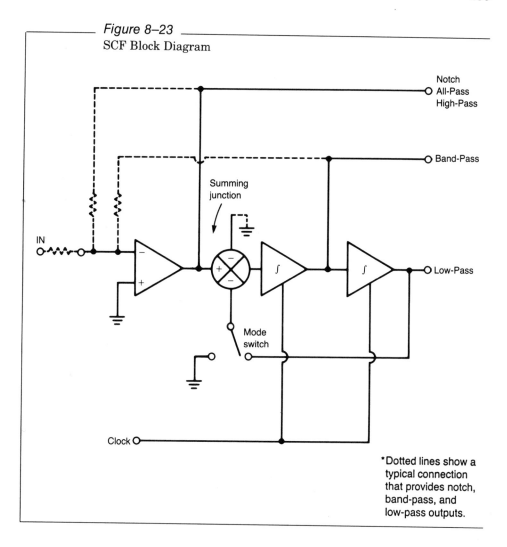

Figure 8–23

SCF Block Diagram

*Dotted lines show a typical connection that provides notch, band-pass, and low-pass outputs.

SUMMARY

Chapters 7 and 8 have provided a view of the application of operational amplifiers to the filter field. The simple single-order filters with their 20 dB/decade roll-off characteristics became the basis for 40 dB/decade second-order filters as the voltage-controlled-voltage-source (VCVS) and multiple-feedback configurations developed.

The use of positive feedback and a capacitor to simulate an LC tuned circuit forms the basis for VCVS filters. As with LC tuned circuits, the shape of the frequency response curve of the VCVS filter is somewhat determined by the damping of the filter. Responses varying from relatively flat to very peaked characteristics are found by selecting filter damping. It should be noted that a more easily controlled VCVS filter configuration, called the equal-component-value Sallen-Key filter, is often used when damping factor must be conveniently adjusted.

Multiple-feedback second-order filters use both resistive and capacitive feedback. When filter adjustment is not required, multiple-feedback filters are most often used. Band-pass filters employing multiple-feedback configurations are also common, although combinations of high-pass and low-pass filters may be found.

A truly universal filter is the state-variable filter. Although it uses at least three op amps, it does have high-pass, low-pass, and band-pass outputs available simultaneously. Biquadratic filters are also used but are quite complex.

Notch, all-pass, constant-time-delay, and high-order filters all find application using op amps. Further information on these complex filters is found in the Bibliography.

══ QUESTIONS ══════════════════════

1. Define the following terms: (a) second-order filter, (b) damping factor, (c) voltage-controlled-voltage-source filter, (d) Butterworth response, (e) Chebyshev response, (f) Bessel response, (g) multiple-feedback filter, (h) state-variable filter, (i) biquadratic filter, (j) twin-T filter, (k) all-pass filter, (l) constant-time-delay filter, and (m) elliptical filter.

2. Explain what is meant when it is stated that low-pass and high-pass filters are reciprocal.

3. What is the purpose of DC feedback in active filters?

4. What is the purpose of AC feedback in active filters?

5. List the parameters that may be controlled in a Sallen-Key filter. Explain by using a typical schematic diagram if necessary.

6. Discuss the differences and similarities of unity gain and equal-component-value VCVS filters.

7. What controls the filter response shape in a unity gain VCVS filter? Explain.

8. What controls the filter response shape in an equal-component-value VCVS filter? Explain.

9. Discuss the advantages and disadvantages of multiple-feedback second-order filters when compared with VCVS filters.

10. In what type of applications would a multiple-feedback filter most likely be found? Why?

11. Show by a block diagram how a wide-band pass-filter could be implemented using second-order low- and high-pass sections. Explain how it works.

12. Repeat Question 11 for a multiple-feedback circuit.

13. Discuss the advantages and disadvantages of state-variable filters.

14. Using a simplified diagram, explain the operation of a typical state-variable filter.

15. Discuss the advantages and disadvantages of biquadratic filters.

16. Using a simplified diagram, explain the operation of a biquadratic filter.

17. Show by simplified diagrams two different methods that could be used to implement active notch filters.

18. Explain why high-order filters have much steeper roll-off characteristics than single- and second-order filters.

19. Why must damping factors be different in each section of high-order filters?

20. Draw a block diagram of a fifth-order low-pass filter. Show as many characteristics of each section as you can.

21. Discuss the advantages and disadvantages of switched-capacitor filters.

═══ PROBLEMS ═══════════════════════════════

1. In Figure 8–3, $R_1 = 3.3$ kΩ, $R_f = 0$ Ω, and $C_1 = 0.015$ μF. Determine (a) passband gain, (b) cutoff frequency, and (c) damping factor. Draw the frequency response graph.

2. What changes would be necessary to increase the cutoff frequency in Problem 1 by a factor of 2?

3. In Figure 8–4, $R_1 = 4.7$ kΩ, $C_2 = 0.033$ μF, $R_f = 27$ kΩ, and $R_x = 47$ kΩ. Determine (a) passband gain, (b) cutoff frequency, and (c) damping factor. Draw the frequency response graph.

4. What changes would be necessary to increase the cutoff frequency in Problem 3 by a factor of 2?

5. In Figure 8–5, $R_1 = R_2 = R_3 = 6.8$ kΩ. $C_1 = 0.1$ μF and $C_2 = 0.022$ μF. Determine (a) passband gain, (b) cutoff frequency, and (c) damping factor. Draw the frequency response graph.

6. What changes would be necessary to decrease the cutoff frequency in Problem 5 by a factor of 2?

7. In Figure 8–7, R_1 = 68 kΩ, R_2 = 2.7 kΩ, R_3 = 180 kΩ, and C = 0.01 µF. Determine (a) cutoff frequency, (b) passband gain, (c) Q, and (d) bandwidth.

8. In Figure 8–11, R_f is increased from 6.8 kΩ to 11 kΩ. Determine (a) low-pass cutoff frequency, (b) high-pass cutoff frequency, (c) center frequency of band-pass section, (d) low-pass gain, (e) high-pass gain, and (f) band-pass gain.

9. Repeat Problem 8, but also change R_b to 10 kΩ.

10. In Figure 8–14, C_1 and C_2 are changed from 1000 pF to 470 pF. Determine (a) low-pass gain, (b) cutoff frequency, and (c) Q.

11. Show the changes necessary to Figure 8–17 to obtain a null frequency of 100 Hz.

12. Redraw Figure 8–20 as a fifth-order low-pass filter with the same cutoff frequency. Show all component values.

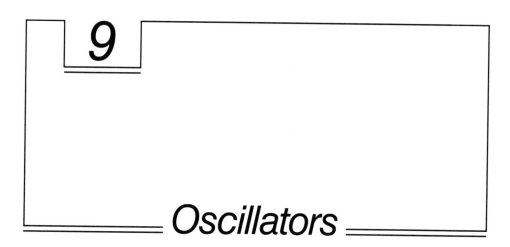

Oscillators

INTRODUCTION

Prior to this chapter, we discussed the use of operational amplifiers in signal-processing circuits. Input signals were amplified, attenuated, phase shifted, and so forth. Now we are going to talk about the *generation* of electronic signals.

An electronic circuit that provides an AC output with no external AC input is called an **oscillator.** In simplified form, all that is necessary to form an oscillator is an amplifier and a phase-shifting network. Actually, oscillators are easy to make. If we are not careful, many

Figure 9–1
Oscillation Requirements

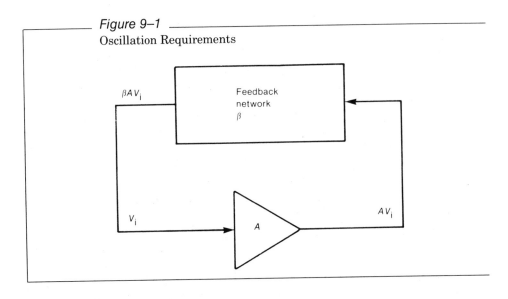

op-amp-based amplifiers will oscillate even though we want them only to amplify. Figure 9–1 shows in a simplified block diagram what is required to form an oscillator. An amplifier and a feedback network are all that is needed. As already noted, any op amp will have a known gain and phase shift that depends on both internal and external components. Whatever is applied to the input of the op amp will be amplified by the op amp's gain. In Figure 9–1, the output of the op amp is shown connected to a feedback network. Such networks have both attenuation and, if there are reactive elements like capacitors or inductors present, phase shift. Note that the output of the feedback network is connected back to the input of the op amp. Therefore, the input to the op amp is a function of

1. the gain of the op amp,
2. the phase shift of the op amp,
3. the attenuation of the feedback network, and
4. the phase shift of the feedback network.

Now for the criteria that establish oscillation. The gain of the amplifier must be at least enough to make up for the attenuation of the feedback network. The loop gain, then, must be equal to or greater than 1 to provide enough input to the amplifier to make up for the losses in the feedback network. Furthermore, if the oscillator is to generate an electronic signal at a specified frequency, the phase shift of the fed-back signal must be 0° at the specified frequency. In other words, the input must be in phase with itself. The frequency of oscillation is thus determined by the phase shift, while the ability to oscillate is determined by the loop gain of the circuit. An oscillator must therefore meet the following two criteria:

$$\text{Loop gain } (\beta A) \geqslant 1$$
$$\text{Loop phase shift } = 0°$$

In passing, one additional point should be made. The closer the loop gain is to 1 without being less than 1, the more **sinusoidal** will be the output. Large loop gains tend to ensure oscillation but also cause distorted sine wave output.

SINUSOIDAL (SINE WAVE) GENERATORS

One of the most familiar forms of electronic signals is the **sine wave.** It is a periodic waveform found in audio systems, radios, televisions, control systems, and many other devices. Operational amplifiers are used extensively in modern sine wave oscillator circuits.

Phase Shift Oscillator

One of the simplest sine wave oscillators is the **phase shift oscillator.** It is a classic illustration of the basic criteria for oscillation. Figure 9–2 is a schematic diagram showing the details of a phase shift oscillator. Amplification is provided by the op amp, while phase shift is provided by the three-section *RC* network.

Figure 9–2
Phase Shift Oscillator

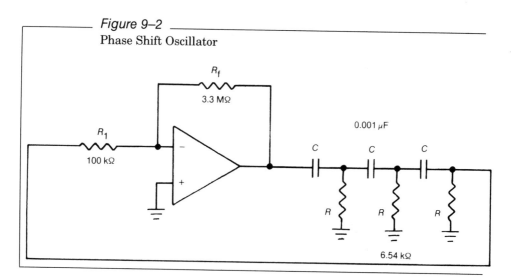

First let's discuss the RC network. A single RC network, you may recall, can shift the phase between input and output from $0°$ to almost $90°$. As phase shift approaches $90°$, however, the attenuation of the network becomes restrictive. Since $180°$ of phase shift is needed (the op amp will furnish $180°$ also), three RC networks in cascade are used. With $60°$ of phase shift, there is still a usable amount of signal at the network output. Three $60°$ phase shifts provide the required $180°$. Signal attenuation also results, though. The mathematicians can show that three $60°$ networks in cascade will attenuate the input signal by a factor of 29. Therefore, the output of the three-section RC network will be $180°$ out of phase with the input and attenuated by a factor of 29.

Now for the amplifier. Since the op amp is going to provide $180°$ of phase shift, the input signal must be supplied to the inverting input. To make up for the attenuation of the phase-shifting network, the op amp gain must be at least 29. The R_f-R_1 combination establishes op amp gain in the conventional manner. Let's analyze the phase shift oscillator in Figure 9–2 to see whether the criteria for oscillation have been met. Example 9–1 shows the required calculations.

_____ *Example 9–1* _____

Calculate the frequency of oscillation, phase shift of the RC networks, and amplifier gain for the phase shift oscillator of Figure 9–2.

Solution

$$f = \frac{1}{2\pi RC\sqrt{6}} = \frac{1}{(6.28)(6.54 \times 10^3 \times 0.001 \times 10^{-6})\sqrt{6}}$$

$$= 9935 \text{ Hz}$$

$$\phi = \tan^{-1}\frac{1}{2\pi fRC}$$

$$= \tan^{-1}\frac{1}{(6.28)(9935)(6.54 \times 10^3 \times 0.001 \times 10^{-6})}$$

$$= \tan^{-1} 2.45 = 68°$$

$$A_V = \frac{R_f}{R_1} = \frac{3.3}{0.1} = 33$$

It has been stated that each of the RC sections in the feedback network must contribute $60°$ of phase shift. This is not exactly true; the total phase shift of all three sections must be $180°$. Each of the RC sections is loaded by the following section, and the phase angle calculation for single sections will be slightly in error. For example, the values of C and R used in Figure 9–2 and Example 9–1 yield a phase shift of $68°$. This is well within reason, however, and when following sections are connected, the phase shift will be slightly less. Now for the final check. The attenuation of the three-section RC network is 29, and the amplifier gain must be at least 29 to make up for it. As shown in Example 9–1, the values for R_f and R_1 establish a gain of 33. All criteria for oscillation have been met. Phase shift is correct, and adequate gain has been provided to make up for network losses.

The principles and formulas of this discussion are adequate for troubleshooting a malfunctioning phase shift oscillator. If the circuit does not oscillate, the loop may be broken and amplifier gain checked by inserting a test input. Replacing the op amp or gain-determining components generally brings the circuit back to operation. Distorted output is most often the result of excessive gain and can be checked in the same manner. If gain is correct and oscillation still does not occur, the phase-shifting network can be checked for both attenuation and total phase shift. Off-frequency operation will usually be traced to problems in the RC sections also. With just a bit of ingenuity and knowledge, then, the phase shift oscillator will become easy to understand and use.

Wien Bridge Oscillator

The **Wien bridge oscillator** is another example of meeting the criteria for oscillation. It includes an amplifier with means to establish the required gain, and a phase-shifting network to determine the required phase shift. The Wien bridge oscillator gets its name from the form of bridge circuit used to establish phase shift and gain. Figure 9–3A is a schematic diagram of a Wien bridge oscillator. The more conventional manner of drawing the circuit is shown in Figure 9–3B.

Frequency of oscillation is established by the values of R and C in the positive feedback loop. When both of the resistors and both of the capacitors in the feedback loop are of equal value, the conventional formula for oscillator frequency is used ($f_o = 1/2\pi RC$). Understanding the principle of the Wien bridge requires a review of the fundamentals of series and parallel RC circuits. At a specific frequency, the phase of the voltage across the parallel branch of a series RC and a parallel RC network in series is the same as the phase of the applied voltage across the total network. A lagging phase angle exists when frequency increases above the specified frequency. Decreasing frequency below the specified frequency results in a leading phase angle. Only at the specified frequency is the phase angle of the input to the network equal to the phase angle of the output. If connected as shown in Figure 9–3B, then one of the criteria for oscillation exists; that is, the input and output of the op amp are in phase.

There is a problem, however. The Wien bridge attenuates the signal by a factor of approximately 3. If, however, the gain of the amplifier

Figure 9–3
Wien Bridge Oscillator

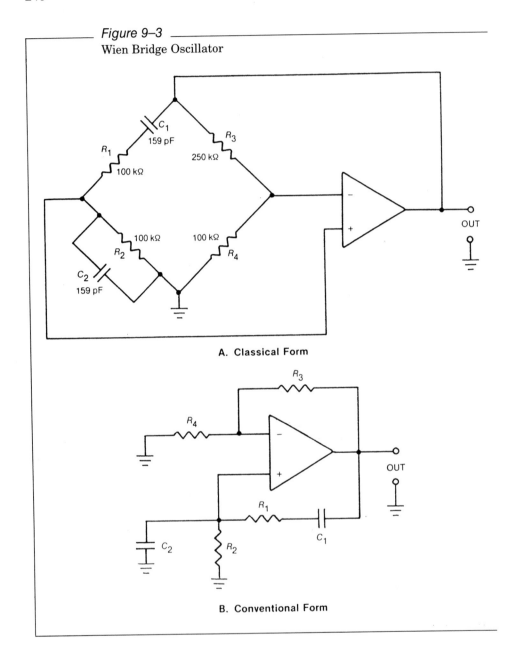

A. Classical Form

B. Conventional Form

is equal to or greater than 3, then the second criterion for oscillation exists. R_3 and R_4 are, therefore, selected to provide a noninverting amplifier gain of at least 3 ($A_V = 1 + R_3/R_4$). From the bridge viewpoint, then, the leg with the RC circuits is one branch of the bridge, while the resistive leg is the other branch. However, it is more convenient to draw the circuit in the more conventional form of Figure 9–3B.

Evaluation of the oscillator of Figure 9–3B follows the usual pattern.

___ *Example 9–2* _____

Calculate the frequency of oscillation, phase shift of the RC networks, and amplifier gain for the Wien bridge oscillator of Figure 9–3A.

Solution

$$f_o = \frac{1}{2\pi RC} = \frac{1}{(6.28)(100 \times 10^3)(159 \times 10^{-12})}$$

$$= 10 \text{ kHz}$$

$$\phi = \tan^{-1}\frac{1}{2\pi fRC} = \tan^{-1}\frac{1}{(6.28)(10 \times 10^3)(100 \times 10^3)(159 \times 10^{-12})}$$

$$= \tan^{-1} = 1 = 45°$$

$$A_V = 1 + \frac{R_3}{R_4} = 1 + \frac{250{,}000}{100{,}000} = 1 + 2.5$$

$$= 3.5$$

_____

Unfortunately, operation of the Wien bridge oscillator is critical in terms of negative and positive feedback balance. If the positive feedback increases above the design value, the amplifier may saturate and distort the sine wave output. An increase in negative feedback will in most cases cause oscillation to cease. Most Wien bridge oscillators are constructed as shown in Figure 9–4. The negative feedback gain-determining circuit is modified to include a nonlinear element such as a thermistor or a small incandescent lamp. A lamp or a positive temperature-coefficient thermistor will increase the resistance of the circuit as the output of the amplifier rises. Negative feedback will increase to counteract the increased output, and the output will remain relatively constant. Decreasing output causes the lamp or positive temperature-coefficient thermistor to decrease its resistance and thus reduce negative feedback and bring the output back to the design value. Use of a lamp or thermistor for stability purposes has its drawbacks, but it is an improvement over no stabilization at all. Other more complex methods of stabilization may be used, depending on requirements. However, for

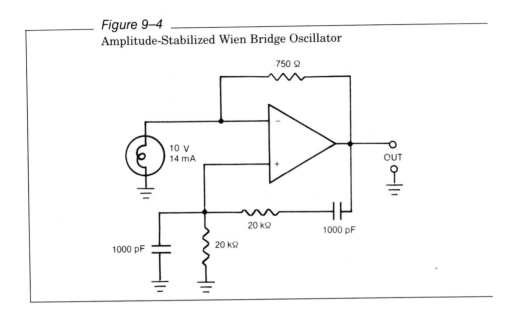

Figure 9–4
Amplitude-Stabilized Wien Bridge Oscillator

simple oscillator requirements, the circuit shown in Figure 9–4 is quite adequate.

The reader is encouraged to apply the values shown for the Wien bridge oscillators of Figures 9–3 and 9–4 to verify the information concerning gain, frequency, and phase shift. The relevant equations are as follows:

$$A_V = 1 + \frac{R_3}{R_4}$$

$$f_o = \frac{1}{2\pi RC}$$

$$\phi = \tan^{-1}\frac{1}{2\pi fRC}$$

Troubleshooting Wien bridge oscillators follows the same general procedures discussed with phase shift oscillators.

Twin-T Oscillator

The characteristics of the **twin-T, or parallel-T, network** can be used to precisely control the frequency of an oscillator. Twin-T characteristics were discussed in Chapter 8. The primary characteristic used in twin-T oscillators is that of *zero transmission* at a given frequency. In other

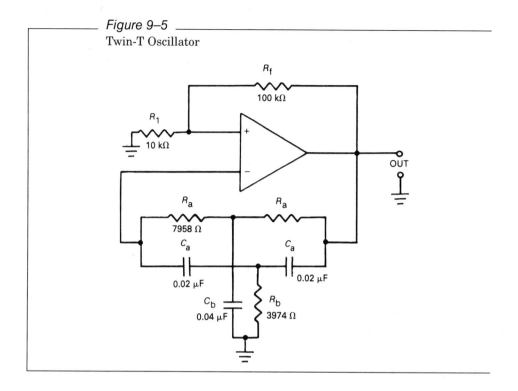

Figure 9–5

Twin-T Oscillator

words, at some specified frequency, the twin-T filter will almost completely attenuate the input signal. At frequencies both below and above
the filter's notch frequency, transmission through the filter will be only
slightly attenuated.

Figure 9–5 is a schematic diagram for an oscillator using a twin-
T filter. Frequency is controlled by the component values of the twin-T
filter. Oscillator frequency is found by the equation $f_o = 1/2\pi RC$ when
the R and C relationships are $R_b = R_a/2$ and $C_b = 2C_a$. The twin-T
network is connected from output of the op amp back to the inverting
input. At frequencies both below and above f_o, the negative feedback is
adequate to keep the circuit from oscillating. However, at f_o, the filter
blocks all feedback from the output, and oscillation can occur if adequate
gain is available. The R_f-R_1 network provides positive feedback to sustain oscillation. Usually a ratio of about 10 to 1 for R_f and R_1 is adequate.

It is relatively easy to verify the operation of a twin-T oscillator.
The following values will be used to demonstrate analysis of this circuit:

$$R_a = 7958 \ \Omega \qquad R_f = 100 \ \mathrm{k}\Omega \qquad C_a = 0.02 \ \mu\mathrm{F}$$
$$R_b = 3974 \ \Omega \qquad R_1 = 10 \ \mathrm{k}\Omega \qquad C_b = 0.04 \ \mu\mathrm{F}$$

The R_f to R_1 ratio is correct ($100/10 = 10/1$). Oscillator frequency should be about 1 kHz with the frequency-determining component values listed. If the circuit does not oscillate, the following steps should be taken:

1. Verify component values, especially in the twin-T filter.
2. Check the twin-T filter attenuation characteristics. If the filter is not completely balanced, attenuation may not be adequate to reduce negative feedback sufficiently to permit oscillation.
3. Verify that the op amp gain is that gain determined by the R_f-R_1 combination.

As can be seen, the twin-T oscillator is a relatively simple circuit. When component values are as designed, the circuit output frequency and amplitude are stable and accurate. The twin-T oscillator is used in many applications that require an accurate fixed audio frequency.

Quadrature Oscillators

There are many applications in electronic communications and elsewhere that require sine waves of the same frequency but 90° out of phase with each other. The term used to describe the 90° phase relationships is *quadrature,* and oscillators that generate the sine and **cosine** (90° out of phase) **waves** are called **quadrature oscillators.** An oscillator circuit that provides both sine and cosine waves is shown in Figure 9–6.

The operating principle of the quadrature oscillator of Figure 9–6 is that of *integrating* a sine wave. Integrators were mentioned during discussion of active filters, where it was pointed out that the output of an integrator is 90° out of phase with its input. Inverting integrators are used, so the actual output of the integrating amplifier is $-90°$ + 180° (the inversion of the amplifier). The second inverting integrator provides the same phase shifts. Therefore, 180° of phase shift appears between the input of the first inverting integrator and the output of the second. The output of the second inverting integrator is routed back to the *noninverting* input of the first inverting integrator. Since there is 180° difference between the inverting and the noninverting inputs of an op amp, the total phase shift around the feedback loop is 360°. The criterion of 0° phase shift for oscillation to occur has thus been met. Although the gain of an integrator has not yet been discussed, it is sufficient to meet the criterion for oscillation. When the integrator is discussed in detail in Chapter 10, the gain factor will be verified.

With both basic criteria for oscillation satisfied, the circuit of Figure 9–6 will oscillate. It should be noted, however, that R_1 must be less

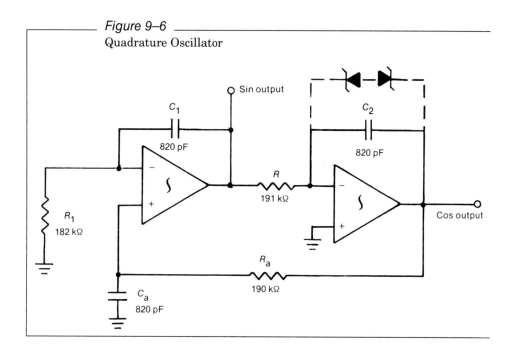

Figure 9–6

Quadrature Oscillator

than or equal to R to ensure enough unbalance for the circuit to begin oscillation. Frequency of oscillation is once again calculated with the formula $f_o = 1/2\pi RC$, where $C = C_1 = C_2$. The component values shown will result in an oscillator frequency of about 1 kHz. Quadrature oscillators of this type are usually operated at a fixed frequency because of the need for highly precise components.

Other than the requirement for precision components, only one difficulty exists with the use of the dual-integrating quadrature oscillator. The unbalance required to ensure that the oscillator starts when first turned on causes the output amplitude to slowly increase. Saturation and resultant distortion ultimately will occur unless some means to limit output amplitude is provided. The usual method of limiting is to connect two back-to-back zener diodes across one of the integrators. Although the limiting effect of the diodes generates a small amount of distortion on the cosine output, the filtering effect of the R_a and C_a sections will remove most of the distortion from the sine output.

The biquadratic filter discussed in Chapter 8 is also applicable to quadrature oscillators. The principle of biquadratic filter operation is based on the use of dual integrators. It is only necessary to supply the correct component values and feedback paths to convert the biquadratic filter into a quadrature oscillator.

LC Oscillators

Oscillators that use inductors and capacitors as frequency-determining elements are seldom found in audio frequency applications. The physical size of components makes such oscillators impractical. However, as frequencies get higher, the physical size of inductors and capacitors gets smaller, and radio frequency oscillators commonly use LC resonant circuits for frequency control.

An easy way to get started with LC oscillators is to revise the basic oscillator block diagram shown in Figure 9–1. By expanding the feedback block, as in Figure 9–7, the general concept of LC oscillators can be seen. The basic requirements for oscillation do not change just because higher frequencies are used. The way feedback is managed does change, however. Two impedances, Z_1 and Z_2 in series, paralleled by a third impedance, Z_3, is a convenient way to view the feedback network. The combination of all three impedances determines the frequency of oscillation. The percentage of output returned to the input (feedback factor) is a function of voltage division by Z_1 and Z_2.

If Z_3 is a capacitor, then Z_1 and Z_2 must be mutually coupled inductors. That's what it takes for a resonant LC circuit. An oscillator that has a tapped inductor is called a **Hartley oscillator** and has been used since the days of the first vacuum tube. In fact, there really is no reason

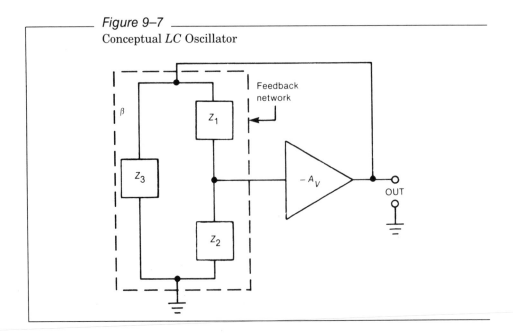

Figure 9–7
Conceptual *LC* Oscillator

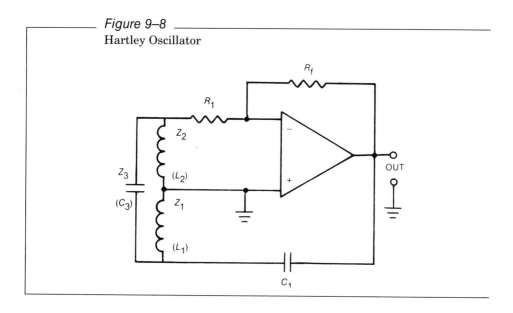

Figure 9–8

Hartley Oscillator

to use an op amp as the active device in Hartley oscillators operating at radio frequencies. A single transistor works quite well and is probably cheaper. However, op amps *can* serve as the active device, so we will analyze a simple op-amp-based Hartley oscillator (Figure 9–8).

Z_1, Z_2, and Z_3 are L_1, L_2, and C_3, respectively. The L and C combination determines the frequency of oscillation, which may be calculated by the formula $f_o = 1/2\pi \sqrt{LC}$. Recall that the criteria for oscillation are 0° total phase shift around the feedback loop and enough amplifier gain to make up for circuit losses. First consider the phase shift. Since the amplifier is operating in the inverting mode, 180° of phase shift is contributed by the op amp. In studying basic fundamentals, it was found that 180° of phase shift also appeared from one end of an inductor to the other end. Therefore, a total of 360° (0°) of phase shift is present in the circuit. Gain losses in the circuit are a function of the inductor in the feedback loop and, in simplified form, are expressed as the ratio of L_1 to L_2. Amplifier gain must be established by the R_f and R_1 feedback path to overcome the circuit losses.

The analysis in Example 9–3 will use the following component values (in henrys, farads, and ohms):

$$L_1 = 0.4 \text{ mH} \qquad C_3 = 0.001 \text{ μF} \qquad R_f = 220 \text{ k}\Omega$$
$$L_2 = 0.1 \text{ mH} \qquad C_1 = 0.1 \text{ μF} \qquad R_1 = 50 \text{ k}\Omega$$

_____ *Example 9–3* _____

Calculate the frequency of oscillation and the amplifier gain for the circuit of Figure 9–8. Note that $L = L_1 + L_2$.

Solution

$$f = \frac{1}{2\pi\sqrt{LC}} = \frac{1}{(6.28)\sqrt{(0.5 \times 10^{-3})(0.001 \times 10^{-6})}} \approx 225 \text{ kHz}$$

$$A_V = \frac{R_f}{R_1} = \frac{220}{50} = 4.4$$

The amount of gain needed to sustain oscillation is found by the ratio of L_1 to L_2, or $0.4/0.1 = 4$. Op amp gain is thus adequate to overcome the losses in the feedback network. C_1 is included only for the purpose of isolating the input from any DC offset at the output.

The **Colpitts oscillator** is the "dual" of the Hartley oscillator. That is, the capacitor is replaced by an inductor, and the inductive divider is replaced by a capacitive divider. Feedback is the same, losses and f_o are calculated in the same manner, and gain is determined again by the ratio of R_f to R_1. For the component values shown in Figure 9–9, the output frequency of the Colpitts oscillator is approximately 690 kHz. Feedback loop loss is calculated as 2, which is easily overcome by the R_f to R_1 ratio of 2.4. Once again, a coupling capacitor C_4 isolates the input from the output for any DC offsets.

Both the Hartley and the Colpitts oscillators are used in applications where variable frequency output is required. Typical uses are in AM/FM radios and in television sets. There are some communication applications, however, where highly stable frequency output is neces-

_____ *Figure 9–9* _____
Colpitts Oscillator

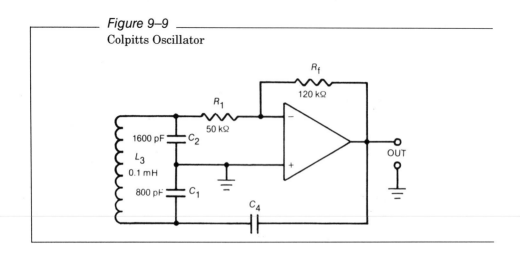

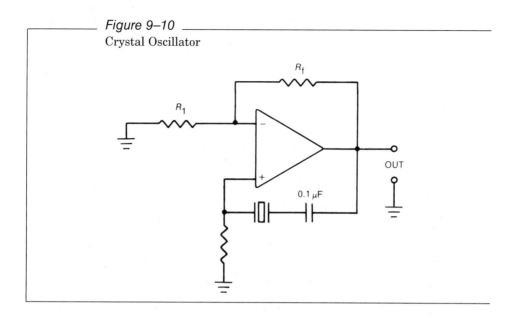

Figure 9–10

Crystal Oscillator

sary. Temperature variations and vibration tend to cause frequency changes in *LC* tuned oscillators. Citizen's band transceivers and mobile radiotelephones, for example, cannot tolerate the frequency variations that occur in *LC* tuned oscillators. Frequency stability can be achieved by using a **quartz crystal** as the frequency-determining element.

Quartz crystals have the property of mechanical vibration at a stable frequency when a voltage is applied across the crystal. The frequency is basically determined by the mechanical dimensions of the crystal. From an electrical viewpoint, the quartz crystal behaves as though it were a very high Q series resonant circuit whose L and C are insensitive to temperature changes and other outside influences. When connected as shown in Figure 9–10, the series resonant properties of the crystal allow adequate positive feedback for oscillation to occur *only* at the crystal's resonant frequency. At all frequencies other than resonance, the impedance of the crystal is quite high, thus reducing positive feedback to a minimum. Furthermore, only at resonance will the feedback loop phase shift requirement be 0°. All that remains is to provide sufficient gain to make up for what little losses the crystal has at resonance. The conventional R_f and R_1 divider provides control of gain. Often R_f is made variable so that the exact amount of gain required for sine wave purity and reliable oscillator startup may be adjustable. Note that excessive gain will cause saturation and cutoff in the op amp. Rectangular (square) waves may thus be obtained from the crystal oscillator.

Crystal oscillators are used in applications requiring good frequency stability. Communications equipment such as CB and cellular telephones use crystal oscillators to maintain the required frequency accuracy and stability. Another crystal oscillator application is the microcomputer, in which a stable and accurate source of clock pulses is needed. Many manufacturers supply linear IC oscillator chips.

NONSINUSOIDAL WAVEFORM GENERATORS

All waveforms that are not actual sine waves or direct derivatives such as a cosine wave are considered in this section. Concepts and circuits capable of supplying **square waves, pulses, triangular waves,** and **sawtooth waves** are discussed. First, however, the action of a simple electronic component, the capacitor, should be reviewed.

Basic Fundamentals

Almost all nonsinusoidal waveform generators depend on the charge and discharge characteristics of the capacitor. *Capacitance* is sometimes defined as the property of a circuit (or device) that opposes a change in voltage. In other words, if the voltage applied to a capacitive circuit changes, the voltage across the capacitor cannot change instantaneously. It takes *time* for the change to occur. The actual amount of time needed for a specified change is a function of many factors—for example, the voltage presently existing across the capacitor, the new voltage, the value of capacitance, and any resistance in the circuit.

The design engineer uses complicated exponential equations to calculate charge and discharge characteristics of circuits containing resistance and capacitance (*RC* circuits). Analysis and troubleshooting of *RC* circuits, however, can be performed using graphical methods. The exponential equation is simplified and plotted as a **universal time constant curve,** as shown in Figure 9–11. A circuit's **time constant** is

Figure 9–11

Universal Time Constant Curve

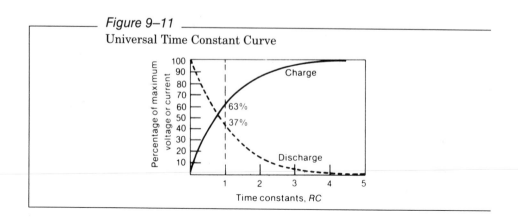

merely the product of R and C, or $T = R \times C$. Time constant is defined as the time (T) in seconds (s) required for the voltage across the capacitor to rise to 63.2% of the applied voltage. The time constant curve may also be turned upside down to represent the discharge characteristics of an RC circuit. This is shown by the dashed line in Figure 9–11. During discharge, the time constant of the circuit is the time it takes for the capacitor to discharge 63.2%, which is equivalent to 36.8% of the starting value. In Figure 9–11, the percentage of the total voltage applied to the circuit is used as the vertical axis and the time constant is used as the horizontal axis. Given the applied voltage, resistance, and capacitance, the voltage across the capacitor at any time may be easily obtained. Consider Examples 9–4 and 9–5.

_____ *Example 9–4* _____

A simple circuit consists of a 100 V battery, a 1 MΩ resistor, and a 1 μF capacitor in series. What is the time constant of the circuit? How long does it take for the voltage across the capacitor to reach 80 V? How long does it take for the voltage across the capacitor (V_C) to reach 100 V?

Solution 1

Time constant (T):

$$T = R \times C = 1{,}000{,}000 \times 0.000001 = 1 \text{ s}$$

Solution 2

Time (T) for V_C to equal 80 V: From the graph, 80 V is reached in 1.7 time constants. Thus,

$$T = 1.7 \times T = 1.7 \times 1 = 1.7 \text{ s}$$

Solution 3

Time for V_C to equal 100 V: Theoretically, the voltage will never reach 100 V. The following percentages of applied voltage have been calculated from an exponential equation.

$$1\,T = 63.2\% \text{ of applied voltage}$$
$$2\,T = 86.5\% \text{ of applied voltage}$$
$$3\,T = 95\% \text{ of applied voltage}$$
$$4\,T = 98.2\% \text{ of applied voltage}$$
$$5\,T = 99.3\% \text{ of applied voltage}$$
$$6\,T = 99.8\% \text{ of applied voltage}$$

Therefore, for all practical purposes, the voltage across the capacitor reaches the applied voltage within about 5 time constants.

Example 9–5 _____

How long will it take for the voltage across a 0.047 μF capacitor to rise to 2.5 V if 5 V is applied to it in series with a 20,000 Ω resistor?

Solution

2.5 V is 50% of 5 V. The 50% point on the time constant graph occurs at about 0.7 time constant. Thus,

$$T = R \times C = 0.047 \text{ μF} \times 20,000 \text{ Ω} = 0.00094 \text{ s} = 0.94 \text{ ms}$$

The time for V_C to equal 2.5 V is $0.7 \times T$, or 0.7×0.94 ms, which is 0.658 ms.

Thus, by the use of the universal time constant curve, it is possible to determine the voltage across a capacitor in an RC circuit at any time. It is only necessary to know the applied voltage and to calculate the time constant of the circuit. Similarly, it is possible to determine the voltage across a fully charged capacitor at any time during discharge. Consider the RC circuit of Example 9–5 with the capacitor fully charged to 5 V. Disconnect the charging source and connect the 20,000 Ω resistor directly across the 0.047 μF capacitor. The 5 V that existed across the charged capacitor will begin to drop in the manner shown by the dashed discharge curve of Figure 9–11. How long will it take for the voltage to drop to 1.84 V? 1.84 V is 36.8% of 5 V, which occurs on the discharge curve at 1 T. Since the time constant of the 0.047 μF capacitor and the 20,000 Ω resistor is 0.94 ms, it will take that time for V_C to reach 1.84 V.

These basic concepts of capacitor charge and discharge are used throughout discussion of nonsinusoidal waveform generators. Some slight modifications may be needed as practical circuits are shown, but in general the ideas just presented will suffice. Application of these ideas and use of the universal time constant chart will provide adequate tools for waveform generator analysis and troubleshooting.

Square Wave Oscillators

A number of nonsinusoidal waveshapes are encountered in electronics. Most of them are easily generated using op amp circuits. One of the most fundamental of nonsinusoidal waves is the _square wave_. As shown in Figure 9–12A, the square wave is symmetrical about some reference axis, often zero. Both positive and negative amplitudes are equal, and both halves of the complete cycle of the square wave have the same period.

The steep slope of the op amp's **voltage transfer characteristic**

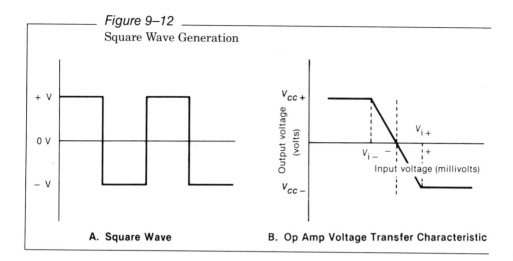

Figure 9–12

Square Wave Generation

A. Square Wave   **B. Op Amp Voltage Transfer Characteristic**

(Figure 9–12B) is used to generate square waves. Voltage transfer characteristics are graphs of input voltage versus output voltage. Note particularly that the output voltage scale is in volts (V), while the input voltage scale is in millivolts (mV). It takes just a few microvolts (μV) difference between the inverting and the noninverting inputs to force the output voltage from V_{cc+} to V_{cc-}. When the inverting input terminal is more positive than the noninverting input terminal, negative saturation will occur. The output voltage will remain at V_{cc-} even though the differential input voltage increases. When the inverting input terminal is less positive than the noninverting input terminal, positive saturation occurs. The output voltage remains at V_{cc+}.

A simple square wave generator is shown in Figure 9–13A. The noninverting input is grounded and serves as a reference voltage (0 V) for the inverting input. With both inverting and noninverting inputs at 0 V, the output voltage will also be 0 V (except for input offset voltages and so forth). However, when power is applied, the probability that the inverting input will have *exactly* 0 V is very poor. Even if both inputs do start out the same, noise generated by system components would be enough to cause an input voltage differential. Assume that the inverting input momentarily became positive in respect to the noninverting input (0 V). The output voltage would be forced to V_{cc-}. Capacitor C begins to charge toward V_{cc-} through resistor R. As soon as the capacitor charges to a few millivolts negative, the output changes to V_{cc+}. C now charges toward V_{cc+}. When C charges to a few millivolts positive, the output switches back to V_{cc-}. The duration of the square wave is determined by the RC time constant, as will shortly be seen.

The square wave generator shown in Figure 9–13 is somewhat impractical. Noise alone is sufficient to cause the generator to operate

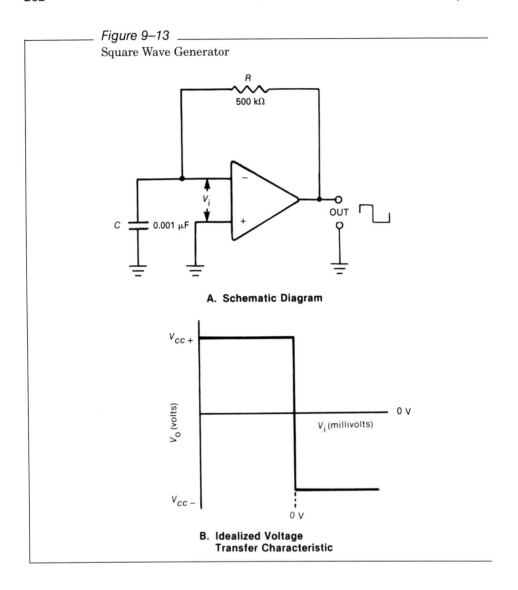

Figure 9–13

Square Wave Generator

A. Schematic Diagram

**B. Idealized Voltage
Transfer Characteristic**

because of the steep slope of the voltage transfer characteristic (high gain) shown in Figure 9–13B. Input offset and drift also can cause difficulties. The circuit of Figure 9–14A removes some of these problems. Voltage divider R_2/R_1 provides **hysteresis** for the op amp. An op amp circuit is said to have hysteresis when its output switches from V_{cc+} to V_{cc-} under one input condition but does not switch back to V_{cc+} until another condition exists. In other words, it switches from V_{cc+} at a specific voltage differential between op amp inputs and back to V_{cc+} at a different voltage differential. With hysteresis, the transfer characteristic of the op amp circuit appears as shown in Figure 9–14B. Note the

Figure 9–14

Square Wave Generator with Hysteresis

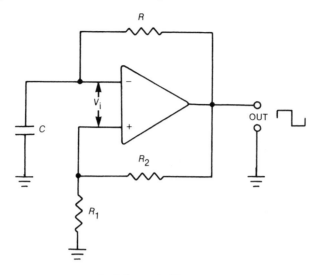

A. Schematic Diagram

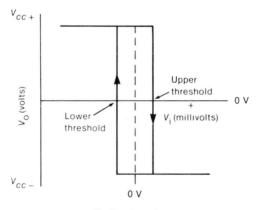

B. Hysteresis

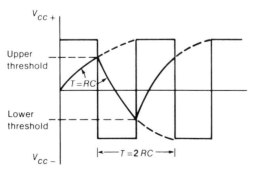

C. Waveforms

existence of two switching points instead of only one. At the upper threshold voltage, the circuit switches from V_{cc+} to V_{cc-}. The opposite action occurs at the lower threshold point. A range of input voltage called the *hysteresis voltage* exists during which no switching can occur. The upper and lower threshold voltages can be determined by considering the schematic diagram of Figure 9–14A. The actual reference is determined by the divider ratio and the output voltage. When the output voltage is at V_{cc+}, the reference voltage at the noninverting input of the op amp will no longer be 0 but will be a fraction of the + output. The timing capacitor has to charge longer to reach this new reference and the switching point. Likewise, when the output voltage is at V_{cc-}, the reference voltage at the noninverting input will be a fraction of the − output. The timing capacitor must charge to the − reference rather than to 0. Therefore, switching occurs at the two reference points, not at zero voltage. The difference between the upper and lower threshold is the hysteresis voltage. Designers usually select a hysteresis voltage only large enough to ensure that false triggering on noise does not occur. Although not shown, it should be noted that the switching points do not have to be centered about 0 V. When $R_1 = R_2$, which is the most common situation, the period of the square wave can be calculated from the following formula:

$$T = 2RC$$

where R = resistance in ohms (Ω) and C = capacity in farads (F). This formula is only approximate but is much easier to use than the more complex exponential equation. The waveform drawing in Figure 9–14C shows the relationship between capacitor charging and output waveshape.

Two variations from the basic square wave generator are seen in Figure 9–15. Note the 5 kΩ resistor and dual zener diodes at the output of the op amp. The normal low impedance output is available directly from the op amp output terminal. In some cases, however, operation at + and − saturation does not yield perfect square waves. Use of the 5 kΩ series resistor and the zener diodes will square up the output at the expense of a lower output voltage. The clamped output is limited to the zener voltage of the diodes.

Although operational amplifiers make good square wave generators, the task is often left to special-purpose integrated circuits. Comparators, discussed in Chapter 11, often are better than operational amplifiers when generation of square waves is required. The very steep voltage transfer characteristic (Figure 9–15) generally results in faster switching. In digital applications, **bistable** and **astable flip-flop** circuits perform the function of a square wave generator. Timer chips spe-

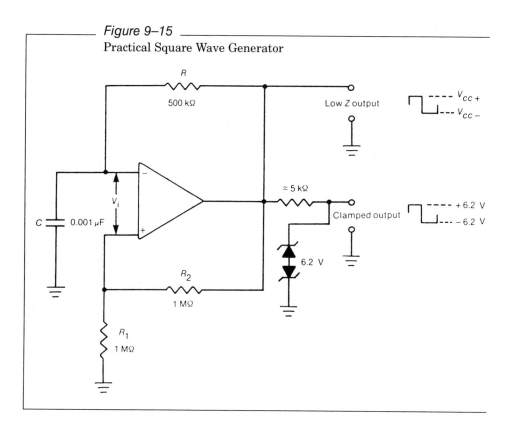

Figure 9–15

Practical Square Wave Generator

cifically designed to precisely generate square waves or rectangular waves find common use.

Pulse Generator

A *pulse generator* is really nothing more than an **astable multivibrator** (square wave generator) with unequal on and off times. The circuit of Figure 9–14A is modified as shown in Figure 9–16. Note that the same scheme is used to establish circuit hysteresis. The major change exists in the timing portion of the circuit. Diode D_1 is inserted in the charge path for the timing capacitor so that the capacitor can charge only when the op amp output is at a positive potential. When the op amp output switches to a negative potential, D_2 is forward biased and the timing capacitor discharges through the 1 MΩ resistor. Note that the discharge resistor is 10 times greater than the charge resistor. Therefore, the output will have unequal on and off times.

The general principle of operation is the same as that of the

Figure 9–16

Pulse Generator

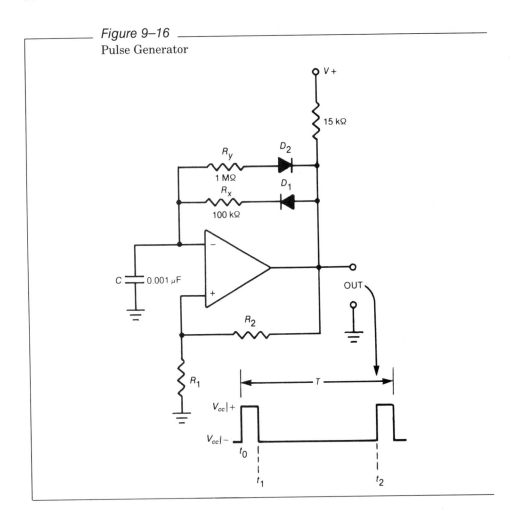

square wave generator. Voltage appearing across the timing capacitor (connected to the inverting input of the op amp) is compared to the voltage at the noninverting input of the op amp. The actual reference voltage at the noninverting input is determined by the values of the two divider resistors, the positive supply voltage (V_{cc+}), and the output voltage. Let's assume that the output voltage has just switched to V_{cc-}, which means the timing capacitor voltage has risen to the + switching voltage. D_1 disconnects the charging path, and D_2 connects the discharge path. When the timing capacitor voltage reaches the upper switching threshold voltage, the output changes back to V_{cc+}. D_2 disconnects the discharge path, and D_1 connects the charge path. The timing capacitor charges toward V_{cc+}. When the timing capacitor voltage reaches the upper switching threshold, the output again changes. The cycle continues, alternately charging and discharging the timing capacitor. Since the charge and discharge times are unequal, the on and off times of the output are unequal.

Operational characteristics of the pulse generator of Figure 9–16 can be determined using techniques similar to those used with the square wave generator. In the case of the pulse generator, though, two separate time constants must be calculated. One time constant determines the charge time of the timing capacitor, while the other determines the discharge time. When the output voltage is at V_{cc+}, the capacitor charges through R_x and D_1. The time constant is calculated as follows:

$$T = R_x \times C = 100,000 \ \Omega \times 0.001 \ \mu F = 0.0001 \ s = 0.1 \ ms$$

During this time period, the output will be at V_{cc+}. This "on" time is labeled as t_1 in Figure 9–16.

When the on time expires, the output switches to V_{cc-}. The timing capacitor discharges through D_2 and R_y. The discharge time constant is calculated as follows:

$$T = R_y \times C = 1,000,000 \ \Omega \times 0.001 \ \mu F = 0.001 \ s = 1 \ ms$$

During the discharge time period, the output will be at V_{cc-}. This "off" time is labeled as t_2 in Figure 9–16.

Thus, the output will be at V_{cc+} for 0.1 ms and at V_{cc-} for 1 ms. The on-off cycle then repeats over and over. If the frequency of the repetitions is of interest, it may be calculated using the relationship $f = 1/T$, where T is the sum of both on and off times. In this case, $T = 0.0001 + 0.001$, or 0.0011 s. f, then, is the reciprocal of T, or 1/0.0011, or approximately 909 Hz. However, pulse generator calculations have the same ground rules used with the square wave generator. R_1 and R_2 must be equal, and the final calculations are only within 10%. Any component variations from the noted values will cause inaccuracies in the calculations.

Another type of pulse generator is the *one-shot*, or **monostable multivibrator.** This is not a "free-running" multivibrator but requires an external stimulus to cause operation. When turned on, it provides an output pulse of a given amplitude and period and then turns itself off. The one-shot multivibrator is used in many electronic devices to supply a constant-amplitude, constant-period pulse from a less-than-perfect input stimulus. For example, a photocell may be used to count objects as they pass on a moving conveyor belt. The photocell output is not a perfect pulse, and if applied to a counting device, could result in an inaccurate count. A one-shot multivibrator, triggered by the photocell output, would supply a more perfect pulse and ensure counting accuracy.

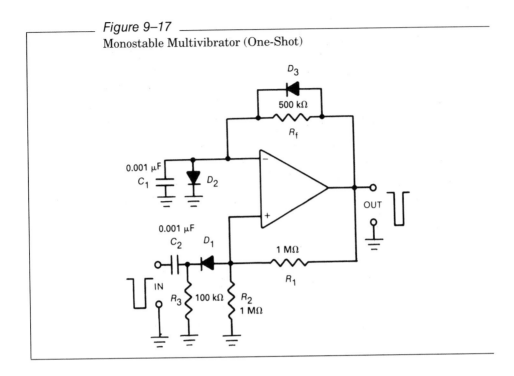

Figure 9–17

Monostable Multivibrator (One-Shot)

A one-shot multivibrator is easily formed from the square wave generator circuit of Figure 9–14. Two diodes in the timing circuit and components to process the input trigger are all that is necessary. Figure 9–17 is typical of op amp one-shot multivibrators found in modern electronic devices. Positive feedback from output to noninverting input is identical to that used in both square wave and pulse generators. Timing components are also the same, consisting of the timing capacitor C_1 and the timing resistor R_f. Diode D_2 across the timing capacitor is the component that prevents the circuit from behaving like a square wave generator.

Let's begin circuit analysis by assuming that the output voltage is at V_{cc+}. Positive feedback from the R_1-R_2 divider causes a fixed + voltage to be placed on the noninverting input. If the inverting input voltage is less than the noninverting input voltage, then the circuit will be "latched" in the state with the output voltage at V_{cc+}. Without D_2, the timing capacitor would charge toward V_{cc+}, and the circuit would change state when the inverting input voltage exceeded the noninverting input voltage. However, as soon as the voltage across the timing capacitor rises to about 0.6 V, D_2 conducts and "clamps" the inverting input at that voltage. Therefore, the circuit remains in the on condition, with the output voltage at V_{cc+}.

Since the inverting input voltage is clamped by D_2, it is necessary to change the noninverting input to cause the output voltage to change. The input portion of the one-shot circuit allows a change of adequate amplitude at the noninverting input. A negative-going signal at the input terminal of the one-shot will cause the noninverting input of the op amp to become less than the diode-clamped voltage at the inverting input. Capacitor C_2 and resistor R_3 form a **differentiating circuit** that allows only the fast-rising leading edge of the trigger input to be applied to the op amp. (Note that D_1 will only allow the negative-going portion of the trigger to pass.) When the noninverting input of the op amp becomes less positive than the inverting input, the output changes to V_{cc-}. The positive feedback now supplies a portion of the negative output to the noninverting input, causing the one-shot circuit to latch into the off condition. The input trigger, by the way, is now "disconnected" because of D_1 diode action. Timing capacitor C_1 now begins to charge toward V_{cc-} through the timing resistor R_f. D_2 is reverse biased and does not enter into the charging process.

When the − voltage across the timing capacitor becomes more negative than the − voltage on the noninverting input, the one-shot output returns to V_{cc+}. The amount of time that the one-shot output remains at V_{cc-} is determined by the time constant of the timing components and the value of the positive feedback resistors. (D_3 is used only to provide a quick discharge of the timing capacitor following completion of the timing cycle. Without D_3, closely spaced trigger inputs could result in improper circuit operation because the inverting input had not returned to its resting value of 0.6 V.) The output of the one-shot of Figure 9–17, then, is a negative-going pulse whose presence is initiated by a trigger input and whose length is a function of the timing capacitor and resistor. Output pulse duration can be calculated in the same manner as for the pulse generator, with similar errors due to approximations. Appendix C (program 3) contains a BASIC computer program that performs monostable multivibrator calculations.

WAVEFORM GENERATOR

The 8038 type linear integrated circuit, available from many manufacturers, is a popular answer to the need for a circuit that will supply more than one type of waveform. The 8038 is a precision waveform generator capable of producing sine, square, triangular, sawtooth and pulse waveforms with a minimum number of external components and adjustments. Its operating frequency can be selected over nine decades of frequency, from 0.001 Hz to 1 MHz, by the choice of external RC components. The frequency of oscillation is highly stable over a wide range of temperature and supply voltage changes. The frequency

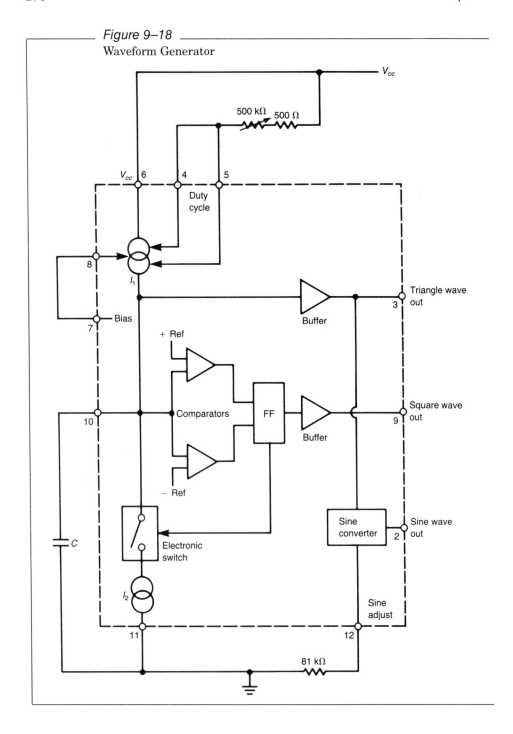

Figure 9–18
Waveform Generator

control, sweep, and modulation can be accomplished with an external control voltage without affecting the output waveform quality. Each of the three basic waveform outputs—sine, triangle, and square—are available simultaneously, from independent output terminals.

Figure 9–18 is a functional block diagram of the 8038 showing both internal functions and common external connections. R and C determine the output frequency by the formula $f = 0.15/RC$. The 8038 operates on the principle of linear charge and discharge of external capacitor C. The resulting triangle wave is the source of both the square and the sine wave. The square wave across C is buffered and becomes the triangle wave output. The triangle wave output also feeds the sine converter to obtain the sine wave output. The flip-flop output is buffered and becomes the square wave output.

Two current sources (I_1 and I_2) alternately charge and discharge C. When current source I_1 drives the triangle wave amplitude above the positive internal reference voltage, the output of comparator #1 changes state. The flip-flop switches from current source I_1 to I_2 and C discharges. When the triangle wave output falls below the negative internal reference voltage, the output of comparator #2 changes state. The flip-flop switches back to I_1 and C begins to charge again. Thus a triangle wave is generated.

Current source I_1 is provided with external controls. By separating pins 4 and 5 and using two resistors instead of a single resistor, waveform duty cycle can be adjusted. In addition, a control voltage can be applied to I_1 via pin 8 to vary or "sweep" the waveform generator's output frequency. In Figure 9–18, the sweep input is connected to an internal bias reference voltage.

Sine wave symmetry can be set by the resistor connected between pin 12 and ground. It should also be noted that the 8038 requires an external load resistor. The value is usually between 10 kΩ and 15 kΩ.

In a single linear IC we can obtain many of the commonly required waveforms. Frequency is adjustable, can be swept, and the waveform's duty cycle changed. The 8038 is a valuable addition to today's technology.

Square wave, pulse, and one-shot functions are also furnished by special timer integrated circuits. In many cases, the same operations may be performed with less components and at less cost by use of timer and other special-purpose ICs as discussed in Chapter 11.

SUMMARY

The application of operational amplifiers to signal-generation circuits has been shown in Chapter 9. Traditional sine wave oscillator circuits are very similar to the amplifier circuits already discussed. The many different forms of sine wave oscillators are merely amplifiers with positive feedback. Frequency-dependent networks, whether capacitive and resistive or capacitive and inductive, ensure that the positive feedback occurs only at a specific frequency. Thus, the output of the sine wave oscillators is a sine wave at a discrete frequency. No other frequencies are present.

Nonsinusoidal generators are amplifiers that automatically switch from V_{cc+} to V_{cc-} or some other defined references. The switching action causes outputs that transition rapidly from V_{cc+} to V_{cc-} at a rate usually determined by an RC network. Outputs may be either symmetrical (on and off times are equal) or nonsymmetrical (on and off times are different). Outputs do not have to be continuous, however. One-shot oscillators show how a single output pulse can be generated.

═══ QUESTIONS ═══

1. Define the following terms: (a) sine wave, (b) oscillator, (c) phase shift oscillator, (d) Wien bridge oscillator, (e) twin-T oscillator, (f) quadrature oscillator, (g) LC oscillator, (h) RC time constant, (i) hysteresis, (j) square wave generator, (k) pulse generator, and (l) one-shot.

2. Explain what is required in order for a circuit to oscillate. You may use a diagram if necessary.

3. What establishes the phase shift criterion for oscillation in a phase shift oscillator? The gain criterion?

4. Could two phase shift networks be used in place of the three networks shown in Figure 9–2? Explain.

5. What is the *minimum* gain required for the phase shift oscillator of Figure 9–2 to oscillate? Why is it a minimum gain?

6. Discuss the steps necessary to troubleshoot a phase shift oscillator that is not oscillating.

7. What establishes the phase shift criterion for oscillation in a Wien bridge oscillator? The gain criterion?

8. List the identifying characteristics of a Wien bridge oscillator.

9. What is the purpose of the nonlinear element in a Wien bridge oscillator?

10. Discuss the steps necessary to troubleshoot a Wien bridge oscillator that is not oscillating.

11. List the identifying characteristics of a twin-T oscillator.

12. What establishes the phase shift criterion for oscillation in a twin-T oscillator? The gain criterion?

13. List the identifying characteristics of a quadrature oscillator.

14. What establishes the phase shift criterion for oscillation in a quadrature oscillator? The gain criterion?

15. List the advantages and disadvantages of a quadrature oscillator when compared with other sinusoidal oscillators.

16. Explain how you could tell the difference between a Colpitts and a Hartley LC oscillator. You may use a schematic diagram if desired.

17. List the advantages and disadvantages of a crystal oscillator when compared with Colpitts and Hartley oscillators.

18. What is the purpose of a universal time constant curve?

19. How does a square wave differ from a sine wave? How are they the same?

20. Explain how an operational amplifier can generate a square wave.

21. Discuss why hysteresis is a desirable factor to be incorporated into a square wave generator.

22. What is the difference between a pulse generator and a square wave generator? List any similarities also.

23. Explain how a square wave generator can be converted to a pulse generator. You may use a schematic diagram if desired.

24. Explain how a pulse generator can be converted to a one-shot. You may use a schematic diagram if desired.

25. Discuss where a one-shot might be used.

PROBLEMS

1. In Figure 9–2, $C = 0.16$ µF, $R = 560$ Ω, $R_1 = 5.6$ kΩ, and $R_f = 180$ kΩ. Determine (a) frequency of oscillation and (b) gain.

2. In Figure 9–4, change the frequency-determining C to 0.1 µF and the frequency-determining R to 33 kΩ. What is the new frequency of oscillation?

3. In Figure 9–5, change R_a to 6.8 kΩ, C_a to 0.047 µF, and R_1 to 13.6 kΩ. Maintain the relationships shown in Figure 9–5. What is the new frequency of oscillation?

4. In Figure 9–6, change R to 10 kΩ and C to 0.033 µF. Maintain the relationships shown in Figure 9–6. What is the new frequency of oscillation?

5. In Figure 9–8, L_1 is 0.8 mH, L_2 is 0.2 mH, and C_3 is 500 pF. R_f and R_1 establish adequate gain. What is the frequency of oscillation?

6. Assume $V_{cc+} = +15$ V, $V_{cc-} = -15$ V, $R = 0.68$ MΩ, and $C = 0.0047$. Draw the

output waveform for the circuit of Figure 9–13. Label amplitude, frequency, and time on the waveform drawing.

7. Repeat Problem 6 for Figure 9–14 if R_1 = 100 kΩ and R_2 = 100 kΩ.

8. Repeat Problem 6 for Figure 9–15 if R_1 = 100 kΩ and R_2 = 100 kΩ.

9. In Figure 9–16, calculate the on time and the off time for C values of (a) 0.0001 µF, (b) 0.047 µF, and (c) 0.0033 µF. Draw appropriate waveforms.

10. Draw waveforms showing operation of the circuit shown in Figure 9–17.

Mathematical
Operations

OBJECTIVES   After studying Chapter 10, you will be able to

1. Identify the characteristics of an adder and its principles of operation.
2. Explain how an adder circuit multiplies and averages.
3. Identify the characteristics of an integrator and its principles of operation.
4. Identify the time and frequency response of an integrator.
5. Identify the characteristics of a differentiator and its principles of operation.
6. Identify the time and frequency response of a differentiator.
7. Identify the characteristics of log and antilog amplifiers and their principles of operation.
8. Explain how to multiply numbers with log and antilog amplifiers.
9. Discuss the principles of operation of two- and four-quadrant multipliers.
10. Describe how to multiply and divide with analog multipliers.

_____ *INTRODUCTION* _____

It is only fitting that the subject of mathematical operations be discussed and related to operational amplifiers. Even before integrated circuits were born, operational amplifiers were being used in *analog* computers. As noted much earlier in this book, it was in the analog computer field that the designers saw maximum use for their brainchild, the integrated circuit operational amplifier. But, as we have already seen, the designers had not counted on the ingenuity of people. The use of operational amplifiers in analog computers is actually one of the lesser of today's applications.

The concept of electronic circuits performing mathematical operations is a very useful one. Much of an engineer's training is in the field of mathematics, and having electronic circuits that will perform mathematical operations provides the engineer with yet another important tool. Since the application of electronics is designed mathematically, the engineer can easily implement the operations. Today's engineer does not have to design the electronic implementations—the functional blocks in the form of operational amplifiers are already there. It should be noted that mathematical operations are sometimes called *wave-shaping* operations.

SUMMING CIRCUITS

An op amp circuit that takes its name from the analog computer field is the **adder**, or summing circuit. Originally used to perform analog addition, it now has many uses in other types of electronic equipment. Its operation, however, is perhaps easier to visualize when considered from the addition function.

Addition

Figure 10–1 is a diagram of an op amp circuit that algebraically sums two voltages. If it is assumed that each of the two voltages represents a number, then the sum of those two numbers can be obtained. As soon as the operation of the circuit is determined, actual examples of addition can be shown.

The **summing amplifier** is nothing more than a special case of an inverting amplifier. The basic rules already established for inverter amplifier operation must be assumed for summing amplifier operation. First, in the ideal inverting amplifier with no input signal present, the output is 0. For the output to be 0, the voltage differential between the inverting and noninverting inputs must be 0. If the noninverting input is connected to ground (0 V), then the inverting input must also be at 0 V. A *virtual ground* thus appears at the inverting input terminal. Second, because of the extremely high input impedance of the op amp, negligible input current flows to the op amp. Any current trying to flow in the op amp input circuit due to circuit input voltage(s) will be canceled by current flow in the feedback circuit (R_f).

In order to simplify the original analysis, all of the resistors in the circuit of Figure 10–1 are assumed to be equal. Let's first consider the currents in the circuit. For the op amp input current to be 0, the feedback current must equal any current due to the circuit input voltages. If a voltage is present at both circuit inputs, then a current I_1 will flow due to V_1. Likewise, a current I_2 will flow due to V_2. Both currents

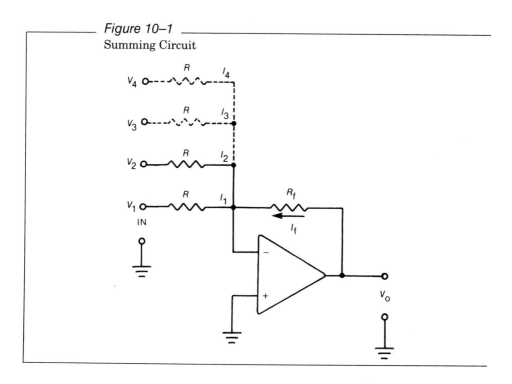

Figure 10–1

Summing Circuit

combine at the inverting input of the op amp to equal $I_1 + I_2$. But the sum of the input currents cannot flow in the op amp input circuit. It must flow through R_f, such that $I_1 + I_2 = I_f$.

Since the inverting input of the op amp is at virtual ground, the currents may be calculated by the following simple Ohm's law relationships:

$$I_1 = \frac{V_1}{R}$$

$$I_2 = \frac{V_2}{R}$$

$$I_f = \frac{-V_o}{R}$$

Note the use of $-V_o$ in the feedback current formula. V_o must be used in the negative form because inputs to the op amp are applied at the inverting input terminal. Substituting in the total current formula gives:

$$I_1 + I_2 = I_f$$

$$\frac{V_1}{R} + \frac{V_2}{R} = \frac{-V_o}{R}$$

Removing the common R from all three terms, we have:

$$V_1 + V_2 = -V_o$$

or

$$V_o = -(V_1 + V_2) \tag{10–1}$$

Therefore, the output of the summing circuit is the inverted algebraic sum of the inputs. The same general equation holds for more than two inputs if all resistors have the same resistance value. If AC voltage inputs are used instead of DC, each voltage term *must* include phase information.

An example will illustrate the use of a summing circuit. In Figure 10–1, let's use 100 kΩ resistors for all Rs. V_1 is $+5$ V and V_2 is $+1.5$ V. V_o, according to Equation 10–1, will be $-(5 + 1.5)$, or -6.5 V. Some caution must be exercised, however. The output voltage cannot exceed the supply voltages for the op amp. Therefore, do not try to add voltages whose sum will be greater than V_{cc+} or V_{cc-}. Circuit designers generally restrict input voltages to well below those that will result in either positive or negative output saturation voltage.

What would have to be done to the circuit in Figure 10–1 if it was necessary to determine the sum of four input voltages? According to the earlier discussion, as many inputs as desired may be used. Figure 10–1 shows the original summing circuit modified for four inputs. Once again, all resistor values are assumed to be equal. The output voltage formula becomes:

$$V_o = -(V_1 + V_2 + V_3 + V_4)$$

Any four voltage values may be summed with this circuit, as long as their sum does not result in saturation of the op amp output. For example, if $V_1 = 1.2$ V, $V_2 = -0.8$ V, $V_3 = 2.6$ V, and $V_4 = -0.3$ V, V_o would equal $-(1.2 + -0.8 + 2.6 + -0.3)$, or -2.7 V. Thus, the summing circuit is able to solve any simple arithmetic problem requiring algebraic addition of a number of variables. In addition to the restriction on output saturation, one more restriction exists. Only equations of the form $x + y + z + \cdots$ (where $x = y = z = \cdots$) may be used. If the equation to be solved is of the form $2x + 3y + z + \cdots$, the following methods must be used.

Inputs to a summing amplifier may be **scaled** to allow solution of equations of the form $2x + 3y + z + \cdots$ (where $2x = 3y = z = \cdots$). That is, changing the value of the series resistor for the appropriate input will change the *multiplier* for each input. The basic summing circuit really is providing the solution to an equation of the form $1x + 1y + 1z + \cdots$. Applying what is known about inverting amplifiers and feedback, the general expression for summing circuit output is:

$$V_o = -\left[V_1\left(\frac{R_f}{R_1}\right) + V_2\left(\frac{R_f}{R_2}\right) + V_3\left(\frac{R_f}{R_3}\right) + \cdots \right] \qquad \textbf{(10–2)}$$

In the discussion of the basic summing circuit (see Figure 10–1), R_f and all other resistors were assumed to have the same resistance—that is, 100 kΩ. Each of the multipliers in Equation 10–2 would, therefore, be 1 (100,000/100,000). Let's redraw the circuit to solve for a general expression of the form $2x + 3y + z$. See Figure 10–2. Three input terminals are required. The input terminal to which the voltage representing x is applied will need a series resistor such that $R_f/R_x = 2$. If R_f is fixed at 100 kΩ, then $R_x = R_f/2$, or 100,000/2 = 50,000 Ω. R_y must be 33,333 Ω and R_z must be 100,000 Ω as determined in the same manner. In this manner, any algebraic equation involving simple sums of products may be solved using appropriate resistors to scale input voltages.

Figure 10–2
Solution of $2x + 3y + z$

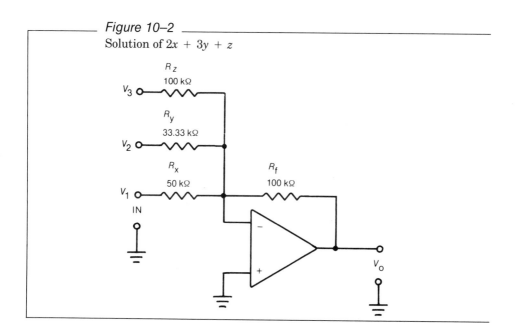

Multiplication

The technique just discussed also demonstrates how multiplication may be accomplished with op amp circuits. Operation may be explained using the basic equation for an inverting amplifier:

$$V_o = -A \times V_i$$

The gain (A) of an op amp inverter is determined by the resistance of the feedback resistor and the input resistor such that

$$V_o = -\left(\frac{R_f}{R_i}\right) \times V_i \qquad (10\text{--}3)$$

Note that the expression just developed looks very much like the expression for the scaled summing circuit. Each of the inputs for the scaled summing circuit included the variable *and* a multiplier. That multiplier was the ratio of R_f to R_i. Thus, all that is necessary to perform multiplication with op amp circuits is to select the appropriate ratio of the feedback resistor to the input resistor of an inverter. A fractional multiplier (equivalent to division) is just as easy to obtain. In the case of division, however, the input resistor will be *larger* than the feedback resistor. For example, to divide by 2, R_f/R_i must equal 1/2. Thus, $R_i = 2 \times R_f$. If $R_f = 100 \text{ k}\Omega$, $R_i = 200 \text{ k}\Omega$ for division by 2.

Averaging

Another special case of the summing circuit is where all input resistors are identical, but R_f is equal to the value of an input resistor divided by the number (n) of input resistors. Under these circumstances, the output voltage will be the *average* of all input voltages. Therefore, if $R_1 = R_2 = R_3 = \cdots = R_n$ and $R_f = R_1/n$, then

$$V_o = -\frac{(V_1 + V_2 + V_3 + \cdots + V_n)}{n} \qquad (10\text{--}4)$$

Circumstances exist where the inverted algebraic sum of the inputs is inconvenient. It may be converted to the actual direct sum merely by using the unity gain inverter circuit discussed in earlier chapters. Direct-sum circuits (Figure 10–3) are also used, but the advantages of simplicity disappear. More resistors of equal value and close tolerance are needed. For V_o to equal $V_1 + V_2$, the following conditions must exist: $R_f/R_1 = R_f'/R_1' + R_f'/R_2'$ and $R_f' = R_1' = R_f'$. Modern op amps tend to make the unity inverter scheme more reliable and accurate than the direct-sum circuit.

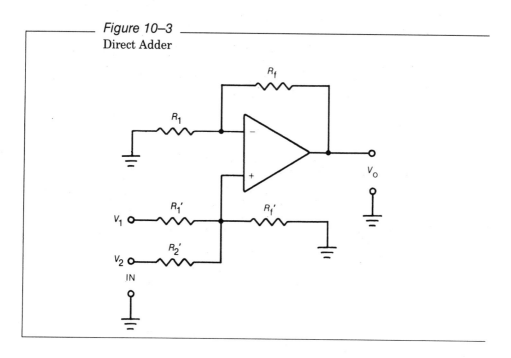

Figure 10–3
Direct Adder

Subtracting

When the difference between two inputs is required, a **subtractor,** or **difference amplifier,** is used. Figure 10–4 is a diagram of a difference amplifier circuit. In the most simplified case, when all resistors are of equal value, the output voltage is the difference between V_2 and V_1. The circuit functions as a combination inverting and noninverting amplifier. Two components thus exist in the output voltage. The inverting amplifier contributes a component determined by the following expression:

$$V_o = -\left(\frac{R_f}{R_1}\right) \times V_1 \qquad (10\text{–}5)$$

This is the inverter amplifier gain multiplied by the input voltage at V_1. The contribution of the noninverting amplifier is determined as follows:

$$V_o = A \times \left(\frac{R_3}{R_2 + R_3}\right) \times V_2$$

$$= \left(1 + \frac{R_f}{R_1}\right) \times \left(\frac{R_3}{R_2 + R_3}\right) \times V_2 \qquad (10\text{–}6)$$

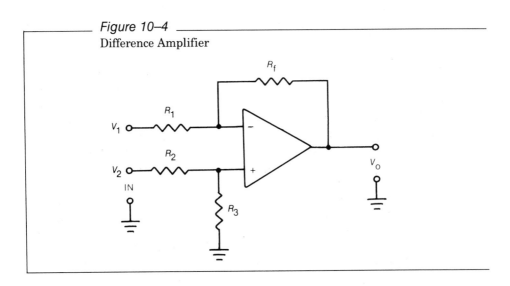

Figure 10–4

Difference Amplifier

Note the gain expression for the noninverting amplifier and the reduction of V_2 by the voltage divider action of R_2 and R_3. The final output voltage is thus the sum of the noninverting amplifier and the inverting amplifier contributions. Since the sign of the inverting amplifier contribution is negative, the actual output is the difference between the noninverting amplifier and the inverting amplifier contributions. With equal resistors, the noninverting amplifier contributes $1 \times V_2$. The inverting amplifier contributes $-(1 \times V_1)$. Therefore, when all resistors are equal, the net result is $V_o = V_2 - V_1$. If either or both of the inputs are scaled (different resistor values), the full equation for V_o (Equation 10–6) must be used to determine V_o.

Applications of Summing Circuits

An excellent example of the use of the difference amplifier is found in the instrumentation field. Many measurements made in electronics use *bridge* circuits such as the resistive bridge shown in Figure 10–5. (Capacitive, inductive, and mixed-component bridges are also used. Resistive bridges, however, are easier to understand.) Consider that all four resistors are *exactly* equal. Basic fundamentals of electronics tell us that a voltage applied to two equal resistors in series (R_4 and R_7) will be divided by 2 at the junction of the resistors. Thus, V_1 will be exactly $V_{ref}/2$. Likewise, V_2 will also be exactly $V_{ref}/2$, making V_1 and V_2 equal. In real-life applications, one of the resistors (R_7, perhaps) is used to sense or measure some physical parameter such as temperature. Special resistors that have large resistance variation with temperature change

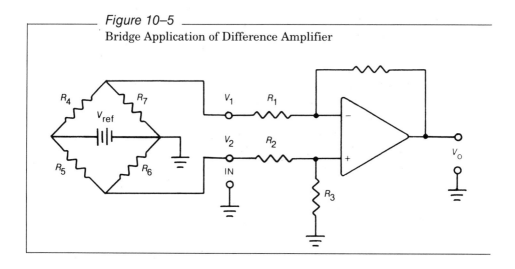

Figure 10–5

Bridge Application of Difference Amplifier

(thermistors) are used. If the resistance of R_7 no longer equals the resistance of R_4, then the bridge will no longer be balanced. V_1 will no longer be the same as V_2 because the voltage dividers are no longer equal. The difference may be quite small with minute temperature changes. Use of the difference amplifier just discussed will provide accurate and, if desired, amplified indication of the difference between V_1 and V_2. Furthermore, any loading effect of a measuring instrument is removed because of the high input impedance and low output impedance of the difference amplifier circuit. Here, again, op amps have come to the rescue.

Although much of the discussion of summing circuits has revolved around arithmetic and algebraic uses, many other applications are found. Many public address sound systems require more than one microphone or program source to be amplified at the same time. It may even be necessary in some broadcasting applications to have two or three microphones and even a tape deck or record player all available for use together. Orchestras often must combine the sounds from various electronic instruments and microphones. The summing circuit effectively adds or **mixes** the sound sources. Figure 10–6 is a simplified diagram of such a mixing arrangement using a summing circuit. Each of the program sources has its separate control so that the amount of sound from each source may be adjusted to the desired loudness. Mixing occurs at the junction of the input resistors (R_1 through R_4) and the feedback resistor (R_f). The amplification of each program source is determined by the ratio of R_f and the appropriate input resistor. Output voltage of the summing circuit is the inverted algebraic sum of all four inputs. Additional amplifiers must, of course, follow to increase the power of the summed program sources.

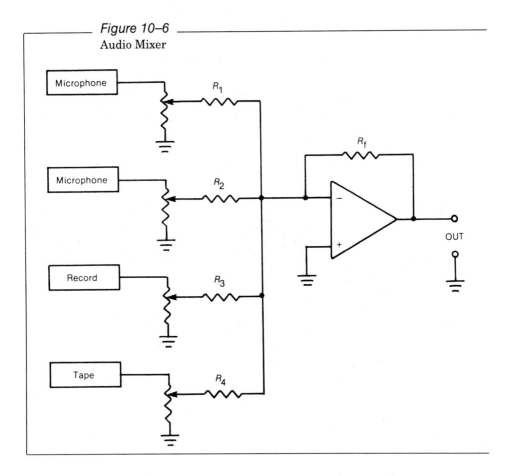

Figure 10–6
Audio Mixer

INTEGRATION

An integrator performs the mathematical operation of **integration,** which provides the area under the curve of the input function. But our interest here is more in how circuits function—let's look at an integrator circuit and determine how it operates.

Concepts of Integration

Figure 10–7A is the schematic diagram of a simple integrator. Note that it very much resembles a common inverter amplifier, except that the feedback component is a capacitor instead of a resistor. Operation of the integrator circuit can be explained by establishing some initial conditions. As with any basic op amp circuit, it is assumed that the voltage differential between the inverting and noninverting inputs is 0 with no

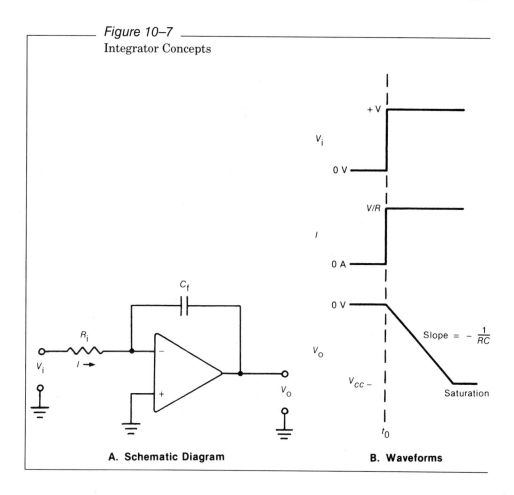

Figure 10–7
Integrator Concepts

A. Schematic Diagram

B. Waveforms

input signal. Furthermore, no current flows in either the inverting or noninverting input circuits of the op amp. Under these circumstances, there is no input to the op amp, and, consequently, there is no output. With no input and no output, there is no voltage differential between input and output, and no voltage exists across capacitor C_f. The capacitor is, therefore, in a discharged state.

Now let's cause the input to the integrator to change instantaneously from 0 V to some positive voltage, as shown at t_0 in Figure 10–7B. Application of the input voltage will cause current to flow in R_i. Since no current can flow in the op amp input circuit, the current must flow through the capacitor. The capacitive current must equal the current through the resistor to maintain op amp input current at 0. Since the input voltage is constant, the current through the resistor is constant. The matching current through the capacitor must also be constant. Recall, from your basic studies, that a constant current applied through a capacitor causes the voltage across the capacitor to change linearly. Therefore, in order to maintain a constant current through the capacitor as it charges, the voltage at the output of the op amp must change linearly. As long as the input voltage remains positive, the op amp output voltage will fall linearly within the range of the op amp and its supply voltage. In other words, the negative ramp cannot continue forever.

When the input to the integrator goes from a positive voltage to a negative voltage, the opposite condition exists. The capacitor must now try to charge in the opposite direction, and the output voltage becomes a positive-going ramp. Integrator output must be defined in terms of both voltage and time. The change in integrator output voltage is a function of the time constant formed by R_i and C_f. An actual example will be shown shortly.

Another way of looking at the operation of the integrator is to realize that one end of the capacitor is at the output of the op amp, while the other end is at ground potential. Remember, if the noninverting input of an op amp is grounded, then the inverting input must also be at a virtual ground to maintain the input differential voltage at 0. If it were not for C_f, the output voltage would try to be very large. In fact, it would *try* to reach a value equal to the open-loop gain of the op amp times the input voltage. Even though it cannot go that high, the integrating capacitor C_f will be trying to charge to that voltage. Since it will only be able to charge to a very small fraction of the fictitious very-high voltage, only a very small part at the beginning of the time constant curve is used. The beginning portion of the time constant curve is linear, and the resulting output of the integrator is thus quite linear.

In mathematical terms, the output of an integrator is the time integral of the input multiplied by a gain factor $(1/RC)$. The effect of the RC time constant can be shown by the schematic example in Figure 10–8A. It is convenient to use a 1 s time constant with $C_f = 1\ \mu F$ and $R_i = 1\ M\Omega$. When the input changes from 0 V to $+1$ V, the output begins to change linearly from 0 V toward some negative voltage as the integration process occurs. A 1 s time constant $(R \times C)$ results in a voltage change of 1 V in 1 s. See Figure 10–8B. Changing R_i to 100,000 Ω will change the time constant to 0.1 s. Applying the same input now results in an output change of 10 V in 1 s. Thus, the gain of the integrator is determined by the RC time constant of the integrator.

Practical Integrator

The integrator circuit of Figures 10–7 and 10–8 is a theoretical circuit. Real-life integrators must consider some additional factors. For example, any bias current that flows or any offset voltage that is present will

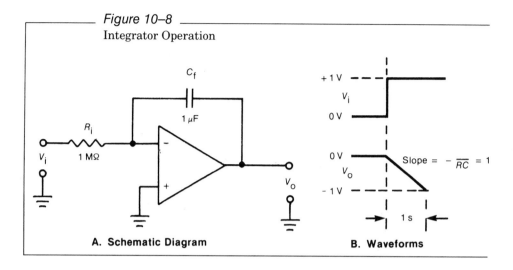

Figure 10–8

Integrator Operation

A. Schematic Diagram

B. Waveforms

appear to the integrator as an input signal. Integration will occur, and the output voltage will change. Bias current can be combatted by using FET op amps that have very low bias current ratings. A resistor may also be added at the noninverting input. Just as in other cases where bias current was to be minimized, the value of the resistor is calculated by the following formula:

$$R = R_i + R_s$$

where R_s is the input source resistance. Offset voltage effects may be minimized by using low output offset voltage op amps. A very large feedback resistor ($R_f = 10 \times R_i$) also helps to discharge the integrating capacitor when offset voltages are present. R_f also helps to stabilize the low-frequency and DC gain of the op amp but does make the integrator less ideal. Without R_f, the op amp effectively operates in an open-loop configuration, which may result in unstable operation. The most common "fix" for offset voltage problems is to reset the integrator periodically by shorting out and discharging the integrating capacitor. A field effect transistor (FET) is connected directly across the integrating capacitor. Prior to each integrating period, the FET is turned on, and the capacitor is discharged. The output voltage thus starts at 0. The input to be integrated also turns off the FET, and the output is allowed to rise for the integrating period. When the input to be integrated returns to 0, the FET is again turned on, and the capacitor is discharged. Many variations of the integrator circuit are seen, but the concepts shown in Figure 10–9 will provide enough background to allow analysis of integrator operation.

Figure 10–9
Practical Integrator

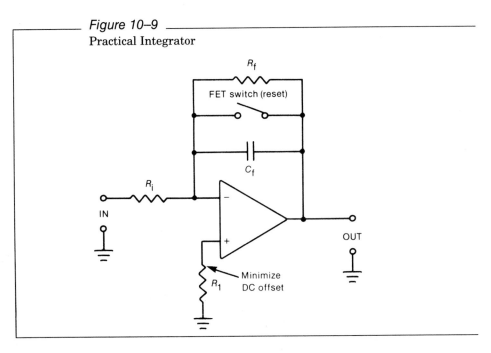

Figure 10–10
Integrator Frequency Response

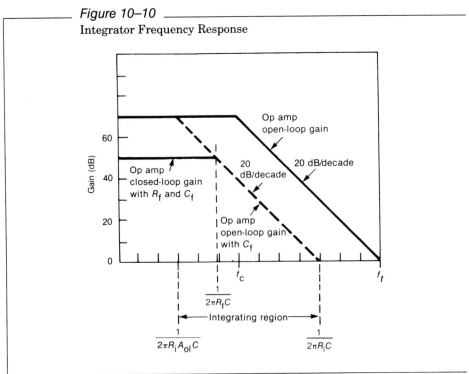

Integrator Frequency Response

Another way to look at the integrator is to examine its response to different input frequencies. The important points for discussion of the integrator (Figure 10–9) are shown on Figure 10–10. For example, the frequency response of the op amp by itself is shown for reference. Considering that the op amp is frequency compensated for normal operation, it will have the normal open-loop gain A_{ol} until the cutoff frequency (f_c) is reached. The gain then drops off at a rate of 20 dB/decade to the unity gain frequency (f_t). As noted before, the basic op amp acts very much like a low-pass filter whose cutoff frequency is determined by internal characteristics of the op amp. The integrator circuit has the same type of frequency response, as shown in Figure 10–10. The cutoff frequency and unity gain frequency are much lower because of the RC time constant, but the 20 dB/decade characteristic remains. Addition of R_f causes predictable results. Low-frequency gain is reduced, and the cutoff frequency is extended just as with conventional inverter amplifier and low-pass filter circuits. The frequency range over which integration occurs is identified in Figure 10–10, as are the important frequencies associated with integration.

The response of an integrator to various input signals is shown in Figure 10–11. Use of Figure 10–11 will make circuit analysis easier. Integrator applications are discussed in Chapter 8, Chapter 13, and Chapter 15.

—————— DIFFERENTIATION ——————————————

Differentiation is the mathematical process of finding the instantaneous rate of change of an input. The mathematical symbol for differentiation is dx/dt, where dx represents a small change in variable x and dt represents a small change in time. Differentiation is the opposite of integration. In fact, as may be seen in Figure 10–12, interchanging R and C in the integrator circuit results in a differentiator. Since the differentiator has a capacitor between the input signal source and the op amp input, it will respond *only* to the input signal change. Generally, the RC time constant is small compared to the input interval. This same type of circuit was encountered during discussion of active filters and should be recognized as having the frequency response of a high-pass filter. As such, it is susceptible to high-frequency noise. In addition, instability can result due to the high open-loop gain at high frequencies.

Figure 10–13 shows the input versus output waveforms for the differentiator circuit. This figure may be used to help analyze circuits in which differentiation is applied. Note that the effect of differentiation is

Figure 10–11
Integrator Responses

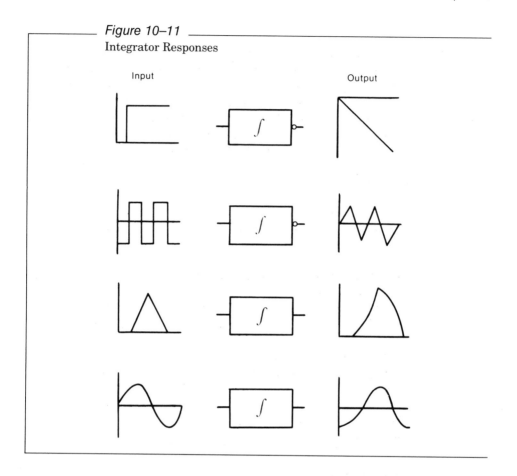

opposite to the effect of integration, as may be seen by referring to Figures 10–11 and 10–13. As an example, a square wave applied to an integrator results in a triangular wave output. Applying a triangular wave to a differentiator results in a square wave output. Thus, the integrator and differentiator provide opposite functions. Note that a positive-going input gives a negative-going output.

Practical Differentiator

A practical differentiator is shown in Figure 10–14. Two components are added to the circuit of Figure 10–12 to combat the high-frequency noise susceptibility and instability. A resistor R_c is added in series with the input capacitor C to give a 20 dB/decade high-frequency roll-off characteristic. Feedback capacitor C_c is added to provide more high-frequency feedback. Both components act to reduce high-frequency gain and improve differentiator stability.

Figure 10–12

Differentiator Concepts

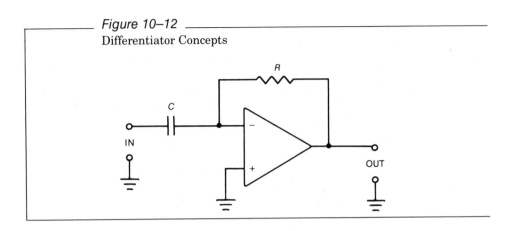

Figure 10–13

Differentiator Responses

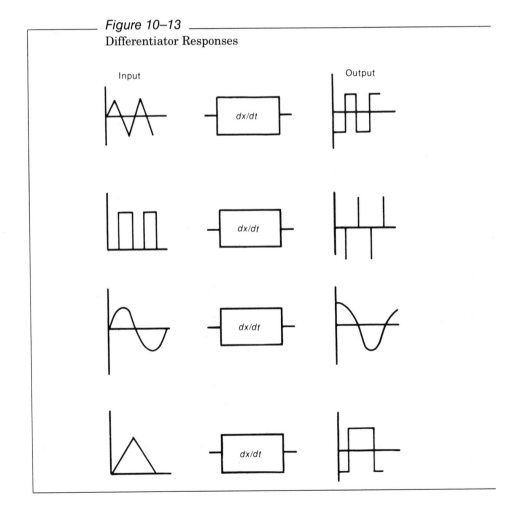

Differentiator Frequency Response

When the overall frequency response of the differentiator in Figure 10–14 is examined (see Figure 10–15), some interesting characteristics come to light. Basic response of the op amp is shown for reference, and the results of adding the various circuit components are shown. The frequency response of the theoretical differentiator of Figure 10–12 is that of a high-pass filter with a 20 dB/decade roll-off characteristic. Feedback resistor R establishes the closed-loop gain. Addition of R_c sets the low-frequency cutoff frequency. Without C_c, the high-frequency cutoff frequency would be determined by the characteristics of the op amp. Adding C_c reduces high-frequency gain and ultimately the high-frequency cutoff frequency. Note that the actual frequency response of the practical differentiator is that of a band-pass filter. The important frequencies are defined on the graph of Figure 10–15. It is particularly interesting to note that differentiation, filtering, and integration all occur with the differentiator. Proper differentiator design results in a stable op amp circuit that meets the mathematical definition of differentiation.

—————— *LOGARITHMIC AMPLIFIERS* ——————

Another application of op amps is in the area of calculations and operations requiring logarithmic functions. Some mathematics and a

Figure 10–14 ————————————————————————————
Practical Differentiator

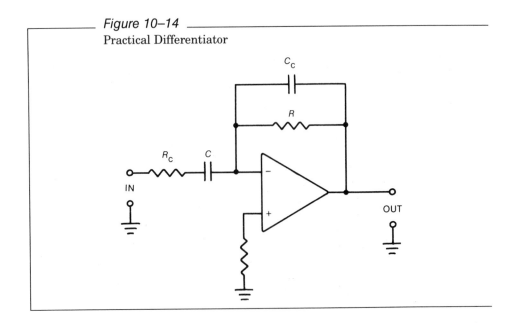

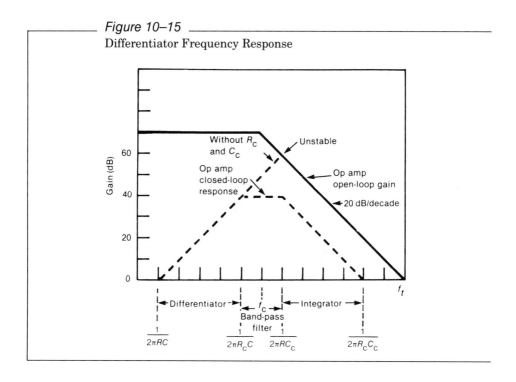

Figure 10–15

Differentiator Frequency Response

large number of electronic operations require manipulation of logarithmic quantities. A logarithm of a number, you may recall, is an exponent that defines the power to which a defined base must be raised to equal that number. Since logarithms are exponents, they may be manipulated as exponents, thus simplifying mathematical operations. Multiplication, for example, is performed by adding exponents. The square of a number is obtained by multiplying the logarithm of the number by 2 and then converting from logarithms back to the normal number system. Arithmetic operations, then, are simplified by one degree of difficulty.

Concepts of Logarithmic Amplifiers

In order for op amps to use logarithmic operations, some circuit must be devised that has logarithmic characteristics. Fortunately, the plot of a bipolar transistor's base-emitter voltage (V_{be}) against its collector-current characteristic (I_c), as shown in Figure 10–16A, closely approximates a logarithmic curve. Thus, when a bipolar transistor is used in the feedback loop of an inverter amplifier, the output of the op amp is proportional to the logarithm of the input. Figure 10–16B shows the simple connections necessary to obtain logarithmic operation from an op amp. It should be noted that the conventional solid-state diode also possesses

Figure 10–16

Logarithmic Amplifier Concepts

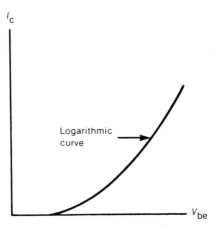

A. V_{be} versus I_c Transistor Characteristic

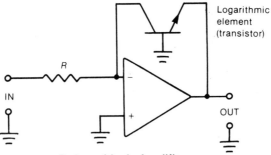

B. Logarithmic Amplifier

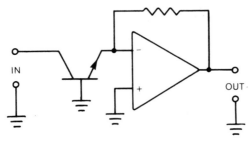

C. Antilogarithmic Amplifier

the same logarithmic characteristic and may be used in place of the bipolar transistor. The transistor, however, is the most effective and most commonly used feedback element in **logarithmic amplifiers.**

It may also be necessary to reverse the logarithmic procedure— that is, to take the *antilog* of a number. The **antilog amplifier** circuit (Figure 10–16C) is as simple as the log circuit (Figure 10–16B). It is merely necessary to interchange the transistor (the logarithmic element) and the input resistor. The output of the op amp is now proportional to the antilog of the input.

The circuits shown are simplified. Bipolar transistors, unfortunately, change their characteristics drastically as temperature changes. Logarithmic circuits must provide appropriate compensation. Precautions must be taken to protect against bias current and offset voltage errors. If high-quality op amps are not used, conventional balance techniques should be employed. Modern logarithmic amplifier circuits rarely use discrete transistors and op amps. Logarithmic op amps are a common item, containing *both* the logarithmic element and the op amp (see Figure 10–17). Both op amp and logarithmic element connections are connected to external pins for maximum flexibility. If a log amplifier is desired, the logarithmic element is connected in the negative feedback loop. Antilog amplifiers are formed by connecting the logarithmic element in series with the inverting input.

Logarithmic Amplifier Applications

Let's consider how two numbers can be multiplied using a logarithmic amplifier. Multiplication is performed by adding the logarithms of both numbers and then taking the antilog of the sum. Figure 10–18A shows

Figure 10–17

Logarithmic Op Amp

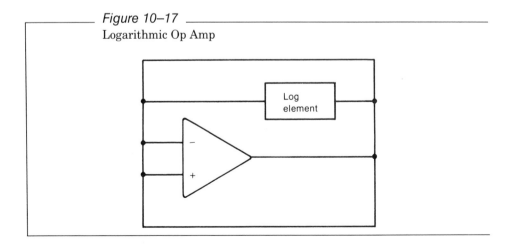

Figure 10–18

Mathematical Operations with Log Amps

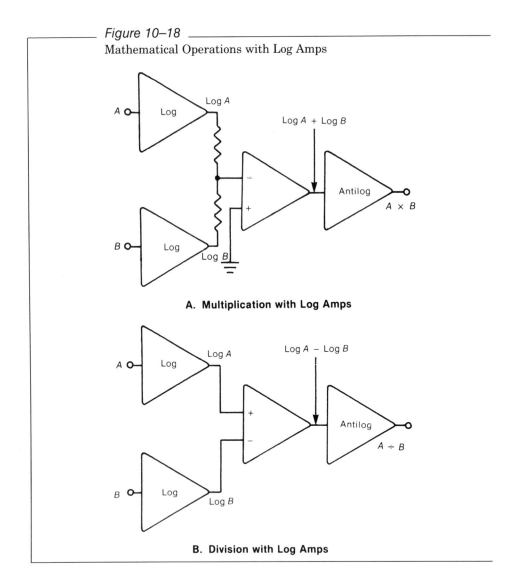

A. Multiplication with Log Amps

B. Division with Log Amps

a functional diagram of a circuit that will do this. Both log amplifiers are formed by connecting the logarithmic element of the log amplifier IC in the feedback network of the included op amp. They are shown merely as "log" amplifiers on the functional diagram. Outputs of both log amplifiers are summed in a conventional op amp summer circuit. The resulting sum is used as input to an antilog amplifier, whose output then will be the product of both inputs. Division is equally easy. It is only necessary to replace the summing circuit of Figure 10–18A with a difference amplifier circuit (see Figure 10–18B). Division is performed

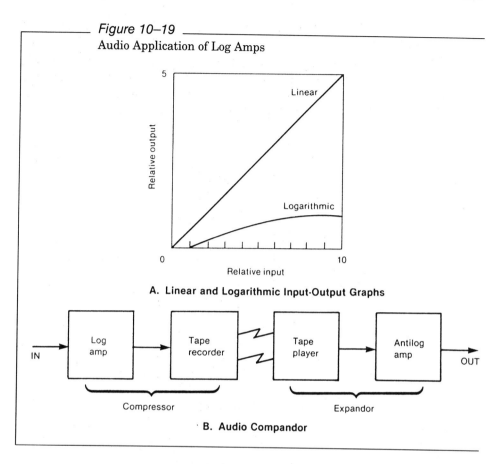

Figure 10–19

Audio Application of Log Amps

A. Linear and Logarithmic Input-Output Graphs

B. Audio Compandor

by subtracting the logarithm of the divisor from the logarithm of the dividend. Taking the antilog of the result yields the quotient.

Another possible application of log amps is in the field of audio recording. Quite often the range of loudness of material to be recorded is greater than recording equipment and media (records or tape) can accommodate. If the information to be recorded is passed through a log amp, the range will be effectively "compressed." The curves of linear and logarithmic input-output relationships show why compression takes place (Figure 10–19A). When played back through a conventional amplifier, however, the recorded material does not "sound right." Higher-volume passages tend to be distorted. But, if played back through an antilog amp, the compressed passages are expanded because of the reverse characteristic of the antilog amplifier. In fact, the combination of both log and antilog circuits is commonly called a **compandor** (compressor-expandor) and is used in many audio applications. Figure 10–19B is a block diagram of such a device.

_____ OTHER MATHEMATICAL CIRCUITS _____

Many other mathematical operations are performed by electronic circuits. They are not necessarily based on operational amplifiers, however. The **analog multiplier,** for example, is a common device.

The earlier discussion of how logarithmic amplifiers combined with operational amplifiers can perform multiplication and division was oversimplified. A review of Figure 10–18 and the associated text will show that a potential problem exists. Consider a simple example such as finding the product of $+2$ and $+3$ using logarithms.

_____ *Example 10–1* _____

Find the product of $+2$ and $+3$ using logarithms.

Solution

$$(+2) \times (+3) = (\log +2) + (\log +3) = 0.3 + 0.477 = 0.777$$
$$\text{antilog } 0.777 \approx 6$$

Therefore,

$$(+2) \times (+3) = 6$$

Note that the numbers, their logarithms, and the antilogarithm were all positive. Should we decide to work with *bipolar* inputs (both $+$ and $-$), logarithmic amplifiers become a problem. The logarithm of a negative number is imaginary, and logarithmic amplifiers cannot easily operate with imaginary numbers. We could, of course, provide circuits to examine the signs of the multiplier and the multiplicand, determine the sign of the results, and work the problem as though the numbers were positive. The sign of the product could then be attached after the product was obtained. This approach requires considerable additional circuitry and may not be a good method.

Special circuits, analog multipliers, easily perform multiplication. Analog multipliers consist of transistors connected in such a way that their output is the product of the multiplicand and the multiplier. Operational amplifiers are used in analog multipliers for isolation and scaling of the output. When one of the two numbers to be multiplied may only be positive and the other may be either positive or negative, a **two-quadrant multiplier** is used. See Figure 10–20A, where the multiplication of $+5$ by any number ranging from $+10$ to -10 is shown. The example shown is $+5$ times both $+8$ and -8. If both numbers may be either positive or negative, a **four-quadrant multiplier** must be employed (see Figure 10–20C). An example showing both $+5$ and -5

Figure 10–20

Analog Multiplication

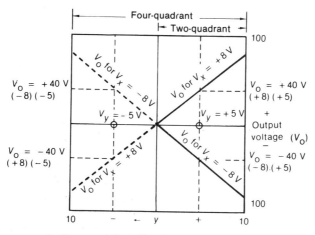

A. Two- and Four-Quadrant Multiplication

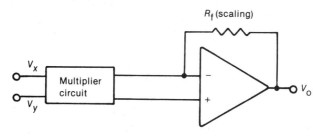

B. Two-Quadrant Multiplier

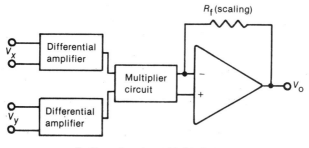

C. Four-Quadrant Multiplier

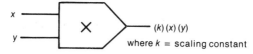

D. Analog Multiplier Symbol

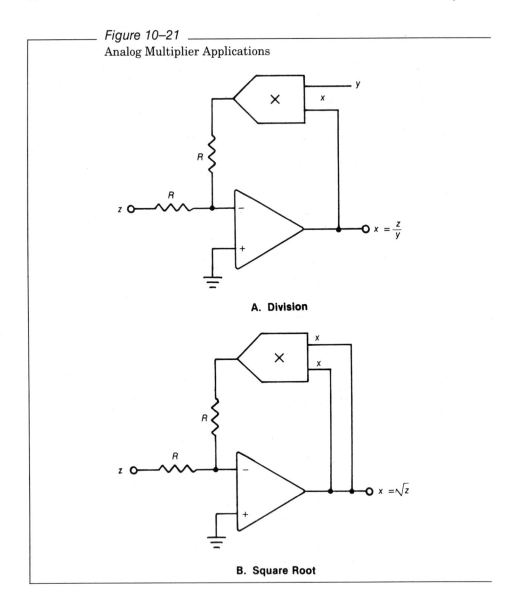

Figure 10–21
Analog Multiplier Applications

A. Division

B. Square Root

times both $+8$ and -8 is also shown in Figure 10–20A. As might be expected, any multiplication concerned with AC inputs *must* employ four-quadrant multipliers. Analog multipliers are used in much the same way as operational amplifiers. In schematic diagrams, a symbol defining the device's function is used (see Figure 10–20D) rather than a detailed internal schematic diagram. Figures 10–20B and 10–20C show functional block diagrams of two- and four-quadrant multipliers, and Figure 10–20D shows the basic functional symbol.

Analog multipliers are often combined with operational amplifiers and logarithmic amplifiers to perform complex mathematical operations. Figures 10–21A and 10–21B show some of these combinations. Many other applications exist. If an operation may be defined mathematically to include multiplication, an analog multiplier may be used. As your background and experience expands, analog multipliers will appear in many unexpected places. Chapters 12 and 13 show some of the unusual applications of the many op-amp-based integrated circuits that we have studied.

SUMMARY

Most of us will probably never use operational amplifiers in the pure sense of performing mathematical operations. However, as shown in this chapter, mathematical operations are easily performed with the aid of operational amplifiers.

The adder, or summing circuit, has been shown to be a simple inverter amplifier with voltages representing numbers combined in resistive dividers. In fact, each of the resistors in the divider arrangement may be a different value so as to scale the inputs and perform sum of products operations. Multiplication and averaging may also be performed by selecting appropriate values of the feedback resistor for the operational amplifier. Subtraction is performed by applying voltages representing numbers to resistive dividers connected to both inverting and noninverting inputs of the operational amplifier.

Integration is performed by substituting a capacitor in place of the resistor in the feedback path of an operational amplifier. Differentiation results when the capacitor replaces the divider resistor instead of the feedback resistor. Both integrators and differentiators may be used as filters, and they may be used to perform their respective mathematical operations.

Logarithmic operations may also be performed using operational amplifiers by placing a bipolar transistor or junction diode in the feedback path of an amplifier circuit. Antilogarithmic functions result when the bipolar transistor or junction diode replaces the divider resistor instead of the feedback resistor.

Analog multipliers are special mathematical circuits that are often used to perform multiplication when both positive and negative numbers must be manipulated. Logarithmic amplifiers cannot function effectively in such cases since the logarithm of a negative number is imaginary. Both two-quadrant and four-quadrant analog multiplier circuits may be needed, depending on whether only one or both of the numbers to be multiplied may be either positive or negative.

In Chapter 10, we have seen many unusual applications for operational amplifiers. We have just scratched the surface, however. Many additional applications will be seen in subsequent chapters.

=== *QUESTIONS* ==

1. What basic operational amplifier circuit configuration is used with summing circuits?

2. Explain the operation of the circuit in Figure 10–1.

3. Why must all of the resistors in Figure 10–1 be the same value?

4. Draw a schematic diagram showing how three voltages could be added using a summing circuit.

5. Draw a schematic diagram showing how to solve the equation $3a + 4b + 2c$.

6. Redraw the diagram drawn in Question 5 to multiply the total equation by 3.

7. Explain the difference between a summing circuit and a difference circuit.

8. Explain the operation of the circuit in Figure 10–7.

9. Discuss the factors that determine the "zero input" conditions of an integrator circuit.

10. Discuss the factors that determine the long-term accuracy of an integrator circuit.

11. Explain why the high-frequency cutoff frequency of an integrator is less than the cutoff frequency of the op amp used in the integrator.

12. A 1000 Hz square wave is applied to an integrator. Draw the output waveform for the integrator output when the cutoff frequency of the integrator is (a) 100 Hz, (b) 1,000 Hz, and (c) 10,000 Hz.

13. Explain the operation of the circuit in Figure 10–12.

14. A 1000 Hz square wave is applied to a differentiator. Draw the output waveform for the differentiator output when the RC time constant is (a) 100 ms, (b) 1,000 ms, and (c) 10,000 ms.

15. Discuss which components in the schematic diagram of Figure 10–14 affect (a) the low-frequency cutoff frequency, (b) the passband, and (c) the high-frequency cutoff frequency of the differentiator. Explain how each component affects the response.

16. Explain the reason for the transistor in the feedback loop of the circuit shown

in Figure 10–16B. Could a FET transistor be substituted for the bipolar transistor? Explain your answer.

17. Repeat Question 16 for Figure 10–16C.

18. List two applications for log/antilog amplifiers, and explain their operation.

19. Why is it difficult to use log/antilog amplifier techniques for multiplication of bipolar numbers?

20. Explain the operation of the divider circuit of Figure 10–21A.

PROBLEMS

1. In Figure 10–1, $R = R_f = 10$ kΩ. $V_1 = 1$ V, $V_2 = 2$ V, $V_3 = 3$ V, and $V_4 = 4$ V. If $V_{cc+} = 15$ V and $V_{cc-} = 15$ V, determine V_o.

2. Repeat Problem 1 for $V_{cc+} = 5$ V and $V_{cc-} = 5$ V.

3. Repeat Problem 1 with R_f *only* changed to 2.5 kΩ.

4. In Figure 10–2, $R_x = 25$ kΩ, $R_y = 50$ kΩ, and $R_z = 200$ kΩ. What equation does the circuit solve?

5. All resistors in Figure 10–4 are 100 kΩ. $V_2 = +6.3$ V and $V_1 = +2.4$ V. Calculate V_o.

6. If V_{cc+} and V_{cc-} are 15 V, how long will it take for the output of the circuit in Figure 10–8 to reach saturation?

7. Over what frequency range will the circuit shown in Figure 10–9 perform as an integrator if $R_i = R_f = 100$ kΩ, and $C_f = 0.01$ µF. Consider the reset switch to be open and $R_1 = 0$ Ω.

8. In Figure 10–14, $R = 60$ kΩ, $C = 0.08$ µF, $R_c = 2$ kΩ, and $C_c = 600$ pF. Calculate the frequency response of the differentiator, and draw the resulting response curve.

9. A 2500 Hz sine wave is applied to the input of the circuit of Figure 10–14. The component values used in Problem 8 are used. Draw the waveform of the output.

10. Repeat Problem 9 using a 2500 Hz square wave.

11

Special-Purpose Op Amps and Linear ICs

OBJECTIVES   After studying Chapter 11, you will be able to

1. Identify the characteristics and applications of comparators, including zero-crossing detectors, level detectors, and window comparators.
2. Identify the characteristics and applications of instrumentation amplifiers, current difference amplifiers, transconductance amplifiers, and modulators.
3. Identify the characteristics and applications of sample-and-hold circuits, timer circuits, and analog signal processors.

INTRODUCTION

Operational amplifier techniques have greatly expanded since their initial applications. Basic operational amplifiers have been modified to interface with digital devices. These op amps are called *comparators* and give a go-no-go type of output based on input relationships. *Instrumentation amplifiers* use basic op amp techniques to amplify minute signals even in the presence of interfering signals. *Current difference amplifiers* (specialized op amps that amplify current difference instead of voltage difference), *transconductance amplifiers* (amplifiers that supply current output rather than voltage output), and even *programmable gain amplifiers* are seeing widespread use. Many large-scale integrated (LSI) circuits are combining operational amplifiers with other components to perform specialized functions. Chapter 11 discusses these special-purpose operational amplifiers and their derivatives.

COMPARATORS

A **comparator** is a special type of operational amplifier. It is like the mythical Centaur, half man and half beast. The comparator is half linear and half digital. It accepts linear inputs and provides digital outputs. For example, if the voltage at the noninverting input is more positive than the voltage at the inverting input, the output is V_{cc+}. If the voltage at the noninverting input is less positive than the voltage at the inverting input, the output is V_{cc-}. Thus, the output of a comparator switches from V_{cc+} to V_{cc-} with no in-between values.

Zero-Crossing Detector

Most comparators switch with less than 2 to 5 mV difference between inverting and noninverting inputs. Some special comparators will even

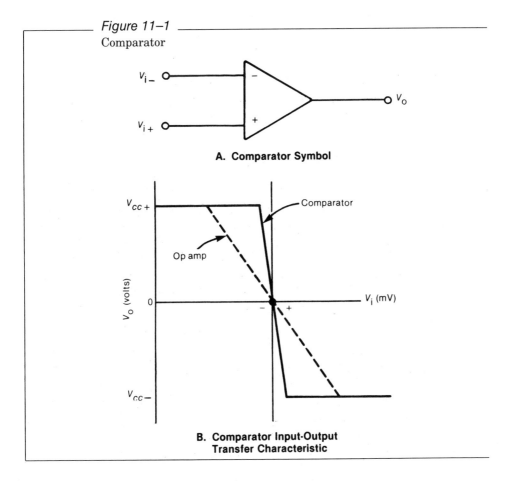

Figure 11–1
Comparator

A. Comparator Symbol

B. Comparator Input-Output Transfer Characteristic

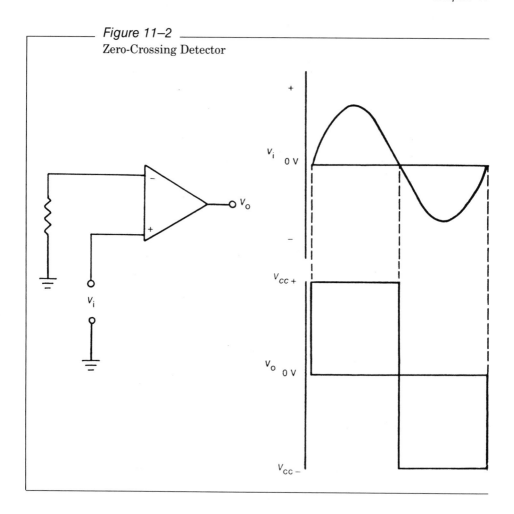

Figure 11–2
Zero-Crossing Detector

switch at input differentials below 100 μV. Figure 11–1A shows the typical comparator symbol, and Figure 11–1B its input-output *transfer
characteristic*. (A conventional operational amplifier's transfer characteristic is shown for comparison.) The very sensitive input characteristic
is obtained by providing extremely high gain and high slew rate during
design. A simple application of comparators is seen in the **zero-crossing detector** of Figure 11–2. Many switching functions for AC-operated
devices perform most effectively when switching occurs at 0 V. Current
flow is low when the AC wave crosses 0, and lower-power switching devices may be used. Furthermore, switching at the zero-crossing point
reduces radio-frequency interference. Typical devices using zero-crossing switching are light dimmers and motor speed controllers. It is only
necessary to ground the inverting input to the comparator and apply

the AC input voltage to the noninverting input. (The AC input will usually have to be scaled with a resistive voltage divider to prevent exceeding comparator input voltage restrictions.) During the portion of the AC cycle that the noninverting input is + in respect to the inverting input, the output voltage will be V_{cc+}. When the AC cycle passes through 0 and into the negative half-cycle, the output switches to V_{cc-}. Again, when the AC cycle passes through 0 going into the positive half-cycle, switching will occur. If a negative output is desired when the input signal is positive, it is only necessary to reverse the inverting and the noninverting input connections. Thus, every time the output of the comparator changes state it will signal that a zero crossing has occurred. It should be mentioned that comparators possess hysteresis, as discussed in Chapter 9 and shown in Figure 9–14B.

Level Detector

The zero-crossing detector may be easily modified to function as a **level detector.** It is often necessary to know when a voltage exceeds a predetermined value. The actual voltage may not be important; just the fact that it has exceeded a specific limit is what matters. By replacing ground as the reference, the comparator is made to switch when the input exceeds the actual reference voltage. Figure 11–3 is a simple example of a level detector. Resistors R_1 and R_2 form a voltage divider that places a + voltage on the inverting input of the comparator. When the input voltage to the noninverting input of the comparator is less than the reference voltage, the comparator output is V_{cc-}. The light-emitting diode (LED) is reverse biased and does not illuminate. Diode D_1 is included in series with the LED to prevent application of high reverse

_____ *Figure 11–3* _____

+ Level Detector

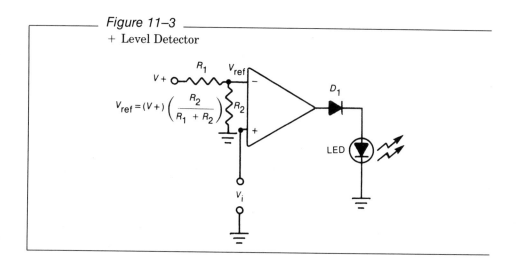

$$V_{ref} = (V+)\left(\frac{R_2}{R_1 + R_2}\right)$$

voltage to the LED under negative voltage output conditions. LEDs cannot tolerate high reverse voltages without damage. When the input voltage to the noninverting input exceeds the reference voltage furnished by the voltage divider, the comparator output switches to V_{cc+}. Diode D_1 and the LED are now forward biased, and the LED illuminates. An indication is thus provided to indicate that the input voltage has exceeded the reference voltage. It is equally easy to use a negative reference voltage and determine when the input voltage exceeds the reference.

Window Comparator

It is sometimes necessary to establish that an input voltage is *between* an upper and a lower limit. The **window comparator** of Figure 11–4 will perform this function. It is designed to provide an indication when a 1000 Ω resistor connected to a test fixture is outside of a required 5% tolerance. The test fixture supplies a constant 2.5 mA of current to the test resistor. An exact 1000 Ω resistor would thus experience a 2.5 V drop, which is applied as the input voltage to the two comparators. The upper comparator has a 2.625 V reference at its inverting input. Calculations will show that a 1000 Ω resistor that is 5% high will actually

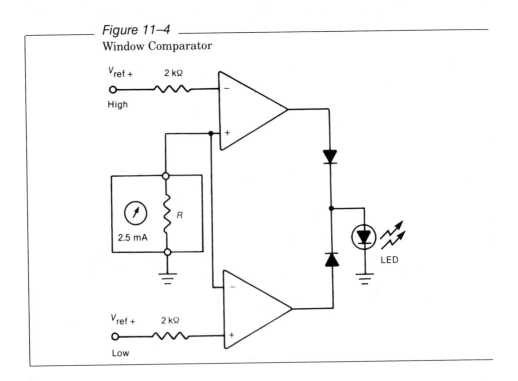

Figure 11–4
Window Comparator

be 1050 Ω. The constant current of the test fixture will cause a voltage drop of 2.625 V, which will cause the top comparator to switch, turning on the LED. Likewise, a resistor that is 5% low will cause the bottom comparator to switch and turn on the LED. In an automatic tester, the LED would be supplemented by an electromechanical device to route the out-of-tolerance resistor to further testing. The general concepts of the *window,* or *limit,* application of comparators is found throughout automatic testing devices.

Comparator Applications

Any operational amplifier application that requires fast switching time can be performed by comparators. Many of the waveform generators, such as square wave and pulse circuits, are actually constructed more effectively using comparators. The use of hysteresis, as discussed in Chapter 9, is also common in comparator circuits. It should be pointed out that operational amplifiers can be used as comparators in low-frequency applications where switching time is not as critical. Comparators, however, are seldom used as operational amplifiers. Designs that optimize switching time usually are highly nonlinear and are not applicable to the usual operational amplifier circuits.

An example of comparator use is seen in Figure 11–5, which is a diagram of a light-controlled one-shot timer. A photodiode operates with light normally present. When the light is interrupted, the circuit output changes from a high to a low state for approximately 60 seconds. Comparator A_1 senses a change in light intensity by comparing a reference voltage applied to the noninverting input with the voltage developed across the photodiode. With normal light falling on the photodiode, its resistance (and the voltage across it) is low. The voltage at the inverting terminal is thus below the reference voltage at the noninverting terminal. Comparator output is at V_{cc+}. Reference voltage is determined by R_3, R_4, and R_5. Two important points should be noted at this time. Positive feedback via R_4 and R_5 establishes hysteresis for the comparator to protect against unstable operation. R_3, in conjunction with R_4 and R_5, establishes a midpoint for the output voltage. The comparator being used has only V_{cc+} applied and is referenced to ground. Any conventional dual comparator IC, such as the 139 series from a number of manufacturers, can be used. The use of R_3 to establish the output operating point has been seen in op amp applications.

When light is removed from the photodiode, its resistance increases. The accompanying voltage increase causes the comparator output to switch to 0 V. Since the voltage across capacitor C_3 cannot change instantaneously, the 15 V negative-going pulse is applied to the inverting input of comparator A_2. The voltage at the inverting input is $+1$ V

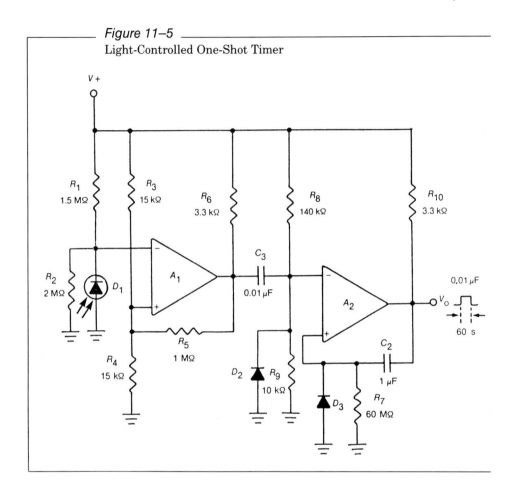

Figure 11–5

Light-Controlled One-Shot Timer

because of divider R_8 and R_9. The negative-going pulse will thus try to make the inverting input highly negative. What happens next depends on the condition of the one-shot configured comparator A_2.

Consider that the output of A_2 is at 0 V and that C_2 is discharged. The noninverting input of A_2 will thus be near 0 V, and consequently A_2 output will also be 0 V. When the negative pulse from A_1 arrives, the inverting input is momentarily made less positive than the noninverting input. A_2 output switches to V_{cc+}. The positive transition is coupled through C_2 and appears across R_7, making the noninverting input positive. A_2 output will remain positive until C_2 charges sufficiently to allow the noninverting input to drop to less than 1 V. The output then returns to 0 V as C_2 discharges rapidly through diode D_3. A_2 output remains positive for a time period determined by the time constant of R_7 and C_2. Therefore, a pulse determined by the RC time constant will occur when light falling on the photodiode is interrupted. Application of the comparator to both voltage comparison and one-shot generation has thus been demonstrated.

Troubleshooting: The light-controlled one-shot timer of Figure 11–5 will be used for a troubleshooting example for this chapter. As stated in the text, removal of light at the photodiode input causes a 60 second duration pulse to be generated at the output. The statement of circuit malfunction is simple—it doesn't work! No output pulse is generated when light is removed from the photodiode. The output of A_2 is a constant positive value.

A troubleshooting technique called "half-splitting" (discussed in more detail in Chapter 15) is used. Simply stated, half-splitting selects a test point approximately halfway through the circuit. Input is applied, and the result at the halfway point is noted. If the result is correct, the last half of the circuit is defective. If the result is not correct, the first half is defective.

In the light-controlled one-shot timer, removal of light from the photodiode causes a negative-going signal at the A_1 output. This is the desired result, so the malfunction is in the second half of the circuit. Now half-split the second half. Does the negative pulse at the output of C_3 reach the negative input of A_2? If it does (the desired result), then the malfunction is associated with the op amp or the output circuit. Assume that the negative input is OK.

What could cause the A_2 output to stay positive even though the negative input returns to the positive reference after the input pulse is complete? Most likely, the positive input remains positive. Either a short to a positive voltage in the op amp or a C_2 short is possible. The C_2 short may be the easiest to check. Assuming C_2 is shorted, the positive input is directly connected to the output of A_2, and the positive output is clamped to a positive value. Replacing C_2 will remove the malfunction.

INSTRUMENTATION AMPLIFIERS

An **instrumentation amplifier** is another special application of operational amplifiers. Instrumentation amplifiers are used in critical data-gathering applications such as research and development activities in the aerospace, automotive, and medical fields.

Concepts of Instrumentation Amplifiers

Instrumentation amplifiers generally must amplify the *difference* between two input signals while simultaneously *not* amplifying any component common to the input signals. The amplifiers must have high input impedance, low output impedance, stable gain, and low drift and offset and must be highly linear. Their description sounds very much like the original description of a perfect (ideal) operational amplifier.

A short review of operational amplifier characteristics is appropriate at this time. Remember that the first stage of an operational amplifier is usually a *differential* amplifier. That is, it amplifies the difference between the two amplifier inputs. In many applications, however, the operational amplifier is used with one of its inputs referred to ground. If neither of the inputs is referred to ground, then the output of the differential amplifier is a function of the *difference* between the inputs. Any component of the input signals common to both inputs is rejected. The rejection capability of the differential amplifier is its *common-mode rejection ratio* (CMRR). Chapter 1 discussed the operation of differential amplifiers. An operational amplifier specially designed to operate in the differential mode is called an instrumentation amplifier. The conventional operational amplifier symbol is used to portray an instrumentation amplifier. As will be seen shortly, however, several operational amplifiers may be required to actually implement the functions of an instrumentation amplifier.

Figure 11–6 represents an amplifier operating in the differential mode. Let's review some of its characteristics. The amplification A_V of the circuit of Figure 11–6 is determined by the ratio of R_f to R_1. R_f and R_3 are usually equal, as are R_1 and R_2. In fact, it is necessary that the resistors be matched within 1% to realize minimum offset voltage and CMRR characteristics. One of the major problems encountered in the use of differential amplifiers is the matching and **tracking** of resistors.

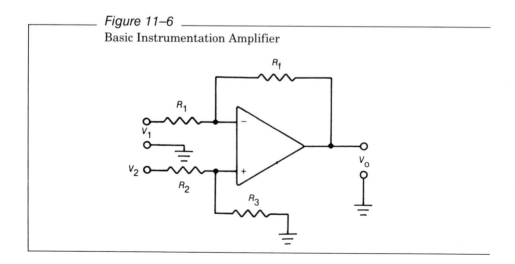

Figure 11–6

Basic Instrumentation Amplifier

(*Tracking* refers to resistors changing value equally as some other parameter such as temperature varies.) Matching and tracking become more difficult as larger values of resistors are used. We are now faced with a dilemma. R_1 and R_2 must be high-value resistors to prevent loading the circuit to be instrumented. If R_1 and R_2 are high-value resistors, then in order to obtain high gain, R_3 and R_f must be very-high-value resistors. Difficulty is sure to be encountered with matching R_f and R_3. If gain is to be varied, R_f and R_3 must be varied an identical amount. Tracking problems will occur. A further problem manifests itself when the actual circuit loading of the differential amplifier inputs is considered. The inverting input's resistance is equal to $R_1 + R_f$. The noninverting input's resistance is $R_2 + R_3$. Therefore, the circuits being instrumented may be loaded differently. Thus, if adequate gain and CMRR characteristics are to be realized, it appears that relatively low-value resistors must be used for R_1 and R_2. All in all, it appears that the conventional operational amplifier and its differential input stage are not satisfactory for instrumentation uses.

Although by no means the only solution, Figure 11–7 shows a commonly used approach to implementing instrumentation amplifier requirements. The loading problem is solved by inserting voltage followers in each input path. With its very high input impedance and low output impedance, the voltage follower reduces circuit loading and still allows the use of low-value resistors for R_1 and R_2. Resistor pairs must

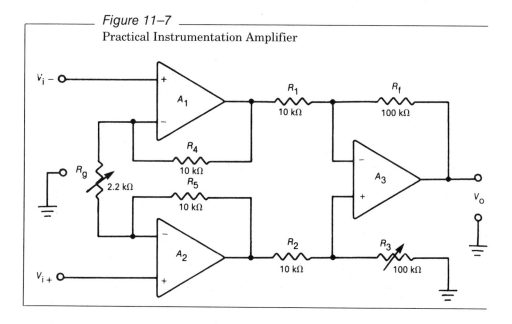

Figure 11–7

Practical Instrumentation Amplifier

still be matched, but the problem is not so difficult with low-value resistors. Also, it is no longer necessary to vary both R_f and R_3 to adjust amplifier gain. R_g provides the gain control. Let's examine the operation of the circuit of Figure 11–7 in more detail.

Three sources of input signals are considered. One source provides an input V_1, while another supplies V_2. The third is common to both other sources and is called the *common-mode input*, or V_{cm}. Both voltage followers share a common input resistor R_g. Normally, R_g would be grounded to establish follower gain according to conventional methods. In the case of the circuit of Figure 11–7, however, the sharing of R_g causes *summing* of "local" feedback with a small portion of the other follower's output. A follower's output, then, contains its amplified noninverting input voltage *minus* a small part of the other follower's output. A third component also exists in each follower's output. The common-mode input V_{cm} exists at both instrumentation amplifier inputs and, consequently, at both follower's outputs. However, the V_{cm} component is equal in amplitude and opposite in phase at each follower's output. The resulting components cancel in R_g. Hence, the common-mode voltage is canceled by the cross-coupled differential amplifier circuit.

Outputs of the voltage followers are fed to the inputs of a conventional differential amplifier A_3. The end result is an output voltage that is the difference between V_2 and V_1. If $R_4 = R_5$, $R_1 = R_2$, and $R_f = R_3$, the gain of the complete instrumentation amplifier is calculated by the following equation:

$$A_V = \frac{R_f}{R_1} \left(1 + \frac{2R_4}{R_g} \right) \tag{11–1}$$

Note that all resistors except R_g and R_3 are fixed. R_g is the gain control, determining the gain of the voltage followers simultaneously. R_3 usually consists of a large fixed resistor and a small variable resistor in series. Its primary purpose is to offer a small amount of adjustment for the output differential amplifier to reduce CMRR to a minimum. Appendix C (program 4) contains a BASIC computer program that calculates instrumentation amplifier gain.

Practical instrumentation amplifiers can be constructed using discrete components and operational amplifiers. A better solution exists, however. All of the components can be constructed on a single chip. Typical examples are Burr-Brown Corporation's 1NA110 and Analog Device's AD524/624. The 1NA110 has field-effect transistor inputs to provide input impedance in the 2×10^{-12} Ω range, and a CMRR rating greater than 106 dB. On-chip gain control resistors allow gain adjustments from 1 to 500.

Instrumentation Amplifier Applications

Instrumentation amplifiers may be formed by using individual op amps and external components, as shown in Figure 11–7. Complete ICs containing all components except the gain and CMRR controls are also commonplace. Some examples of instrumentation amplifier applications follow.

In the medical field, it is often necessary to obtain and record electrical signals generated by the human body. Many of these signals, such as brain waves, give valuable clues to normal and abnormal functioning of the body. Unfortunately, some difficulties are encountered in reliably obtaining these clues. The magnitude of the electrical signals is quite small. Unwanted signals exist along with the desired signals. Most important, the body is susceptible to electrical shock, and the method of data gathering must guard against unwanted electrical current and voltage.

Instrumentation amplifiers can amplify the very weak electrical signals from the body. In fact, the differential configuration of the instrumentation amplifier effectively cancels many of the undesirable common-mode signals. How is the body guarded against electrical shock? It isn't safe to use equipment that "plugs into the wall outlet," because potentially dangerous voltages exist. Figure 11–8 shows a

Figure 11–8

Medical Application of Instrumentation Amplifier

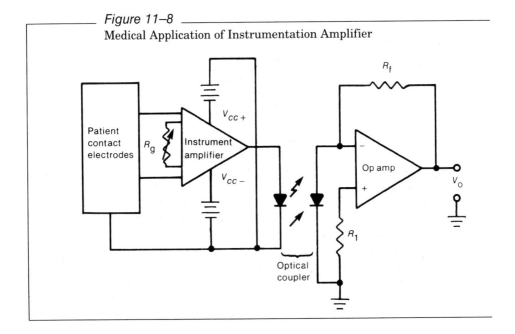

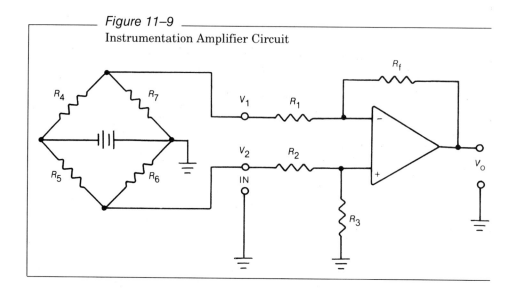

Figure 11–9

Instrumentation Amplifier Circuit

functional diagram of a method to safely obtain electrical data from the body. Electrodes attached to the body supply inputs to the instrumentation amplifier, whose gain is controlled by R_g. Self-contained low-voltage batteries power the instrumentation amplifier so that no connection to a wall-outlet power source is required. The output of the instrumentation amplifier supplies power to an **optical coupler,** which isolates the data-gathering assembly from the recording equipment.

Optical couplers are a combination of light source and photodiode. They are physically and electrically separated from each other. Information is passed by varying light intensity with changing output from the instrumentation amplifier. The changing intensity is detected by the photodiode and amplified by a conventionally connected operational amplifier. Many such assemblies may be used to gather a comprehensive picture of the body's electrical activity. Each of the "channels" is recorded for later analysis.

An excellent example of the use of instrumentation amplifiers was shown in Chapter 10 (Figure 10–5). The instrumentation amplifier is merely a precision difference amplifier. Figure 11–9 shows a typical instrumentation amplifier circuit.

CURRENT DIFFERENCE AMPLIFIERS

Although not strictly an operational amplifier by the definitions used earlier, the **current difference amplifier** is capable of performing many of the operational amplifier functions. The operating principles of the current difference amplifier, and many of its characteristics, differ from those of conventional operational amplifiers.

Conventional operational amplifiers operate on the principle of amplifying the difference between the *voltages* applied to the input terminals. The current difference amplifier operates by amplifying the difference between the *currents* flowing into the input terminals. The amplified current difference flows through an external feedback loop to produce the output voltage. Thus, the output voltage of a current difference amplifier is a function of the difference between the input currents. Current difference amplifiers, sometimes called **Norton amplifiers,** operate from a single rather than dual power supply, which is a major advantage. Compared with the general-purpose type 741 operational amplifier, the current difference amplifier has less voltage gain, lower input impedance, and higher output impedance. It has a slightly higher unity gain frequency than the type 741 operational amplifier, so the gain-bandwidth products are similar.

Current difference amplifiers, such as the 3900 series, have not reached the applications popularity of conventional operational amplifiers. Its original claim to fame was its ability to operate with single rather than dual power supplies. Some special applications that were current-related rather than voltage-related welcomed the current difference amplifier, but in general it was adapted to conventional op amp circuits. We will examine the current difference amplifier only superficially. General characteristics and basic circuits will be discussed, but no attempt will be made to cover detailed circuits.

Since the current difference amplifier operates from a single supply, it is necessary to bias the amplifier so that its output may both increase and decrease. A reference current is supplied to the noninverting input through R_b (see Figure 11–10). Feedback to the inverting input supplies a current to balance the reference current. A general rule of thumb is that the bias resistor R_b should be about $2 \times R_f$ for normal AC operation of current difference amplifiers. Almost all current difference amplifiers operating in the linear mode will have this type of bias circuit.

Unless the circuit to which the current difference amplifier is applied is depending on actual current amplification, it becomes necessary to convert input voltages to input currents. Internal construction of the current difference amplifier "clamps" the input terminals to about 0.7 V, so input voltage variations could not occur once the clamping voltage is reached. The simplest way to convert voltage to current is by inserting a large resistor in series with the signal source. The source then acts as a current generator rather than a voltage generator. Typical inverting and noninverting input circuits are shown in Figure 11–10.

Both inverting and noninverting input circuits look much like conventional op amp input circuits. The gain (*A*) of the inverting

Figure 11–10
Current Difference Amplifier

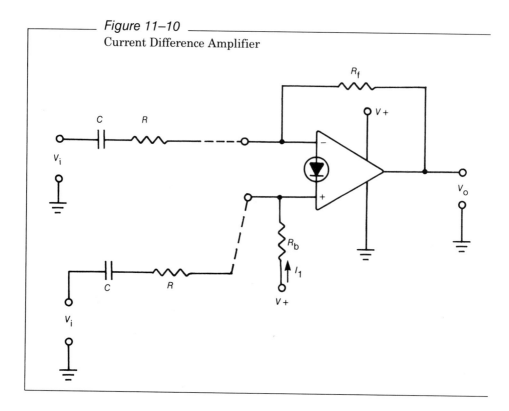

configuration is a function of the series input resistor and the feedback resistor such that

$$A = -\frac{R_f}{R} \qquad (11\text{-}2)$$

Input resistance of the inverting amplifier configuration is equal to the value of the series input resistor. In the noninverting configuration, the gain is

$$A = \frac{R_f}{R + r_d} \qquad (11\text{-}3)$$

where r_d = internal diode resistance. Input resistance of the noninverting amplifier configuration is equal to the sum of the series input resistor value and the internal diode resistance.

Current difference amplifier circuits may be recognized by the unique symbol containing the current generator mark at its input. The current biasing at the noninverting input is also an easily recognized characteristic. Series input resistors will generally be larger than those used in conventional op amp circuits, and a single power supply is used. Otherwise, most conventional op amp circuits already discussed may be implemented with current difference amplifiers.

TRANSCONDUCTANCE AMPLIFIERS

Some electronic circuit applications are best served by amplifiers that supply a *current* output rather than a voltage output. Many oscillator circuits, for example, require control of a capacitor's charging current. Although not extremely popular at the present time, **transconductance amplifiers** are available from a number of manufacturers. Transconductance amplifiers have conventional operational amplifier input characteristics. Their output characteristics, however, are better described by transconductance (g_m) than by voltage gain. Current output of the transconductance amplifier is determined by the following equation:

$$I_o = V_i \times g_m \qquad\qquad \textbf{(11–4)}$$

Furthermore, the output impedance of a transconductance amplifier is high when compared with conventional operational amplifiers. In almost all cases, however, the transconductance amplifier may be used in place of conventional operational amplifiers. It is only necessary to terminate the transconductance amplifier output with a load resistor. The output current of the transconductance amplifier is thus converted to a voltage output. Conventional circuit practices then apply.

Perhaps one of the major advantages of most transconductance amplifiers is the existence of an external control for control of transconductance. By providing external current to the control input of the transconductance amplifier, it is possible to linearly vary the amplifier's transconductance over a wide range. For example, a control current change from 1 μA to 1 mA changes transconductance from approximately 10 μS (microsiemens) to 10,000 μS. Since current output is directly proportional to transconductance, a linear control of output current is provided. When a load resistor terminates the transconductance amplifier, the output voltage that results from output current changes is thus a linear function of the control current. Open-loop gain for a transconductance amplifier connected as a voltage amplifier is

$$A_{ol} = g_m \times R_L \qquad\qquad \textbf{(11–5)}$$

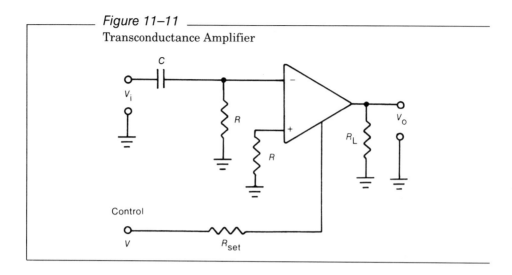

Figure 11–11

Transconductance Amplifier

Figure 11–11 shows an application of the transconductance amplifier. It is a simple differential voltage amplifier with input supplied to the inverting input terminal. Termination of the noninverting and inverting inputs is identical. The unique characteristic of the circuit in Figure 11–11 is that the output voltage is controllable. It is only necessary to supply a variable control voltage to vary the transconductance of the amplifier. (The control voltage is converted to control current by R_{set}.) Gain may be adjusted from maximum to almost zero by changing the control voltage.

An alternating current may also be used as a control input to a transconductance amplifier. If a radio frequency signal is applied to the inverting input and an audio frequency signal is applied to the control input of the transconductance amplifier, the output will be a radio frequency signal varying at an audio frequency rate. This is the definition of an *amplitude-modulated* radio frequency signal (see Figure 11–12). Thus, the transconductance amplifier may be used as an amplitude modulator.

Many other circuits are well suited to the variable-gain transconductance amplifier. Voltage-controlled filters and oscillators are common. The ability to reduce amplification to practically zero also makes the variable-gain transconductance amplifier applicable to switching circuits called *multiplexers*. Application of a current pulse of short duration will turn the amplifier on and allow the signal input to be amplified. A number of such amplifiers may have their outputs connected together and, by sequentially "enabling" each amplifier, a number of different signal sources may be sampled. Figure 11–13 shows the concept of multiplexing. Note that the flip-flop is a digital circuit whose

Figure 11–12

Amplitude Modulator Using Transconductance Amplifier

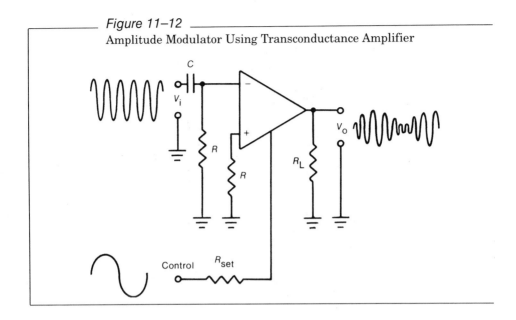

outputs Q and $\bar{Q}$ are applied to separate op amps. When the Q output is positive, the $\bar{Q}$ output is zero, and vice versa. The clock input causes the flip-flop outputs to change, so that one op amp is enabled when the other is disabled.

PROGRAMMABLE AMPLIFIERS

Transconductance amplifiers are not the only operational amplifiers that offer external control of their characteristics. An increasingly popular feature of many op amps is the ability to tailor amplifier characteristics by means of an external input. Early programmable op amps were controlled by a "set" current similar to transconductance amplifiers. Such characteristics as power dissipation, slew rate, gain-bandwidth product, noise figure, and the like all are affected by the "set" current. Unfortunately, all of these characteristics are related, and changing the set current changes all of them. For example, a typical **programmable operational amplifier** can vary slew rate from 0.06 to 6 V/μs by adjusting the set current. Under the same conditions, bandwidth varies from 5 kHz to 10 MHz, bias current changes from 0.4 nA to 50 nA, and supply current requirements go from 1 μA to 1.5 mA. Thus, it is necessary to decide which of the characteristics is most important to adjust. The rest of the characteristics' changes must then be accepted.

Figure 11–13
Multiplexer Concept

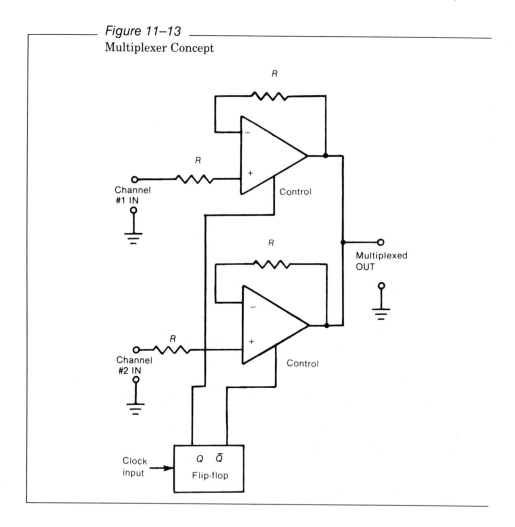

Programmable gain amplifiers (PGAs) can be constructed using conventional operational amplifiers, digital switches (multiplexers), and resistor networks. The resistor networks are used to form the gain-controlling feedback path for the op amp. Selection of the actual resistance in the feedback path is performed by the multiplexer. An eight-position multiplexer can provide 128 switching combinations under control of only three digital inputs. Thus digital switching places the PGA gain under control of a computer in many of today's applications.

Programmable operational amplifiers may be used in **multiplexing** and voltage-controlled oscillator applications much like transconductance amplifiers. The most common applications, however, are in conventional op amp circuits. Programmable op amps allow the use of only one type of amplifier throughout an electronic device. Characteristics for specific portions of the device are selected by the appropriate set current. The wide use of digital computers in instrumentation applications has also had an impact in the use of operational amplifiers. Digitally programmable op amps are beginning to see wide application. Such amplifiers contain circuits on the op amp chip that accept digital signals and convert them to precise set currents for operational amplifier use.

OP-AMP-RELATED INTEGRATED CIRCUITS

As IC technology advances, many of the functions performed by a number of op amps and related components are being incorporated in single *large-scale integrated* (LSI) circuits. Three basic examples from the rapidly growing field of LSI circuits are shown in this section.

Sample-and-Hold Circuits

Another operational amplifier application is found in the instrumentation field. When data are gathered from a number of different locations, it is often necessary to sample the data sequentially and to hold the information for a short period of time. Traditionally, the information was converted to a current or voltage and the energy stored in a capacitor. Unfortunately, any load connected to the capacitor provided a discharge path, and the stored information changed. Modern **sample-and-hold circuits** use operational amplifiers to isolate the storage capacitor from its load. The operation is much like that of a peak detector.

Figure 11–14 shows both the simplified and a practical sample-and-hold circuit. In simplified form (Figure 11–14A), a switch is closed for a short period of time, connecting the parameter to be measured to the sampling capacitor. The capacitor is charged to the input voltage of the data being sampled. Then, when the switch opens, the voltage remains on the capacitor. After the sampling period, the voltage stored on the capacitor is examined and converted to a digital format for transmission and/or permanent storage. In practical form (Figure 11–14B), the sampling switch is most likely an electronic switch such as a field effect transistor. It is turned on at the appropriate time by an electronic sequencing circuit that supplies a precisely timed "on" period. When the switch opens, the capacitor is isolated from the charging source and left connected to the input of the operational amplifier. The voltage present across the capacitor thus provides input to an operational amplifier

Figure 11–14
Sample-and-Hold Concepts

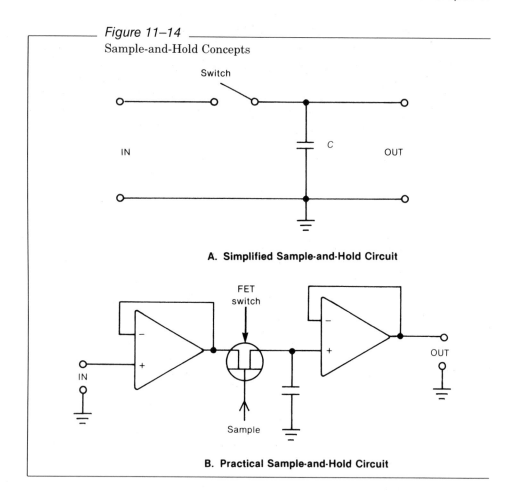

most often connected as a voltage follower. Its high input impedance has little effect on the stored charge, and its low output impedance makes examination of the amount of stored charge easy. For maximum efficiency and accuracy, FET-input operational amplifiers are used because of their extremely high input impedance.

An LSI version of the sample-and-hold circuit is shown in Figure 11–15. Everything necessary to implement a sample-and-hold operation (other than the "hold" capacitor) is included on a single IC chip. All of the input isolation, switching, and output isolation functions are provided with only an external connection to the holding capacitor required. Internal components establish an input-to-output gain of unity. Input impedance is usually well over 100 MΩ, and combinations of FET and junction transistors ensure low offset and drift. All in all, the

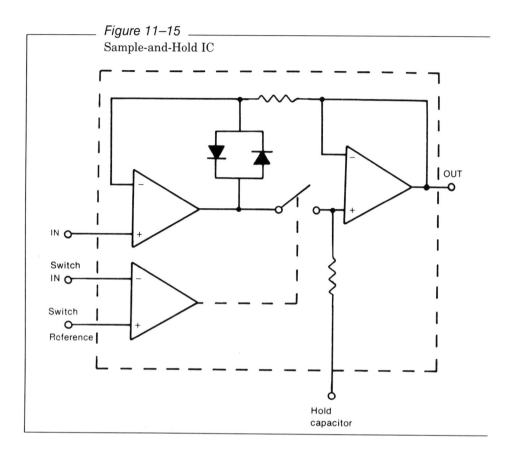

Figure 11–15

Sample-and-Hold IC

sample-and-hold operation is performed much more effectively and in-expensively with LSI ICs than with op amps and other components.

Analog Signal-Processing Subsystem

The **analog signal-processing subsystem** IC (Figure 11–16) takes the sample-and-hold function one step farther. Instead of one input am-plifier, two are provided. Either may be electronically switched to the output voltage follower. Sample-and-hold functions, then, may be per-formed on alternate channels when the hold capacitor is connected. Other "nice-to-have" capabilities are also provided.

For example, each of the differential input amplifiers has both its inverting and noninverting inputs available. The outputs from the volt-age follower may thus be fed back to the input amplifiers to establish both magnitude and polarity control of gain for either of the input chan-nels. Furthermore, the hold capacitor input may be used for loop com-pensation when sample-and-hold operation is not needed. A comparator

Figure 11–16
Analog Signal-Processing Subsystem IC

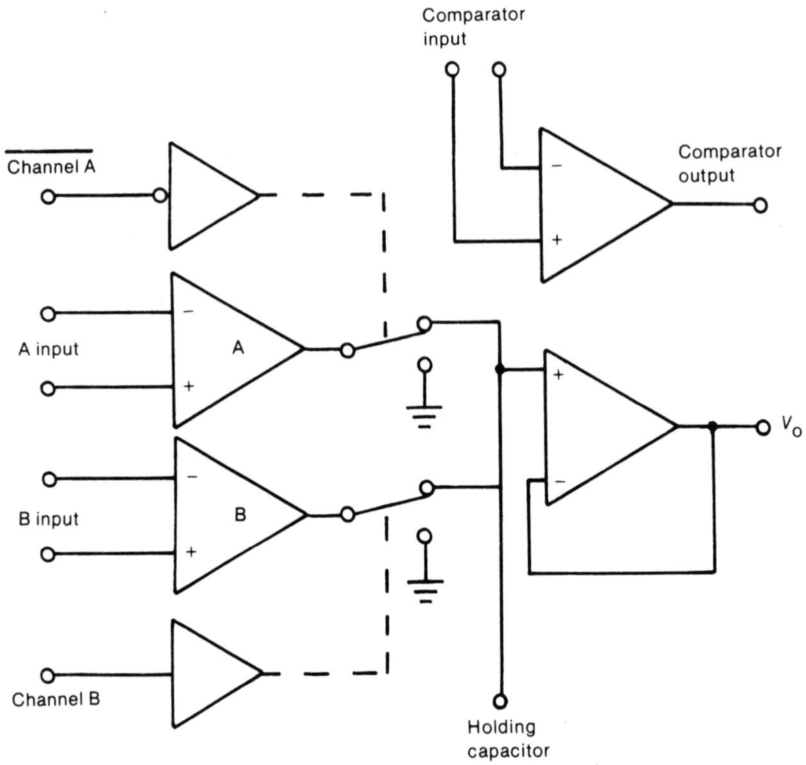

is also included in the analog signal-processing subsystem to further enhance the versatility of the chip.

The many features of the analog signal-processing subsystem make it applicable in several different applications. It can, for example, function quite effectively as a two-channel multiplexer. Either or both channels may be switched on and off to perform the sample-and-hold operation. In fact, with both channels switched off and a high-quality hold capacitor connected, the IC works well in the hold mode. With but a few external components, both analog-to-digital and digital-to-analog conversion can be performed. The IC may even be used to demodulate an amplitude-modulated signal. Considering all of its capabilities, the limitation on use of the analog signal-processing subsystem seems to be only the imagination of the user.

Timer ICs

As noted in Chapter 9, one of the methods of generating nonsinusoidal waveforms is the use of a timer IC. The "old standby" in timer chips is the 555 timer. Many manufacturers supply the 555 timer and its dual equivalent, the 556 dual timer. Included on this IC chip are both digital and analog circuits, resistors, and even a transistor switch. Figure 11–17A is a block diagram of a typical 555 timer. Note that only the external connections relating to this discussion are shown in the figure. See manufacturers' specification sheets for complete details.

The heart of this highly functional IC is a digital circuit called a *set/reset flip-flop*. Flip-flops are circuits that may be in only one of two possible conditions, such as "on" or "off" and "set" or "reset." The set/reset flip-flop in the 555 timer turns off when the reset input is + and the set input is ground and stays off until the set input becomes + and the reset input becomes ground. (The flip-flop inputs respond only to + inputs.) The flip-flop then changes from off to on and remains on until the original conditions reoccur. When the flip-flop is off, its output is 0 V; when on, the output voltage is approximately equal to the + supply voltage. Flip-flop output is applied to an amplifier on the chip so that the flip-flop may be isolated from external influences.

Flip-flop output is also used to control a transistor switch on the chip. The switch is on and the discharge output is grounded (0 V) when the flip-flop is reset, or off. When the flip-flop is set, or on, the switch is off and the discharge output is open-circuited.

Two comparators control the 555 timer's flip-flop. You may recall that a comparator has an output that is of a digital nature, while its inputs are analog. Comparator output voltage is equal to the + supply voltage when the noninverting input is greater than the inverting input. As soon as the noninverting input becomes less than the inverting input, the comparator output voltage changes to 0 V. Note that the comparator outputs are applied to the inputs of the flip-flop.

Also included on the 555 timer IC is a resistive divider made up of three identical resistors. The divider is connected internally from $V+$ to ground (0 V) so that the voltage from $V+$ to ground is divided by 3. Note that $V/3$ is applied to the noninverting input of the lower comparator, while $2V/3$ is connected to the inverting input of the upper comparator. The inverting input of the lower comparator is called *trigger,* while the noninverting input of the upper comparator is called *threshold.*

Let's connect a few external components to the 555 timer, as shown in Figure 11–17B, and demonstrate one of the many waveform generation capabilities of this versatile IC. The circuit of Figure 11–17B generates a rectangular wave, as shown in Figure 11–17C. To determine

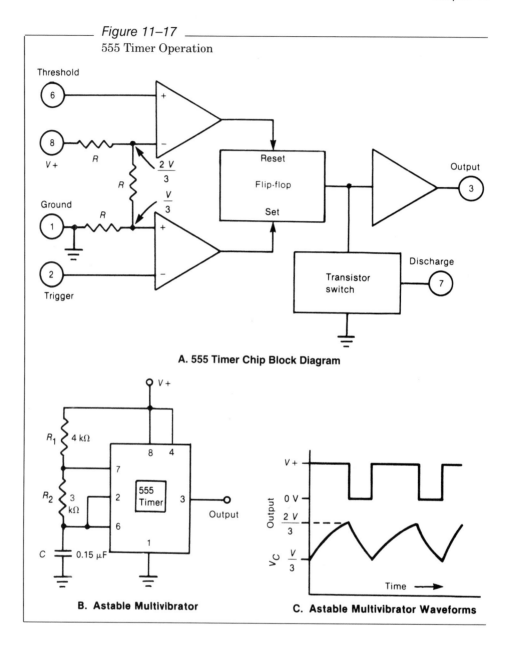

Figure 11-17
555 Timer Operation

A. 555 Timer Chip Block Diagram

B. Astable Multivibrator

C. Astable Multivibrator Waveforms

how this *astable multivibrator* circuit operates, we will assume that C is initially discharged ($V_C = 0$ V) and that power has just been applied. We will also assume $V+ = 6$ V so that the arithmetic will be easier. The internal divider will distribute the 6 V so that the upper comparator's inverting input has $+4$ V applied, while the lower comparator's noninverting input has $+2$ V applied. Let's see what results at initial application of power.

Trigger and threshold inputs are connected together, and since $V_C = 0$ V, those inputs appear to be grounded. The upper comparator thus has a more positive voltage at its inverting input than it does at its noninverting input, and its output will be 0 V. The lower comparator has a more positive voltage at its noninverting input than it does at its inverting input, and its output will be $V+$. The lower comparator will thus set the flip-flop, and the output of the 555 timer will become $V+$. At the same time, the transistor switch turns off, and the discharge output becomes open-circuited.

Thus, upon initial application of power, the output of the 555 timer is $V+$, and the discharge terminal is open-circuited. C begins to charge through R_1 and R_2 at a rate determined by the time constant, $(R_1 + R_2) \times C$. When V_C reaches $V/3$ (2 V), the lower comparator output becomes 0 V. But, since the flip-flop responds only to $+$ inputs, nothing happens. The output remains at $V+$ as C continues to charge. However, when V_C reaches $2V/3$ (4 V), the upper comparator's output changes from 0 V to $V+$. The flip-flop resets, and the output becomes 0 V. At the same time, the discharge terminal becomes short-circuited to ground, and the voltage across C begins to drop as C discharges through R_2. When the voltage across C falls to $V/3$, the lower comparator takes over and sets the flip-flop. The cycle then repeats, with the output at $V+$ as the capacitor charges and at 0 V as the capacitor discharges. Note that the charge time is longer than the discharge time, so the rectangular wave is not a true square wave. Figure 11–17C relates V_C to the output waveform. Appendix C (program 5) contains a BASIC computer program that performs 555 timer calculations.

This is but one of the many types of waveforms that the 555 timer is capable of generating. It is a very versatile chip, and the mix of digital and analog circuits on the chip has resulted in a very useful addition to the electronic world.

Another timer IC is the XR-2240 timer-counter (Figure 11–18), manufactured by Exar. It is a versatile IC that allows selection of many time delays or frequencies from a fixed oscillator circuit. It was originally designed to produce extra-long time delays (from microseconds up to five days) with high accuracy. As shown in Figure 11–18, the XR-2240 contains an internal time-base oscillator, a programmable 8-bit counter, and a control flip-flop.

Figure 11–19A shows the XR-2240 connected as a precision monostable timer. The output of the timer is HIGH until the circuit is triggered on. Then the output goes LOW for a period of time determined by a time-base period set by the RC time constant and the division ratio N. N is determined by the combination of counter outputs connected to the output terminal. The 8-bit counter allows the division ratio to range

Figure 11–18

XR-2240 Timer-Counter

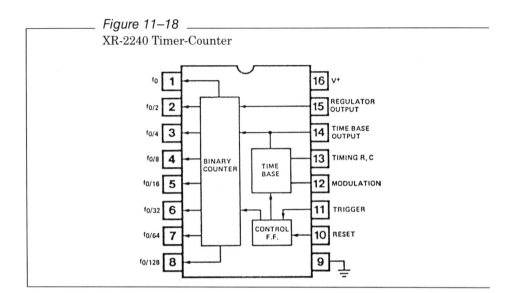

from 1 to 255. For example, if only pin 5 is connected to the output, the duration of the time delay will be $16RC$. By proper choice of output connections, the time delay can be set from $1RC$ to $255RC$.

Example 11–1

In the circuit of Figure 11–19A, $R = 100$ kΩ and $C = .01$ μF. What is the time delay duration if pins 2, 5, and 6 are connected to the output?

Solution

$$T_o = NRC$$

where

$N = 2 + 16 + 32 = 50$

$R = 100$ kΩ

$C = .01$ μF

$$T_o = (50)(100{,}000)(.01 \times 10^{-6})$$
$$= .05 \text{ s}$$
$$= 50 \text{ ms}$$

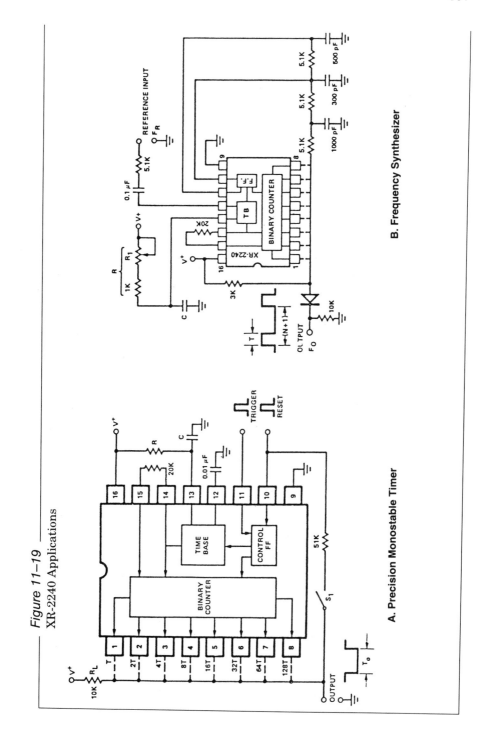

Figure 11–19
XR-2240 Applications

A. Precision Monostable Timer

B. Frequency Synthesizer

_____ *Example 11–2* _____

Repeat Example 11–1 with pins 1 through 8 all connected to the output.

Solution

$$N = 255$$
$$T_o = (255)(100,000)(.01 \times 10^{-6})$$
$$= .255 \text{ s}$$
$$= 255 \text{ ms}$$

When used as a frequency synthesizer, the XR-2240 can both multiply and divide an input reference frequency. Multiplication is accomplished when the internal time-base oscillator locks onto a harmonic of the input reference frequency applied to the synchronization input (pin 12). The division factor is determined by selection of appropriate output pins (pins 1 through 8) connected to the output. Figure 11–19B shows a generalized frequency synthesizer diagram.

The time-base oscillator can easily lock on to as high as the 10th harmonic of the input reference frequency if the time-base oscillator is within about 3% of the desired frequency. A variable resistance as part of the RC frequency determining network allows adjustment of the time-base oscillator. In the circuit of Figure 11–19B, R can range from 1 kΩ to 1 MΩ, and C can range from 0.005 μF to 0.1 μF. It should be noted, however, that the XR-2240 is not a high-frequency device. The maximum output frequency is limited to approximately 200 kHz.

Let's look at a typical application. A 100 Hz output frequency is required, synchronized to the 60 Hz power line. The output frequency of the circuit of Figure 11–19B is determined by

$$f_o = \frac{f_{ref}M}{1 + N}$$

where

f_{ref} = reference frequency
M = multiplication factor
N = division factor

The output frequency is 5/3 times the reference frequency, that is, 100/60. Therefore,

$$f_o = \frac{60 \times 5}{1 + 2}$$

The time-base oscillator should be adjusted to synchronize to the 5th harmonic of the 60 Hz reference, and the divider chain should be connected to divide by two. A 100 Hz output frequency, synchronized to the 60 Hz line frequency, will result.

SUMMARY

Comparators, the first of the special-purpose op amps discussed in Chapter 11, accept linear inputs and provide digital outputs. Their primary function, then, is to compare two voltages at the op amp inputs and supply one of two possible output voltages. Thus, comparators easily interface analog with digital circuits.

By paying special attention to input circuit design, operational amplifiers become instrumentation amplifiers capable of amplifying signals of very small magnitude even in the presence of large interfering signals. Instrumentation amplifiers find application in the medical, aerospace, and automotive fields.

Current difference amplifiers, while not really operational amplifiers, perform op-amp-like functions. They amplify the difference between two input currents, not voltages. Since current must flow in the input circuits, the very high input resistance of conventional op amps is not present. There are even special op amps that provide a current rather than voltage output. These are transconductance amplifiers, and they are most often found with variable-gain capability. Voltage-controlled oscillators, filters, and amplitude modulators can effectively use variable-gain transconductance amplifiers.

Two of the subjects discussed in this chapter show great promise for the future. Programmable amplifiers allow the design of circuits that perform many functions with only a single type of operational amplifier. Cost of design and manufacture is greatly reduced when only one type of device is used.

LSI circuits have already heavily impacted the electronics industry. As soon as enough uses appear for a specific function, the designers of integrated circuits produce a new chip. If there is any disadvantage to LSI circuits, it is that there is little standardization. Manufacturers do not necessarily agree on how much should be included on a chip, and the market sees a proliferation of new devices every year. Still, the use of op-amp-related LSI circuits has allowed electronic devices to become less expensive and smaller, with greater capability—a far cry from the basic type 741 op amp initially discussed in this text.

═══ QUESTIONS ═══

1. Discuss the differences and similarities of operational amplifiers and comparators.

2. Explain in what kind of applications a zero-crossing detector would be advantageous. Draw a schematic diagram if necessary.

3. List the disadvantages of a zero-crossing detector, and show how to improve the listed characteristics.

4. Show an application for a window comparator other than that shown in Figure 11–4. Explain the circuit operation.

5. Discuss what changes would be necessary to the schematic diagram of Figure 11–5 to shorten the output pulse to one-half the present width.

6. What is the primary difference between conventional operational amplifiers and instrumentation amplifiers?

7. Explain how instrumentation amplifiers improve common-mode rejection ratio characteristics of op amps.

8. What determines the gain of the instrumentation amplifier of Figure 11–7?

9. What determines the CMRR of the instrumentation amplifier of Figure 11–7?

10. Discuss the difficulties that exist with the use of electronic devices in medical applications. Explain how instrumentation amplifiers and operational amplifiers have helped solve some of the problems.

11. How does a current difference amplifier differ from conventional operational amplifiers? How are they similar?

12. Can current difference amplifiers be used in the same circuits as conventional operational amplifiers? If not, explain what circuit changes may be required.

13. How does a transconductance amplifier differ from current difference and conventional operational amplifiers? How are they similar?

14. Can transconductance amplifiers be used in the same circuits as conventional operational amplifiers? If not, explain what circuit changes may be required.

15. What parameters may be varied with programmable amplifiers? Are the varied parameters interrelated, and if so, how?

16. Explain the principles of operation of sample-and-hold circuits. Where would these circuits be used?

12

Using Op Amps with Semiconductor Devices

OBJECTIVES After studying Chapter 12, you will be able to

1. Explain how op amps compensate for diode small-signal non-linearity.
2. Show methods of obtaining negative output from precision diodes.
3. Explain how to change the reference level of precision diodes.
4. Show how to obtain full-wave output from precision diodes.
5. List applications of full-wave precision diodes.
6. Describe the uses of peak and peak-to-peak detectors.
7. Discuss reasons for using zener diodes with op amps.
8. Determine where FETs are used in op amp circuits.
9. List applications of bipolar transistors with op amps.
10. Show how op amps can be used in power control circuits.

———— *INTRODUCTION* ————————

   While operational amplifiers can perform many functions with the aid of only passive components such as resistors and capacitors, the use of active components such as diodes, transistors, and other ICs presents many new applications. Chapter 12 investigates how active devices may be combined with op amps to perform additional operations.

   No new operational amplifier ideas are presented in this chapter. However, some of the characteristics of semiconductors are freely used without review. For a review of semiconductor theory, refer to the formulas and data in Appendix B. For additional review, if necessary, refer to any of the multitude of basic semiconductor texts.

DIODES AND OP AMPS

Operational amplifiers can be used to enhance the performance of common semiconductor diodes. One of the disadvantages of semiconductor diodes is that they are nonlinear, especially when small voltage is applied. The graph in Figure 12–1 shows the forward characteristic of a typical semiconductor diode. Note that the response at forward voltages less than 0.7 V is especially nonlinear. Such nonlinearity is usually no problem with power diodes where 0.7 V is a small percentage of the total voltage. In small-signal applications, however, the nonlinearity must be considered.

Precision Diode

If the diode is placed in the negative feedback path, the 0.7 V threshold is effectively divided by the open-loop gain of the op amp. Consider the circuit of Figure 12–2. As the signal applied to the noninverting input becomes positive, the output also becomes positive. The diode becomes forward biased with a very small positive input signal due to the high open-loop gain of the operational amplifier. When the diode becomes forward biased, negative feedback is "connected." The output then follows the input because of the 100% feedback. Any temperature sensitivity of the diode is also reduced by its location in the feedback loop. Therefore, the output of the **precision diode** configuration is as shown in Figure 12–2. The forward characteristics of a precision diode are com-

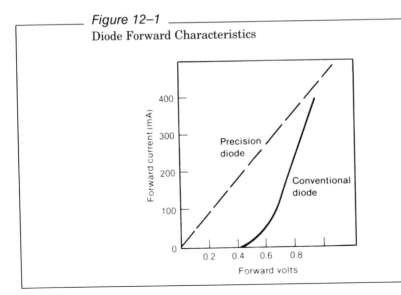

Figure 12–1
Diode Forward Characteristics

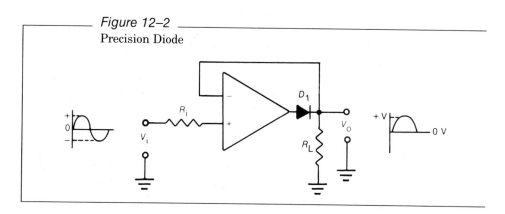

Figure 12–2

Precision Diode

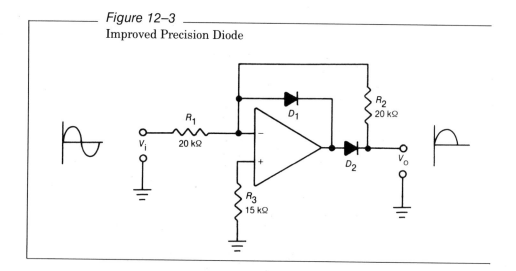

Figure 12–3

Improved Precision Diode

pared with those of a typical semiconductor diode in Figure 12–1. If negative rather than positive output is required, it is only necessary to reverse the diode.

A small modification to the half-wave precision diode rectifier circuit (Figure 12–3) results in higher frequency and more stable operation. The conventional inverting amplifier configuration is used. Both input signal and feedback are applied to the inverting input. A negative-going input signal causes a positive-going output, forward biasing D_2. Resulting current flow through R_2 develops an output signal. When the input signal goes positive, the output goes negative. D_2 is reverse biased, and no current flows through R_2. D_1 becomes forward biased, limiting

Figure 12–4

Clipping and Clamping

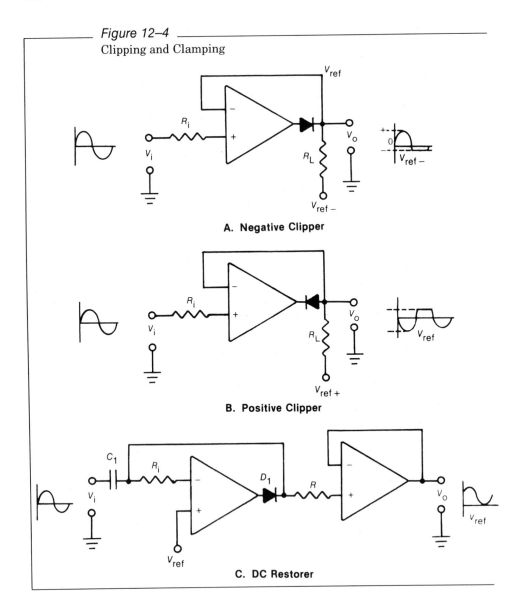

A. Negative Clipper

B. Positive Clipper

C. DC Restorer

the negative output excursion. Saturation of the amplifier is thus prevented, and the amplifier recovers more quickly. High-frequency response may be improved by placing a small capacitor across R_2 to achieve feed-forward compensation.

It is not difficult to establish a reference other than 0 V for the precision diode, as shown in Figures 12–2 and 12–3. Returning R_L in Figure 12–2 to either a positive or negative reference (instead of ground) will do the trick. Figure 12–4 shows how to obtain different reference values. When R_L is returned to a negative reference value, more than a half sine wave is seen at the output (Figure 12–4A). The reference extends below ground, and a portion of the negative sine wave is allowed through. Reversing the diode and changing the reference to a positive voltage allows the opposite situation to occur (Figure 12–4B). When it is necessary to process the complete sine wave without clipping, but to establish other than a 0 V reference, the *DC restorer* of Figure 12–4C may be used. As V_i goes below V_{ref} (negative), D_1 is forward biased. C_1 charges to the peak value of the negative half-cycle, and after the peak has passed, D_1 becomes reverse biased. The charge on C_1 remains, since no discharge path is provided. (Remember, the input resistance of an op amp is very high.) The input waveform thus is applied to the circuit with a reference level determined by V_{ref} and the amplitude of the input waveform. Output level thus is **clamped** to V_{ref}, and the output waveform appears "on top" of the reference level in Figure 12–4C. Clamping to a positive peak level can be obtained by reversing D_1.

Absolute-Value Circuits

A number of different possibilities also exist when full-wave circuits, or **absolute-value circuits,** are required. Figure 12–5 shows one approach. The input and output of an inverting half-wave precision diode circuit, such as shown in Figure 12–3, are combined in the proper amplitude and phase relationships. During the negative half-cycle of the input signal, no output is produced by the inverting half-wave precision diode circuit (see preceding explanation). The input signal is, however, supplied to the input of the inverting summing mixer. Therefore, a positive half-cycle will be produced at the output of the absolute-value

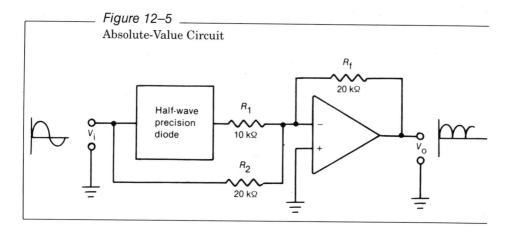

Figure 12–5

Absolute-Value Circuit

circuit during the negative half-cycle of the input signal. During the positive half-cycle of the input signal, the inverting half-wave precision diode circuit produces a negative half-cycle output. At the same time, the input signal is supplying a positive half-cycle. If these half-cycles are mixed in equal proportions, cancellation would occur. Note, however, that the mixing resistors provide twice as much input to the summing point from the half-wave circuit. ($R_1 = 10$ kΩ, while $R_2 = 20$ kΩ.) The net result is as though the input signal were not present during the positive half-cycle. Final circuit output, thus, is the same as would be noted with conventional full-wave rectification, without the nonlinear response at voltages less than 0.7 V. As shown, the output will be the positive absolute value of the input voltage. If the average absolute value is needed, a filter capacitor may be placed in parallel with the summing mixer feedback resistor F_f.

Another variation of the precision absolute-value circuit is shown in Figure 12–6. It provides full-wave rectification by inverting negative polarity input voltages and operates as a unity gain amplifier for positive polarity inputs. For a positive input, two stages of inverting unity gain amplification are used. When the input goes positive, the output of A_1 goes negative. D_2 turns off, and D_1 turns on. Therefore, the junction of R_3 and R_4 is at minus V_i. The voltage at point $\times$ is 0 because D_2 is off and very little A_2 bias current flows in R_2. A_2 operates as an inverting unity gain amplifier, so $V_o = V_i$.

For negative inputs, first-stage gain to point $\times$ is $-2/3$ because D_2 is on, D_1 is off, and 1/3 of the input current flows in R_3 and R_4. The

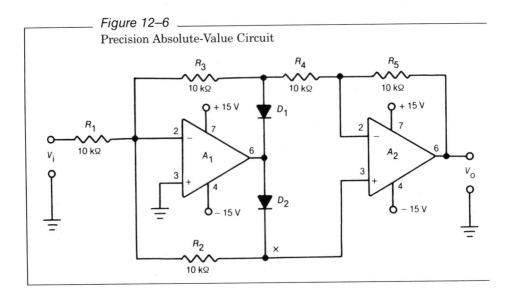

Figure 12–6
Precision Absolute-Value Circuit

second stage operates at a noninverting gain of 1.5 with the voltage at point $\times$ as its input. The overall circuit gain is thus -1. Therefore, V_o will be a positive waveform consisting of the positive half-cycle followed by the "inverted" negative half-cycle. The circuit of Figure 12–6 thus performs the same function as that of Figure 12–5.

Detectors

One application for precision diode circuits is found in the communications field. Information is transmitted from one location to another by changing some characteristic of a radio wave. The amplitude of the radio wave, for example, may be varied by the voice tones and loudness. When the radio wave is received and processed, it is necessary to recover the original information. This function may be performed by a diode and a capacitor connected as a **peak detector.** Figures 12–7A and 12–7B show how an amplitude-modulated radio wave appears before and after it is "detected." The peak detector shown in Figure 12–7C, in effect, allows only positive half-cycles of the radio wave through the diode. The associated capacitor stores the peak value of each of the radio wave half-cycles until the next half-cycle arrives. Then, the capacitor charges to the new value. The voltage across the capacitor is thus a relatively good replica of the original information. Unfortunately, though, the diode is nonlinear and does not reproduce the low-voltage portions of the radio waves faithfully. A precision diode may be substituted for the conventional diode to improve performance, as shown in Figure 12–7D. Selection of appropriate values of capacitance and resistance are important so that maximum output with minimum distortion is achieved.

Occasionally, it becomes necessary to extract the peak-to-peak value of a modulated waveform. The **peak-to-peak detector** of Figure 12–8 performs this function. Both a positive and a negative peak detector are required. (A negative peak detector may be obtained by reversing the diode in Figure 12–7.) The positive peak detector output is applied to the inverting input of an op amp, while the negative peak detector output feeds the noninverting input. The operational amplifier is connected in the adder-subtractor configuration discussed in Chapter 10. Output of the peak-to-peak detector circuit is thus proportional to the peak-to-peak value of the input signal.

Some peak detector applications require that the maximum value of the input signal be detected and then stored for a relatively long time. In other words, the input may be a varying-amplitude signal, but the output must be an indication of the *highest* voltage seen at the input. The conventional precision peak detector, with slight modification, can perform this function. Removal of the resistance used in parallel with the detector capacitor will keep the capacitor from discharging. Other changes are also needed, however. Any attempt to measure the voltage

Figure 12–7 _____
Amplitude Modulation Detection

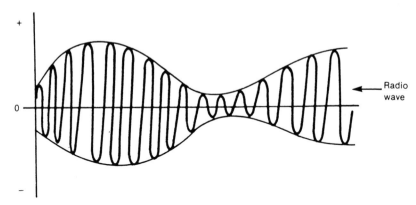

A. Amplitude-Modulated Radio Wave

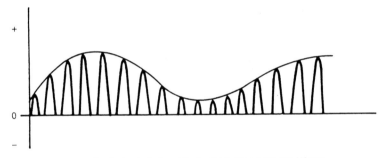

B. Detected Amplitude-Modulated Radio Wave

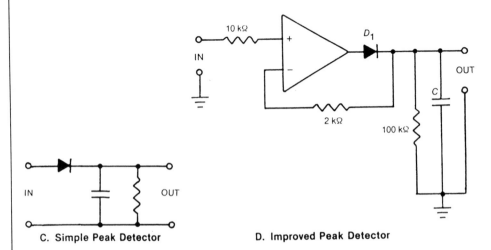

C. Simple Peak Detector

D. Improved Peak Detector

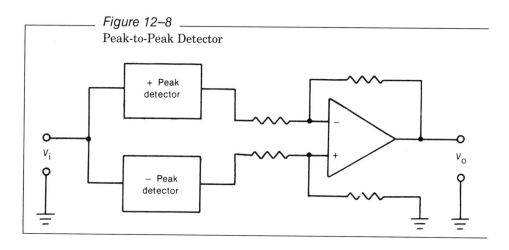

Figure 12–8

Peak-to-Peak Detector

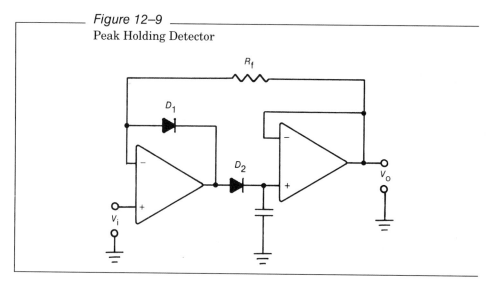

Figure 12–9

Peak Holding Detector

across the capacitor will somewhat discharge it. Therefore, it is common practice to use a unity gain voltage follower to isolate the capacitor. The low output impedance of the follower will allow measurement, whereas its high input impedance will prevent capacitor discharge. A means must also be provided to prevent the capacitor from following the peak value of the input signal when it falls below its "present" peak value. Diode D_2 is connected so that it becomes reverse biased when the output of the precision diode circuit becomes less than the peak voltage stored by the capacitor. Figure 12–9 shows a circuit meeting these requirements.

Zener Diode Applications

Zener diodes also are used with operational amplifiers. In Chapter 9, Figure 9–15 showed back-to-back zener diodes connected to clamp the output of an operational amplifier to specific voltages. Any application that requires a constant voltage drop with varying applied voltage is a prime candidate for zener diodes.

When large signal swings are encountered with operational amplifiers, it is desirable to prevent the output from reaching saturation. A finite time is required for an amplifier to recover from saturation, and, if fast response is necessary, saturation should be prevented. Furthermore, there are circumstances where an operational amplifier must be connected to digital systems. This requires the output voltage to be limited to a value that is less than the op amp swing. The easy way to meet these requirements is to use zener diodes in the feedback path. Figure 12–10 shows a scheme to limit an op amp's output voltage.

If both zener diodes are identical, the output voltage will be limited to $V_z + V_{fd}$, where V_z is the zener value and V_{fd} is the forward voltage drop. A typical value for forward voltage drop is 0.6 V, while numerous zener voltages are available. Assuming zener diodes with a 9.1 V rating, the output circuit of Figure 12–10 will be limited to $+9.7$ V and -9.7 V. If supply voltages are the normal $+15$ V and -15 V, saturation will be avoided.

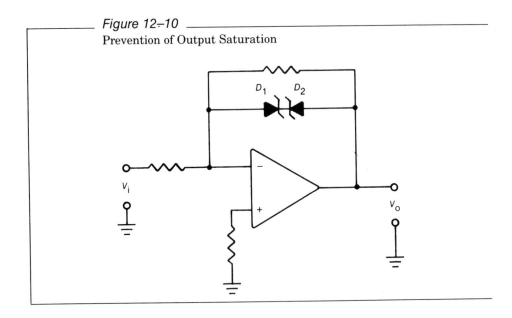

Figure 12–10

Prevention of Output Saturation

FET APPLICATIONS

Field effect transistors are often combined with operational amplifiers to perform functions not available with operational amplifiers alone.

Voltage-Variable Resistors

When the drain-to-source voltage of a field effect transistor is low, variation of the gate-to-source voltage will cause a predictable change in resistance between the drain and source. In other words, the FET acts as a **voltage-variable resistor (VVR).** Figure 12–11A shows a typical graph of the variation in drain-to-source resistance (R_{ds}) with changes in gate-to-source voltage (V_{gs}). This characteristic makes the FET applicable to most electronic circuits that require resistance variation to perform their functions.

Figure 12–11B is a very simple use of an FET in a voltage divider circuit such as a gain or volume control in an audio system. As in any other voltage divider, V_o is determined by V_i and the voltage divider ratio. In the case of Figure 12–11B,

$$V_o = V_i \times \frac{R_{ds}}{R_T} \qquad (12\text{–}1)$$

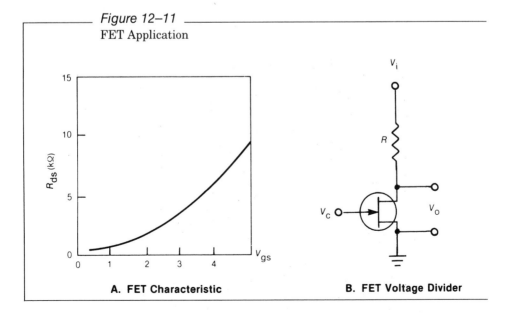

Figure 12–11
FET Application

A. FET Characteristic

B. FET Voltage Divider

where $R_T = R + R_{ds}$. The control voltage (V_c) can be varied either by a potentiometer or an active circuit to control V_o. In typical FETs, V_c variations are from 0 V to a voltage where drain-to-source resistance is highest (called the **pinchoff voltage**). Typically, the pinchoff voltage is in the region of 2 V to 10 V, depending on the FET. Resulting drain-to-source resistance variations will be from near 0 Ω to greater than 15 kΩ. Therefore, the output from a simple FET voltage divider may vary from 0 V to a value determined by the total resistance of the voltage divider.

Gain Control

An FET may be placed in the feedback path of an operational amplifier to control circuit gain. If programmable op amps are available, such additional circuitry is not necessary. However, in many applications, the FET may prove more effective. Figure 12–12 shows two gain control applications of FETs in op amp circuits. In the inverting amplifier configuration (Figure 12–12A), the FET is placed in series with the incoming signal and is used as part of R_i. Since the gain of an inverting op amp circuit is simply $-R_f/R_i$, any variation of R_i will cause a gain change. It is only necessary to provide a small control voltage (V_c) to obtain gain control.

A similar approach is used with the noninverting op amp circuit of Figure 12–12B. The FET is used as part of the feedback voltage divider. Varying V_c will vary the percentage of output voltage fed back to the inverting input, thus varying gain. The usual formula for gain,

$$A = 1 + \frac{R_f}{R_{ds}} \qquad \text{(12–2)}$$

shows that variation of drain-to-source resistance will indeed cause gain variation. Both Figures 12–12A and 12–12B are somewhat idealized. Circuit bias modifications may be necessary to achieve *linear* resistance variation with changes in control voltage. However, the basic circuits as shown are in common use, and modifications for linearity are easily recognized.

Oscillators

The Wien bridge oscillator of Figure 12–13 is another candidate for FETs as voltage-variable resistors. Recall that the balance between negative and positive feedback is critical in Wien bridge oscillators. It is necessary to change the negative feedback if oscillator output rises so

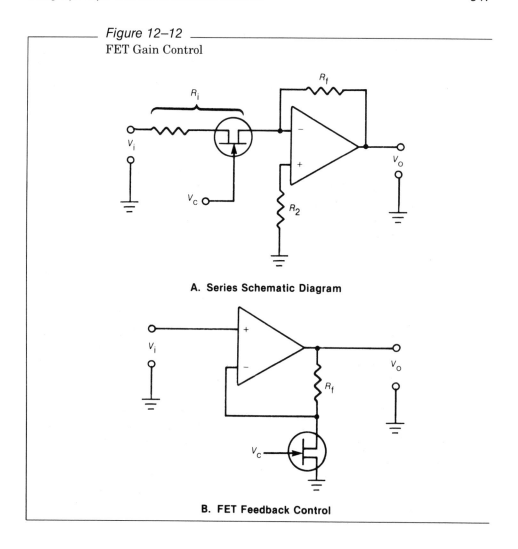

Figure 12–12

FET Gain Control

A. Series Schematic Diagram

B. FET Feedback Control

that a relatively constant output amplitude is maintained. In many Wien bridge oscillators, a small incandescent lamp or diode is used, since its resistance characteristic meets the changing feedback requirement. Unfortunately, it takes time for the lamp to change resistance as the output amplitude of the oscillator changes. The FET can perform the same function without the disadvantage of the thermal time constant of the lamp. Figure 12–13 shows how an FET may be used to stabilize Wien bridge oscillator operation.

The positive feedback is conventional, consisting of R_4-C_3 and R_5-C_4. The negative feedback consists of R_3, C_2, and Q_1 in parallel with

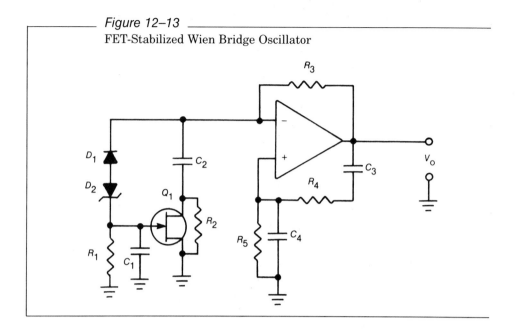

Figure 12–13

FET-Stabilized Wien Bridge Oscillator

R_2. When the output of the operational amplifier exceeds the breakdown voltage of D_1 and D_2, C_1 is charged. The charge stored in C_1 is the gate-to-source voltage of the FET and thus controls the drain-to-source resistance. (C_2 is a DC blocking capacitor to reduce offset voltage and offset current effects.) The parallel combination of R_2 and the drain-to-source resistance of Q_1 thus establishes the percentage of negative feedback. R_1 in conjunction with C_1 actually determines how quickly the FET responds to changes in output amplitude. Their time constant is selected to obtain minimum response time consistent with distortion requirements. Although additional components have been added, the FET-stabilized Wien bridge oscillator is superior to lamp-stabilized circuits in most cases.

FET Switches

FETs are also used as switches in many operational amplifier applications. Sample-and-hold circuits are typical, as was shown in Figure 11–14B. FET switches can have less than 5 Ω resistance when on and a very high resistance, over 200 MΩ, when off. Operating in a switching mode, FETs thus can charge the sampling capacitor through a very low resistance yet present a very high leakage path when off. The same characteristics make FET switches ideal in integrator circuits. As noted in Chapter 11, the integrating capacitor must be periodically discharged (the circuit must be reset) to prevent accumulation of offset errors. The low on-resistance of an FET switch allows short discharge durations. When off, the FET switch has little effect because of its high leakage. The same switching technique is used in various waveform generators that employ integrator circuits. Therefore, when within the power rating of the FET, many circuits can effectively use FET switches.

FET switches also work effectively in audio applications. Most audio entertainment systems require selection of one of many different sources such as records, tape, tuner, and so forth. Relatively complex mechanical switches are often required, and long leads to the front panel may be sources of **hum** pickup and **cross-talk.** The use of FET switches allows the actual switching to remain close to the amplifiers and at the same time reduces the requirements for large switching assemblies. Figure 12–14 is a simplified diagram showing the use of FET switches in an audio system. The FETs act as very high resistances in series with input to the amplifier when their control voltage is 10 V. Grounding the gate (0 V) causes the FET to act as a short circuit, and the selected input is connected to the operational amplifier.

Figure 12–14

FET Switches in Audio Applications

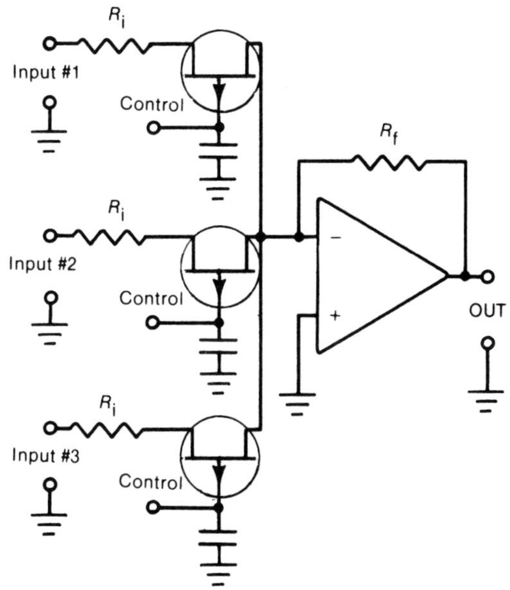

BIPOLAR TRANSISTOR APPLICATIONS

The most common use of bipolar junction transistors with operational amplifiers is to extend the current- or power-handling capability of the operational amplifier. Chapter 3 included a discussion of this subject as related to voltage regulators. A review of the material is suggested at this time.

Power Switches

Power operational amplifiers, now becoming common, can handle many of the applications requiring more current or power capability than conventional operational amplifiers. There are many situations, however, where it is less expensive or more convenient to use a bipolar transistor (or transistors) to accomplish the same task. For example, consider the monitor circuit of an automobile electrical system shown in Figure 12–15. The purpose of the circuit is to constantly monitor the voltage of the electrical system and give an indication when it is either above or below a selected value. The indicating lamp requires more current than the comparator is able to supply. A PNP transistor is therefore used to increase the current-handling capability of the comparator configuration (discussed in Chapter 11). Comparator C_1, as adjusted by R_5, detects the upper limit, whereas C_2, as adjusted by R_6, detects the lower limit.

Let's verify the operation of the circuit. The transistor must be turned off (nonconducting) for the lamp to be turned off. Base-to-emitter voltage on a transistor must be near zero for this condition. The inverted configuration of the PNP transistor, with the emitter connected to the positive voltage, thus requires the base to be near the same positive voltage. Either comparator 1 or comparator 2 can furnish the required positive voltage to the base of the transistor. Remember how a comparator operates? The output switches to V_{cc+} when the noninverting input is at a voltage higher than the inverting input *or* when the inverting input is at a voltage less than the noninverting input. So, we want the comparator 1 output to be switched to V_{cc+} when the input voltage to the circuit is less than the high-voltage threshold. Likewise, we want the comparator 2 output to be switched to V_{cc+} when the input voltage to the circuit is more than the low-voltage threshold. Voltages outside the desired range will not cause either of the comparators to switch, and their outputs will be near zero volts. The PNP transistor will be turned on, and the lamp will be illuminated to warn of an out-of-tolerance condition. A power comparator or power op amp could have been substituted for the combination of comparator and transistor. The circuit shown, however, demonstrates how the same function can be performed with conventional components.

Figure 12–15
Electrical System Monitor

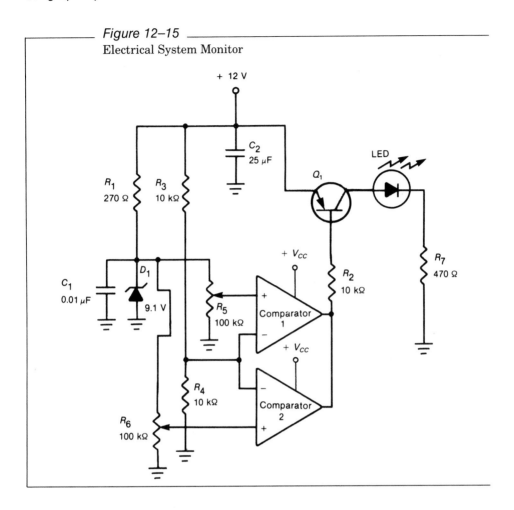

Troubleshooting: During a periodic maintenance check of the electrical system monitor of Figure 12–15, the warning light failed to illuminate for either high- or low-voltage conditions. The troubleshooting example for this chapter will attempt to determine the malfunction.

Let's try half-splitting. We will check the output of the comparators first. Both high- and low-voltage conditions result in low outputs at the appropriate comparators, so the comparators are functioning. Could the malfunction be Q_1?

First, let's put a jumper wire between the collector and emitter of the transistor. If the lamp comes on (which it does), the lamp and associated resistor are OK. Q_1 must be defective or always "turned off" for some reason. That is, the base-to-emitter voltage must be near 0 V.

When measured, the base-to-emitter voltage is near 0 V. An ohmmeter check verifies that a base-to-emitter short exists in Q_1. Replacement of Q_1 will remove the malfunction and allow correct circuit operation.

Current Drivers

The same technique is used to operate other high-current loads such as relays, stepper motors, and heaters. Figure 12–16 is a schematic diagram of a circuit that is used to maintain constant temperature for a frequency-determining crystal in an oscillator circuit. The heater and the temperature sensor are placed in close proximity to the crystal to maintain a constant temperature. Actual temperature is a function of

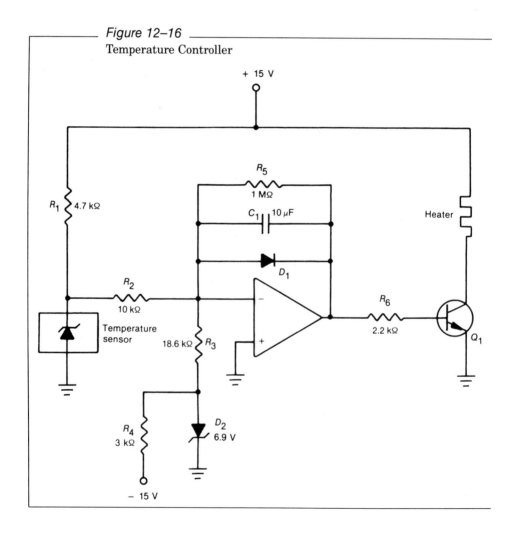

Figure 12–16
Temperature Controller

the current through the heater, which is controlled by transistor Q_1. Control bias for Q_1 is supplied by the operational amplifier connected as an inverting adder. A reference voltage from zener diode D_2 is combined with voltage developed by the temperature sensor to form the input to the operational amplifier. Amplifier gain and frequency response are determined by R_5 and C_1, which are selected to provide the necessary speed of response for the heater control. The temperature sensor is a zener diode whose regulation voltage is proportional to temperature. Any change in temperature causes a voltage change across the sensor. This change is amplified and used to control the current flow through Q_1 and the heater element. The use of R_5 and D_1 for control of low-frequency gain and offset voltage was explained in Chapter 10 during discussion of integrators.

Audio Applications

In audio systems, when output power requirements exceed the capability of an IC operational amplifier, external transistors may be used to boost the power. One approach uses **complementary emitter followers** within the feedback loop, as shown in the schematic diagram of Figure 12–17A. The operational amplifier is the same as discussed in Chapter 5. It is a conventional audio op amp with an internal divider to allow single-ended operation. Both single-ended and stereo applications were shown in Chapter 5.

The operational amplifier in Figure 12–17 supplies the output load (the speaker) directly through R_5 at low power levels. When the power level exceeds about 20 mW, the booster transistors are biased by the load current through R_5. The booster transistors then supply current to the load. Negative feedback is typical in audio amplifiers. Midfrequency gain is established by the R_3-R_2 combination, while C_2 determines the low-frequency roll-off characteristic. High-frequency roll-off is a function of the amplifier, the transistors, and the R_4-C_6 network. The frequency response graph of the circuit showing voltage gain (A_V) versus frequency in hertz for a power output P_o of 10 W is included in Figure 12–17B.

Chapter 10 provided some insight into the use of bipolar transistors as logarithmic elements for mathematical operations. Other applications of bipolar junction transistors are shown in Chapter 13.

POWER CONTROL DEVICES

Control of AC-operated devices often requires more power-handling capability than transistors can easily supply. Other semiconductor

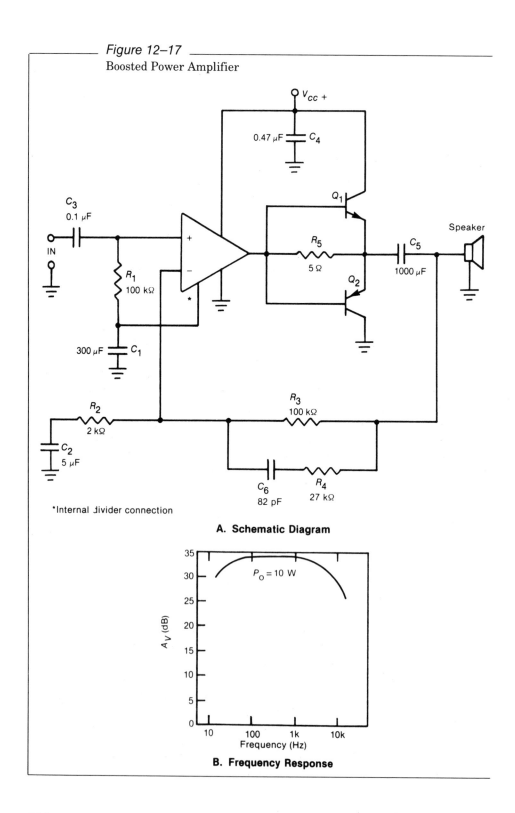

Figure 12–17

Boosted Power Amplifier

*Internal divider connection

A. Schematic Diagram

B. Frequency Response

Figure 12–18

Triac Temperature Controller

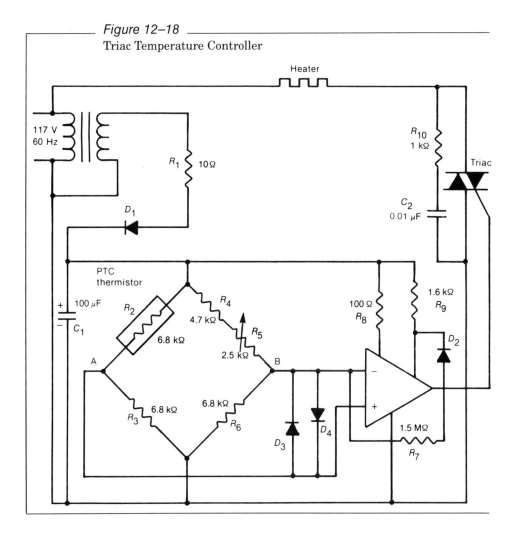

devices such as **silicon-controlled rectifiers (SCRs)** and **triacs** are used in such applications. Unfortunately, most SCRs and triacs require more driving power than most operational amplifiers have available. The solution to this problem is often the addition of bipolar transistor drivers. However, some op amp manufacturers provide power operational amplifiers especially suited to SCR and triac control applications.

Figure 12–18 shows a simple AC-line-operated heater control. A triac is used to control the amount of power supplied to the heater element. The sensor continuously monitors the temperature, supplying control input to the power op amp, which is basically a power amplifier with the usual differential input. Let's investigate the operation of the circuit in Figure 12–18.

Recall that a triac is a bidirectional AC switch that behaves like two SCRs connected back-to-back. The SCR, remember, is only a half-wave device. The triac allows operation on *both* alternations of the AC line. Conduction of the triac is controlled by the input to the gate terminal, just as with an SCR. The bidirectional characteristic of the triac, however, allows control on *both* alternations. Heat output of the electrical heater element will thus be a function of the amount of time per AC cycle that the triac allows current to flow.

The full voltage of the AC line is applied to the heater element in series with the triac. A step-down transformer reduces the line voltage so that it may be rectified and filtered to supply power to the sensing bridge and the power op amp. The sensing bridge, with its sensor and adjusting potentiometer is connected directly across the DC supply. Differential input to the power op amp is from the opposite sides of the bridge. Note the back-to-back diodes connected across the inputs of the op amp. It is possible that relatively high differential voltage may develop across the bridge, and these diodes protect the op amp input.

We can start analysis with the temperature at the sensor *higher* than the desired temperature. Since the sensor has a positive temperature coefficient, its resistance will be higher than normal. The bridge is unbalanced, with point B more positive than point A. Thus, the inverting input of the operational amplifier is more positive than the noninverting input, and the output is low. No drive current is provided to the triac, and it is turned off. Current flow through the heater is zero, and the heater begins to cool.

When the temperature of the sensor falls *below* the desired temperature, its resistance is lower than normal. Under these conditions, the bridge is unbalanced, with point A more positive than point B. The noninverting input of the operational amplifier is more positive than the inverting input, and the output is high. Drive current is provided to the gate of the triac, and current flows through the heater. The on-off cycle of the triac continues to maintain the temperature set by the potentiometer R_5 in one leg of the bridge.

R_7 and D_2 provide negative feedback (hysteresis) to prevent cycling of the controller when the temperature is very near the set temperature. (Hysteresis was discussed in Chapter 9.) R_9 connects DC power to the power output stage of the op amp and is primarily used to set the desired triac gate current when the triac is conducting. The only other unusual combination is R_{10}-C_2. It is used to damp out the rapid surges that occur when the triac switches.

———— *SUMMARY* ————————————————————

In Chapter 12, there are many examples of the use of operational amplifiers to enhance the performance of semiconductor devices. By placing a diode in the feedback loop of an operational amplifier, for example, the small-signal nonlinearity of the diode is effectively removed. Thus, diodes can be used even with signals well below the usual 0.7 V threshold of the silicon device. Both half-wave and full-wave (absolute-value circuit) applications are found throughout modern electronic devices such as communications, audio, analog computing devices, and the like. Zener diodes are even used with operational amplifiers to limit output voltage variations to values required for digital interfacing.

Field effect transistors are combined with operational amplifiers to provide controllable gain without the use of the special-purpose programmable amplifier. The predictable change in source-to-drain resistance as a result of varying gate voltage is used in voltage divider applications such as voltage-variable resistors (VVRs). In some sample-and-hold applications, FETs may also be used as switches, connecting and disconnecting the hold capacitor.

Bipolar transistors are most often used with operational amplifiers to extend power capability. Most operational amplifiers, unless specifically designed for power use, are not capable of controlling the amount of power required for audio amplifiers, power switches, and so on. Bipolar transistors provide this capability. Thus, the marriage of conventional semiconductor devices with operational amplifiers extends the capabilities of both.

=== *QUESTIONS* ===

1. Discuss why diode small-signal nonlinearity is a problem with diodes used in communications but not with diodes used in power rectification applications.

2. Draw a diagram showing how operational amplifiers can be used to compensate for diode small-signal nonlinearity.

3. What is a precision diode?

4. Under what conditions would it be necessary to establish a diode reference level other than 0 V? Show how to establish both − and + reference levels.

5. What is a DC restorer?

6. Draw the input and output waveforms that might be seen in an absolute-value circuit.

7. Explain why the resistor ratios used in Figure 12–6 are important.

8. Using the amplitude-modulated waveform shown in Figure 12–7, draw the output of both a peak and a peak-to-peak detector.

9. Show by schematic diagram two methods of using zener diodes to limit op amp output voltage. Discuss the advantages and disadvantages of each method.

10. Explain how an FET may be used to control gain in an audio system. A diagram may be used, if desired.

11. What is the purpose of the FET shown in the Wien bridge oscillator of Figure 12–13? Are there any advantages to the FET when compared with incandescent lamps?

12. Explain how FETs may be used as switches in analog systems. Draw a diagram, if desired.

13. What is a lamp driver? Why must it be used with operational amplifier circuits?

14. List three applications of bipolar transistors to op amp circuits.

15. Discuss the advantage of the power control circuit of Figure 12–18 over the circuit of Figure 12–16.

13

D/A and A/D
Converters

OBJECTIVES After you study Chapter 13, you will be able to
1. Define analog and digital.
2. Explain the difference between analog and digital.
3. Draw or recognize a block diagram of a typical D/A converter. Explain the function of each of the sub-blocks.
4. Compare and contrast weighted ladder networks and R-$2R$ networks used for D/A conversion.
5. Discuss the advantages and disadvantages of an 8-bit D/A converter versus a 4-bit D/A converter.
6. List four types of A/D converters, ranking them in terms of speed of operation.
7. List four types of A/D converters, ranking them in terms of accuracy.
8. Draw or recognize a functional block diagram of an integrating A/D converter. Explain the principles of operation.
9. Draw or recognize a functional block diagram of a counter A/D converter. Explain the principles of operation.
10. Draw or recognize a functional block diagram of a successive-approximation A/D converter. Explain the principles of operation.
11. Draw or recognize a functional block diagram of a "flash" A/D converter. Explain the principles of operation.

INTRODUCTION

The natural world is **analog.** Today's world is **digital.** What's the difference? Let's look at some examples.

Look at your watch. Does it have hands or does it just have numbers? If it has hands that move, it is analog. If it just has numbers, it is digital. They both show time, but in different ways. An analog watch

359

represents time by the position of hands around a circle. That is, time is related to how far the hands have moved around the circle from some reference point. A distance is measured and marked in hours and minutes. The digital watch actually counts hours, minutes, and seconds. The total number of counts is stored. Electronic circuits in the watch convert those counts into a form that displays them on the face of the watch. The following statement is one way to describe analog and digital devices: *Analog devices measure; digital devices count.*

Now consider a thermometer. Both analog and digital thermometers currently are used. The analog thermometer contains a column of colored alcohol or mercury that expands and contracts with changes in temperature. A scale marked in degrees is attached to the tube containing the liquid. Thus temperature is indicated as the height of a column of liquid. The height varies continuously even as small changes in temperature occur. With a finely divided scale, very small changes could be noted, even down to a hundredth of a degree. Digital thermometers are different. Changes in temperature are converted to electrical form to control the digital indication. At best, most digital thermometers are accurate only to the nearest tenth of a degree. The temperature may be in between values, but indications do not change until the next available digit for readout occurs. Indications are thus in steps, not continuous. (Digital thermometers are capable of closer readings, but require additional components for this capability.)

Thus analog devices display something in terms of something else, for example, temperature in terms of length of a column of mercury. Digital devices, on the other hand, display something in terms of symbols. The symbols usually are digits, or numbers. Digital devices generally operate with greater speed than analog devices, are more versatile, and have memory. These characteristics should be reason enough to use digital electronics.

If we are to use digital devices, we must interface them with the natural world. Consider a typical process control system in a manufacturing plant. Analog information from sensors must be converted into digital form if computers are to manipulate the information. Resulting instructions based on manipulation of information must then be translated into analog form to operate devices controlling the manufacturing environment. Thus we require analog-to-digital (A/D) conversion, and digital-to-analog (D/A) conversion. We will discuss D/A conversion first.

D/A CONVERSION

Concepts

Why are we talking about D/A converters before A/D converters? The natural world (analog) is surely more familiar than the digital world!

However, A/D converters use D/A converter techniques, so we must work with D/A converters first.

Figure 13–1 is a functional diagram of a D/A converter. Digital information is applied to the input of the D/A converter as a binary number on the input lines. Figure 13–2 shows the switching and resistor network sections of a D/A converter in more detail. Each input line is connected to an electronic switch. If the voltage on an input line represents a binary 1, the switch is actuated and the reference voltage is applied to the appropriate resistor in the network. A current flow proportional to the resistor value results. The resistor network, which is the heart of the D/A converter, combines currents from all "active" lines. Resistor network output is a current proportional to the sum of the currents from the active lines. A current-to-voltage converter changes total current flow to an appropriate voltage. The converter also provides

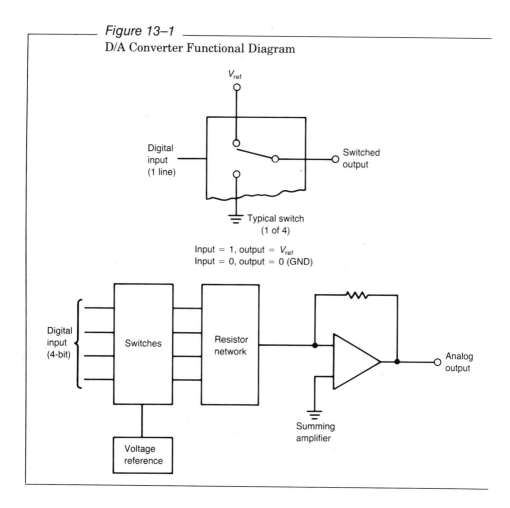

Figure 13–1

D/A Converter Functional Diagram

Figure 13–2

Weighted Ladder Network (D/A Converter)

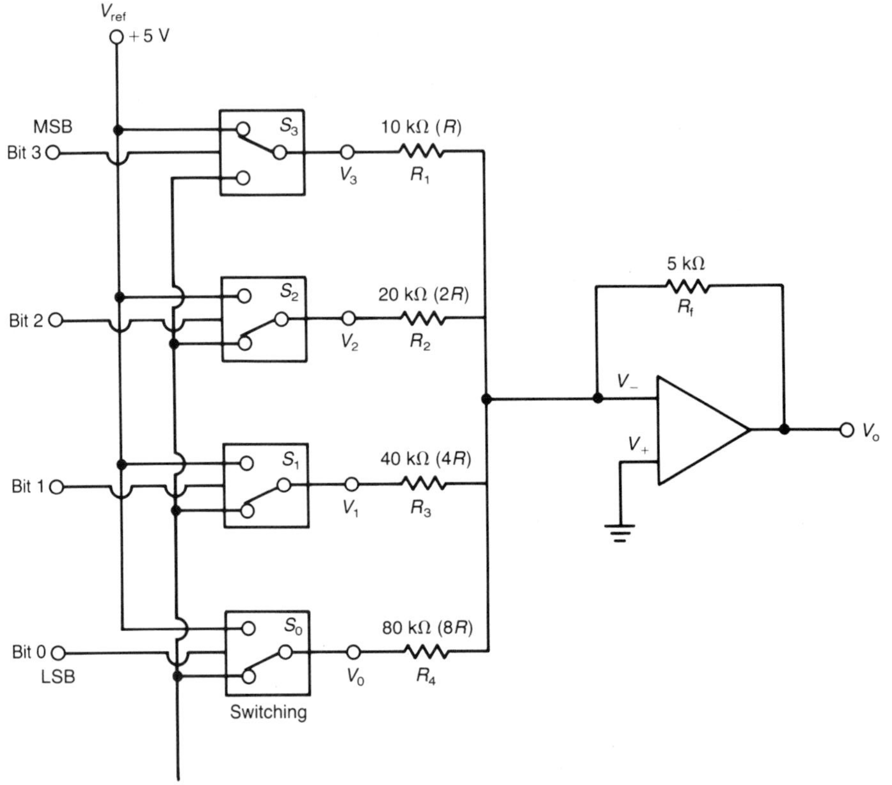

isolation of the network from the load connected to the analog output
terminal.

Weighted Resistor D/A Converters

Since resistor networks are the heart of D/A converters, we should investigate their operation in detail. Actually our investigation turns out
to be a review of Ohm's law and DC network solutions.

Figure 13–2 uses a weighted ladder network. A resistor value is
selected for R_1. Then following resistors are doubled, following a binary
scheme. If R_1 is 10 kΩ, then R_2 is 20 kΩ, and so on until a resistor has
been selected for each bit in the binary input. R_1 is associated with the

most significant bit (MSB) in the binary number to be converted. The weighted ladder network in Figure 13–2 assumes a 4-bit binary number.

As already indicated, input lines carrying a binary 1 will cause the associated switch to activate and connect the reference voltage to its resistor in the network. Input lines carrying a binary 0 will cause the associated switch to connect the resistor to ground. Let's see how the D/A converter works.

Consider that the binary input to the converter is 0001. Switch S_0 will be activated, connecting R_4 to the reference voltage ($+5$ V). All other switches will not be activated. Their associated resistors will be grounded. With S_0 activated, $+5$ V will appear at V_0. Remembering our assumptions from Chapter 2, $V_- = V_4 = 0$ V. The V_- input is thus at virtual ground. The $+5$ V reference appears across R_4. Current flow through R_4 is

$$I_4 = \frac{V_0}{R_4} = \frac{5 \text{ V}}{80 \text{ k}\Omega} = 0.0625 \text{ mA}$$

The current fed back from the operational amplifier output to the inverting output must cancel I_4. That is, $I_f = I_4$. As noted in Chapter 3, output of a current to voltage converter is

$$V_o = -I_f \times R_f$$

The $-$ sign is used because the inverting amplifier configuration is used. Applying the above equation,

$$V_o = -0.0625 \text{ mA} \times 5 \text{ k}\Omega = -0.3125 \text{ V}$$

Now let's try some examples.

Example 13–1

In Figure 13–2, the binary input is 0100. What is the converter output voltage?

Solution

S_1 is activated, applying $+5$ V to R_3. All other resistors are grounded.

$$I_3 = \frac{V_1}{R_3} = \frac{5 \text{ V}}{50 \text{ k}\Omega} = 0.125 \text{ mA}$$

$$V_o = -I_f \times R_f = -0.125 \text{ mA} \times 5 \text{ k}\Omega = -0.625 \text{ V}$$

_____ *Example 13–2* _____

In Figure 13–2, the binary input is 0011. What is the converter output voltage?

Solution

As previously calculated, $I_4 = 0.0625$ mA and $I_3 = 0.125$ mA. Total current flow is $I_4 + I_3$, or 0.1875 mA.

$$V_o = -I_f \times R_f = -0.1875 \text{ mA} \times 5 \text{ k}\Omega = -0.9375 \text{ V}$$

In terms of the value of R, the resistor associated with the most significant bit (MSB) input, the generalized equation for V_o is

$$V_o = I_f \times R_f$$

Converter output voltage for all possible input combinations is shown in Table 13–1. Values were calculated using the generalized equation for V_o.

A potential problem exists with the D/A converter used in the examples. Consider the output voltages for the binary input of 1100 and 1101. Note that there is a difference of 0.3125 V. That is the smallest

_____ *Table 13–1* _____
Weighted Resistor Network

Decimal Equivalent of Binary Input	Input Voltage				Output Voltage
	V_3	V_2	V_1	V_0	V_o
0	0	0	0	0	0
1	0	0	0	5	0.3125
2	0	0	5	0	0.625
3	0	0	5	5	0.9375
4	0	5	0	0	1.25
5	0	5	0	5	1.5625
6	0	5	5	0	1.875
7	0	5	5	5	2.1875
8	5	0	0	0	2.5
9	5	0	0	1	2.8125
10	5	0	5	0	3.125
11	5	0	5	5	3.4375
12	5	5	0	0	3.75
13	5	5	0	5	4.0625
14	5	5	5	0	4.375
15	5	5	5	5	4.6875

change that can occur as input values change. The *resolution* is poor. Most D/A converts use either 8- or 12-line inputs. For the 8-line input, the maximum number of values is 256. Therefore the smallest change will be only 1/256 of 5 V, or 0.0195 V. With 12-line input, the maximum number of values is 4096. The smallest change will be 1/4096 of 5 V, or 0.0012 V. The *resolution* is much better!

D/A converters require that resistors be *very* accurate and temperature stable. As resistor values get large, maintaining accuracy and temperature stability is difficult. The weighted ladder network is especially prone to this problem. The resistor associated with the MSB cannot be too small, or it will load the source of binary data. If we make it too large, by the time the least significant bit (LSB) of the binary input is reached, the resistor required may be extremely large.

Example 13–3

The MSB resistor in an 8-bit weighted ladder network is 10 kΩ. What is the value of the LSB resistor?

Solution

Doubling resistor value for each bit gives the following progression:

> 10 kΩ
> 20 kΩ
> 40 kΩ
> 80 kΩ
> 160 kΩ
> 320 kΩ
> 640 kΩ
> 1280 kΩ

Maintaining accurate conversion requires matching of resistor values to better than 1%. These precise requirements are difficult to achieve as resistor values increase. When in actual use, the current flow through the resistors cause heating. Changes in resistance occur, and resistor values may deviate considerably from the better than 1% requirement. Luckily, there's another way to do it!

R-2R D/A Converter

The *R-2R* ladder network overcomes the requirement for high-resistance, high-accuracy resistors. Figure 13–3 is a functional diagram of an *R-2R* ladder network D/A converter. Note that only two resistor values are used. Input switching is the same as in the weighted ladder network and the reference voltage is +5 V.

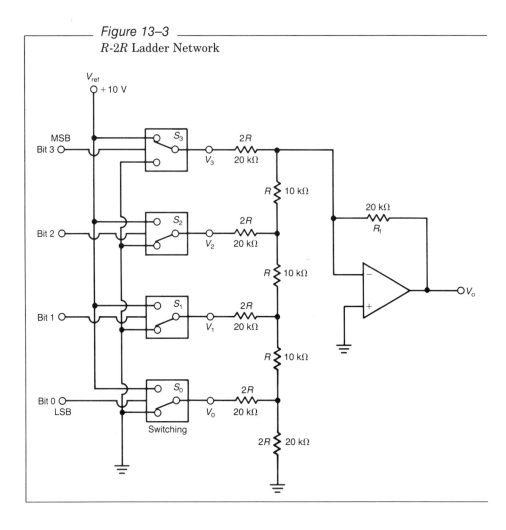

Figure 13-3

R-2R Ladder Network

Explanation of circuit operation assumes that S_3 is activated, and S_0, S_1, and S_2 are not activated. The switch positions are equivalent to a binary input of 1000. Evaluation of the R-$2R$ network can be more complex than for the weighted resistor ladder, but we will pick a simple example. Since the possibility of more than one current source exists, the circuit must be redrawn and converted to its Thevenin equivalent. Fortunately, with only a single source, the task is relatively easy. Figure 13-4 is the Thevenin equivalent of Figure 13-3.

As in the previous explanation, $V_- = V_+ = 0$ V. Since the only current in the circuit is through the $2R$ resistor connected to S_3, calculations are simple.

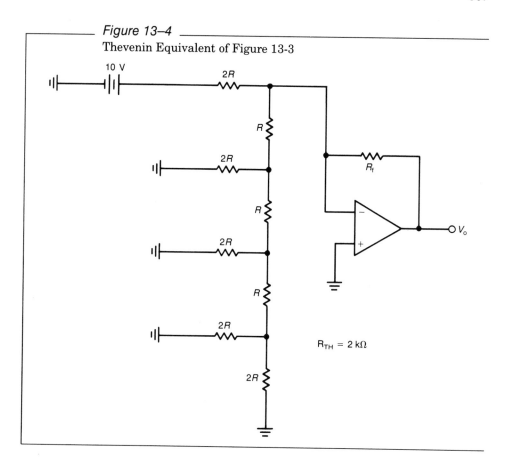

Figure 13–4

Thevenin Equivalent of Figure 13-3

$$I_3 = \frac{V_{ref}}{2R}$$

$$= \frac{5 \text{ V}}{20 \text{ k}\Omega}$$

$$= 0.25 \text{ mA}$$

I_f cancels I_3, and therefore $I_f = 0.25$ mA. As in the previous calculations,

$$V_o = -I_f \times R_f$$

$$= -0.25 \text{ mA} \times 20 \text{ k}\Omega$$

$$= -5 \text{ V}$$

The additional fifteen combinations can be similarly calculated,

Table 13–2

R-2R Network

Decimal Equivalent of Binary Input	Input Voltage				Output Voltage
	V_3	V_2	V_1	V_0	V_o
0	0	0	0	0	0
1	0	0	0	5	0.625
2	0	0	5	0	1.25
3	0	0	5	5	1.875
4	0	5	0	0	2.50
5	0	5	0	5	3.125
6	0	5	5	0	3.750
7	0	5	5	5	4.375
8	5	0	0	0	5.0
9	5	0	0	1	5.625
10	5	0	5	0	6.25
11	5	0	5	5	6.875
12	5	5	0	0	7.50
13	5	5	0	5	8.125
14	5	5	5	0	8.875
15	5	5	5	5	9.375

converting each combination into equivalent Thevenin circuits. Table 13–2 shows V_o for all sixteen possible input combinations.

A generalized equation has been developed for solution of the R-2R ladder network. Entries in Table 13–2 were calculated using the equation for V_o,

$$V_o = -I_f \times R_f$$

The advantage of the circuit of Figure 13–3 is that it requires only two sets of precision resistance values. However, it does require more resistors, and is more difficult to analyze. Both weighted ladder and R-2R networks are found in modern D/A converters.

A Typical D/A Converter

Modern D/A converters have a wide range of capabilities. Some models will accept only four input bits, while others accept up to eighteen bits. The conversion process takes many microseconds in some D/A converters, while others convert in less than a microsecond. Some converters contain their own reference voltage source; others require an external reference. Figure 13–5 is the functional block diagram of a representative D/A converter, model AD558 manufactured by Analog Devices.

Figure 13–5

AD558 D/A Converter

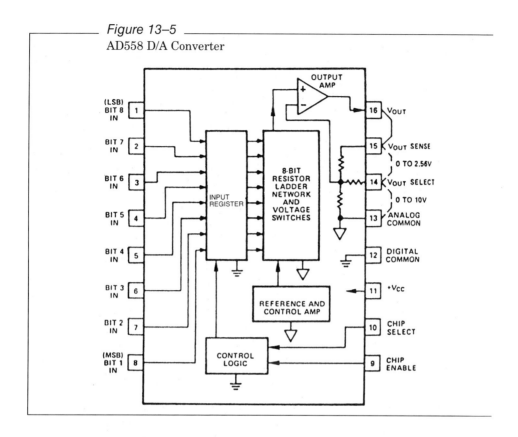

An input register and control logic is provided so that an eight-bit computer "word" can be transferred to the D/A converter. The source of the information to be converted can then go on to other tasks while the conversion takes place. The resistor network is factory adjusted for high accuracy and linearity, as is the precision voltage reference. Finally, the feedback path for the output amplifier is externally accessible. Terminals may be connected to supply either 0 V to 2.56 V or 0 V to 10 V output. The AD558 D/A converter is ideally suited for conversion of microprocessor data to analog form.

Troubleshooting: The D/A converter of Figure 13–5 is used to operate a 10 V analog indicator. Input to the D/A converter is from an eight-bit microcomputer. A malfunction in this circuit will be used as the troubleshooting example for this chapter.

After operating normally for a long period of time, suddenly the analog indicator begins to read consistently low. Let's consider the steps needed to locate and repair the malfunction.

First, the digital input should be verified. If the digital "numbers" provided to the input are correct, we then need to determine whether the output is somehow related to the input. Let's assume that the consistently low output of the D/A converter circuit and analog indicator is low at all readings and is low by the same factor.

A different analog indicator should be substituted to determine whether the malfunction is in the converter or the indicator. Assume the new indicator provides the same output reading. The malfunction is therefore in the converter. What, other than the IC, could cause the malfunction? Examination of Figure 13–5 shows that the only factor affecting output voltage of the IC is the external connections of the output amplifier feedback path.

Upon examination, you would probably find that a cold-solder joint was present from IC pins 13 to 14. This jumper controls the output amplifier feedback path, and the defective jumper would change the feedback ratio, resulting in low output voltage. Repair the cold-solder joint, and correct operation will resume.

_____ A/D CONVERSION _____

Concepts

Now that we have seen how to convert digital information to analog form, let's investigate what it takes to convert analog information to digital form. As mentioned in this chapter's introduction, many manufacturing processes require measurement in analog form. Calculations must be performed using the measured data, and manufacturing decisions made based on the results of the calculations. In many cases, calculations are best made with digital computers. Hence we have a need to convert analog information to digital form.

Previous sections of this chapter showed that resistor networks and switches were most often used to perform digital to analog conversion. We're not quite so lucky when analog to digital conversion takes place. A number of different methods can be used. It will be necessary to investigate integrating A/D converters; tracking, or counter, A/D converters; successive-approximation A/D converters; and "flash" A/D converters.

Flash A/D converters are used when extremely fast conversion (about 1 μs or less) is needed. In the range of 1 to 5 μs, the successive-approximation A/D converters are useful. Tracking, or counter, A/D converters operate near the range of the successive-approximation converters, but do allow tracking of the measured voltage as long as it doesn't vary in large increments. Integrating A/D converters are quite slow (even in the millisecond range) but are extremely immune to noise. You will see the reasons for these characteristics as each of the converters is discussed.

Integrating A/D Converter

Figure 13–6 shows a timing waveform and functional block diagram of an integrating A/D converter. The integrating, or dual-slope, A/D converter is quite slow, taking milliseconds to convert the analog input voltage to its digital equivalent. The integrating action, however, makes the A/D converter quite noise immune.

An integrating operational amplifier is the heart of the A/D converter. Chapters 10 and 15 discuss integrator circuits in detail. The background of those chapters is used to explain operation of the integrating, or dual-slope, A/D converter.

A reset command is issued from external sources to start the integration operation. Reset removes any charge that exists on the integrating capacitor, and sets the counter to zero. The counter then begins counting clock pulses, and the integrator is connected to the analog input voltage to be measured. Note that the input voltage is negative, and the reference voltage is positive. Integrator operation requires opposite

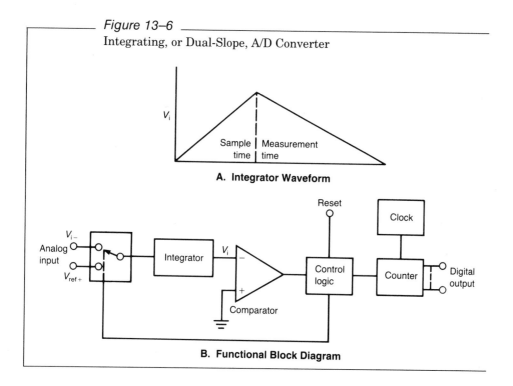

Figure 13–6

Integrating, or Dual-Slope, A/D Converter

A. Integrator Waveform

B. Functional Block Diagram

polarities. Positive input voltage and negative reference voltage constitute an acceptable condition.

The counter is allowed to run for a predetermined length of time, during which the integrating capacitor accumulates charge. Figure 13–6A shows the voltage rising across the capacitor during the fixed time period. The counter is reset at the end of the fixed period, and the integrating capacitor is connected to the reference voltage. Counting resumes and continues until the comparator detects zero voltage across the integrating capacitor. When the comparator detects zero integrator voltage, the counter is stopped. The count in the counter is proportional to the analog input voltage. Counter decoding by the decoder translates the count into a digital representation of the analog input voltage.

Analog input voltage can be calculated using the following formula:

$$V_{an} = (-V_{ref}) \left(\frac{t_v}{t_f} \right)$$

where

V_{ref} = reference voltage

t_v = variable time

t_f = fixed time

_____ *Example 13–4* _____

An integrating, or dual-slope, A/D converter uses a reference voltage of 10 V. The fixed integrating time is 5 ms and the variable integrating time is 3 ms. What is the analog voltage?

Solution

$$V_{an} = (-10) \left(\frac{.003}{.005} \right)$$
$$= (-10)(0.6)$$
$$= 6 \text{ V}$$

Accuracy of an integrating, or dual-slope, A/D converter is primarily related to the reference voltage. Any errors in the integrating components tend to cancel out, since they are used to make both variable and fixed time measurements.

Tracking, or Counter, A/D Converter

Figure 13–7 shows a timing waveform and functional block diagram of a tracking, or counter, A/D converter. An analog voltage is applied to the

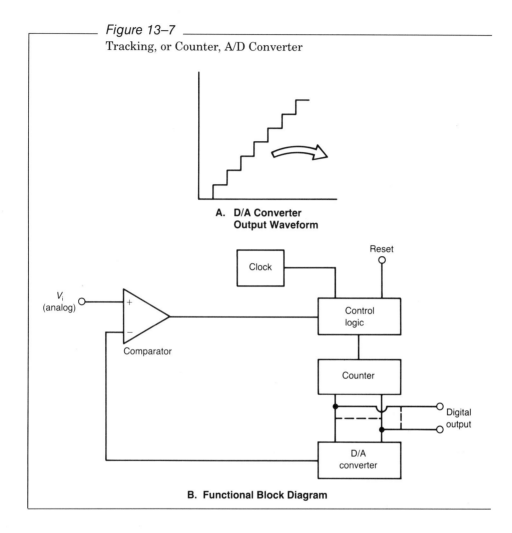

Figure 13–7

Tracking, or Counter, A/D Converter

A. **D/A Converter Output Waveform**

B. **Functional Block Diagram**

converter input, and within a short time, the digital equivalent appears at the output. Since a finite time is required to perform the conversion, a *sample-and-hold* circuit is usually needed so that the input voltage does not change during the conversion process. Sample-and-hold circuits are discussed in Chapter 11.

A tracking, or counter, A/D converter operates in the following manner. Refer to Figure 13–7B. The conversion process begins by external circuits issuing a reset command to the converter. The control logic resets the counter to zero count. Since the counter output is the digital output of the A/D converter, 0 V output is indicated. Consider a + voltage applied to the + input of the comparator. The − input of the comparator is 0 V, because the counter has been reset to zero. The D/A converter converts zero count to 0 V. When the + input of a comparator is greater than the − input, the comparator output is +. The + comparator output to the control logic circuits allows clock pulses to be applied to the counter, which starts counting from 0 upward. As the counter accumulates clock pulses, the output of the counter is converted to analog form by the D/A converter. The output of the D/A converter appears as a staircase waveform, as shown in Figure 13–7A. Comparator output remains + until the staircase output of the D/A converter equals the analog input voltage. The comparator output then goes −, and the counter switches to counting down. After one down count, the D/A converter output is again less than the analog input, and the counter resumes up-counting. Circuits in the control logic recognize the up/down transition as the closest possible match between the analog input voltage and the D/A converter output. The output of the counter is shifted to the latch circuits for storage and readout. The output of the latch circuits is now the digital equivalent of the analog input voltage. If the analog input voltage changes, the counting cycle repeats, and a new value is stored in the latch circuits.

The conversion process using a tracking, or counter, A/D converter is quite slow. It takes a finite time for the counter to count enough clock pulses so that the digital output of the counter equals the analog input voltage. Thus one of the limiting factors with tracking A/D converters is the clock frequency.

Successive-Approximation A/D Converter

Figure 13–8 shows a functional block diagram and a decision chart for a successive-approximation A/D converter. A successive-approximation A/D converter looks very much like the tracking, or counter, A/D converter, but the principle of operation is different. Since it, like the tracking A/D converter, takes a finite time to perform conversion, the analog voltage input should be applied through a sample-and-hold circuit.

Have you ever seen a chemist's balance scale being used? Material to be weighed is placed on one side of the balance. Then weights are added, heaviest weight first, to the opposite side of the scale. If the heaviest weight isn't enough to balance the scale, the next heaviest weight is added. This continues until the scale either balances or there is too much weight, and the scale tips toward the weights. If the scale balances, the sum of all of the weights equals the weight of the material. If the scale tips toward the weights, the last weight added is removed, and a smaller weight is added. This procedure is continued until the scale balances. The same principle is used in the successive-approximation D/A converter.

A shift register rather than a counter is used in the successive-approximation D/A converter. When a conversion starts, the shift reg-

Figure 13–8

Successive-Approximation A/D Converter

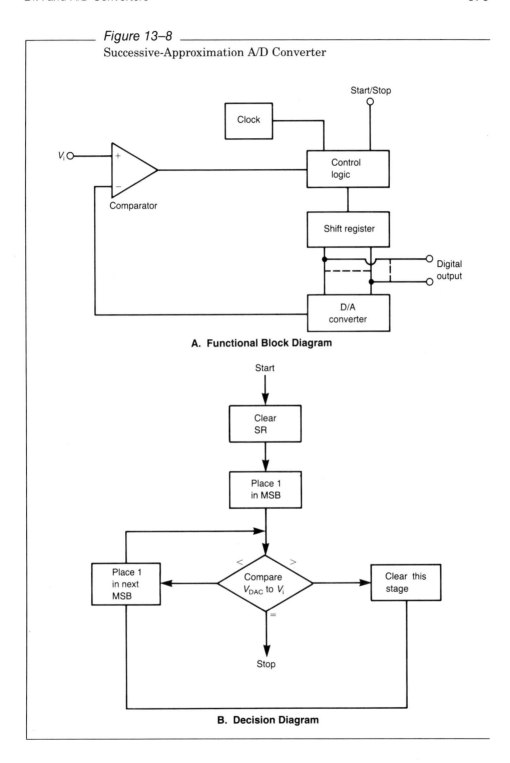

A. Functional Block Diagram

B. Decision Diagram

ister is cleared to all 0's, and a 1 is then placed in the MSB stage. Now we're working like the chemist's scale. The number in the shift register is converted to an analog value, and compared to the input voltage. If the output of the D/A converter is less than the input voltage, a 1 is placed in the next MSB position, and comparison occurs again. If the D/A converter output becomes equal to the input voltage, the conversion process stops, and the number in the shift register is stored in the latches for readout. If the D/A converter output is greater than the input voltage, the last 1 inserted in the shift register is changed to a 0 and a 1 is placed in the next MSB position in the shift register. The flowchart in Figure 13–8B displays the scheme used in the successive-approximation register.

The successive-approximation converter is faster than the tracking A/D converter because all counts do not have to be accumulated.

Parallel, or Flash, A/D Converter

Figure 13–9 is a functional block diagram of a "flash," or parallel A/D converter. Flash conversion is very fast because no counting or bit movement is required. The A/D output can appear within nanoseconds of the application of the analog input voltage to be converted. Such high speed is possible because a comparator is used for *every* possible bit combination. If the output is an 8-bit word, then 2^{n-1}, or 255, comparators are used. Very fast, but lots of parts!

The simplified flash converter shown in Figure 13–9 has four comparators, which means that only 3-bit resolution is possible. As can be seen in Figure 13–9, the analog input voltage is applied to one input of each comparator. The other input of the comparator receives a reference voltage from a voltage divider connected to the converter's reference voltage source. If the analog input voltage exceeds a comparator's reference voltage, that comparator's output will be HIGH. All other comparator outputs will be LOW. A decoder combines the HIGH and LOW outputs to form the digital equivalent of the analog input voltage.

Some Typical A/D Converters

Figure 13–10 is a functional block diagram of the AD7576 8-bit A/D converter manufactured by Analog Devices. It uses the successive-approximation technique, and is microprocessor compatible. Conversion time is approximately 5 μs. Operation is similar to the successive-approximation A/D converter discussed earlier, with minor changes to accommodate microprocessor requirements.

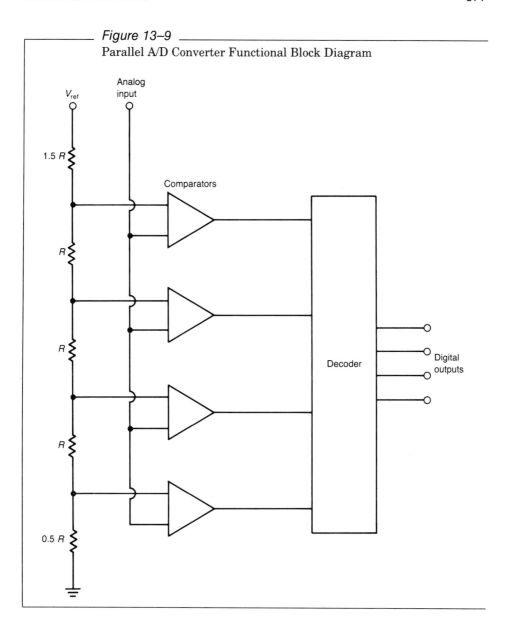

Figure 13–9
Parallel A/D Converter Functional Block Diagram

The control logic function has both microprocessor input and output connections to assure that conversion takes place directly under control of the microprocessor. An external voltage reference is required for the AD7576. Finally, the digital latch circuits include three-state output circuits so that the converter can be "disconnected" from the microprocessor data bus. The AD7576 is a low-power, low-cost A/D converter that

Figure 13–10

AD7576 8-Bit A/D Converter

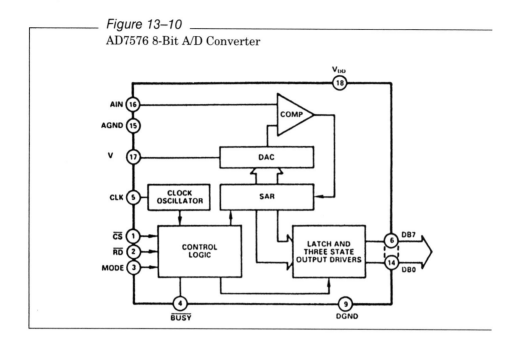

finds many applications in today's manufacturing and process control systems.

A 7-bit flash A/D converter is shown in Figure 13–11. Conversion time is only a few nanoseconds. The ADC-207 flash converter from Datel has 128 comparators that are automatically balanced on every conversion to cancel out errors due to temperature effects. Three-state output is also provided for easy interfacing with other components.

Note that the ADC-207 has two clock phases. Auto-zeroing is performed during phase 1. During phase 2 the analog input voltage is applied to the 128 comparators. All comparator outputs are loaded into latches that feed the 128-to-7 encoder. The encoder converts the latched comparator outputs into a 7-bit binary word that is proportional to the analog input voltage. When the clock initiates the next phase 1 cycle, the encoder output is fed to output latches for temporary storage. A/D converter output is via three-state drivers that are under control of external equipment. Thus the output drivers may be "disconnected" from external equipment.

The ADC-207 can be used in many applications requiring high-speed conversion. Typical uses include TV video digitizing, radar, high-speed digital oscilloscopes, medical imaging (ultrasound), and robotic vision.

_____ *Figure 13–11* _____
ADC-207 Flash Converter Simplified Functional Diagram

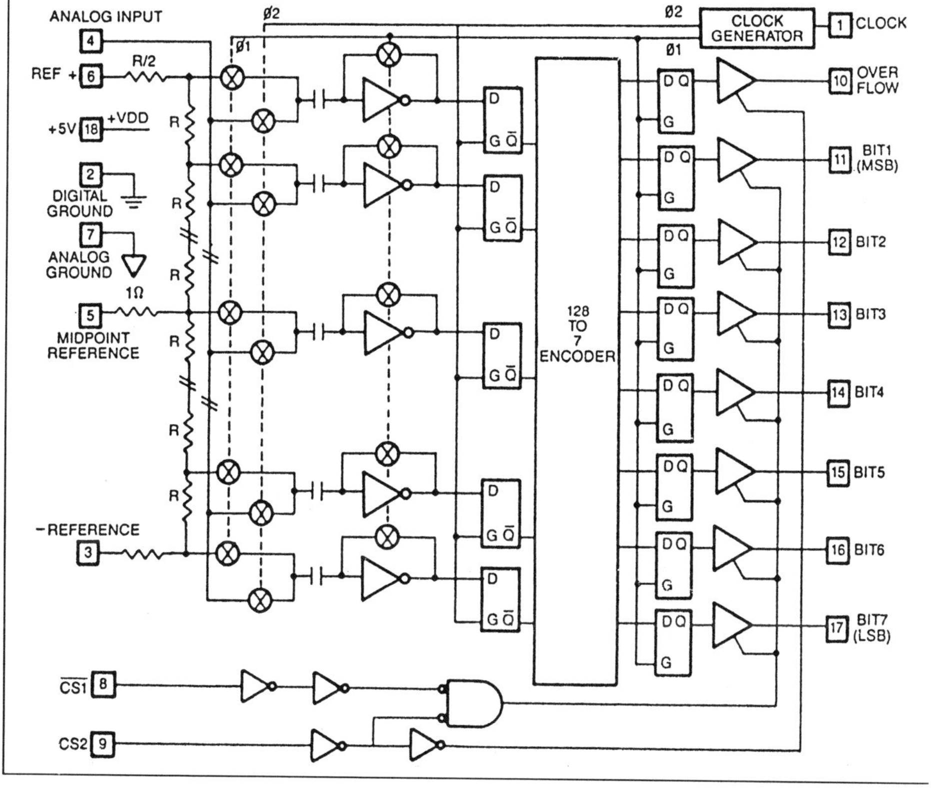

_____ **APPLICATIONS OF D/A AND A/D** _____
CONVERTERS

The concepts of a data acquisition system can be seen in Figure 13–12. Although simplified, it does provide the basic functions that must be performed in order to acquire, process, and display data. Consider the need to acquire data from a remote location such as a space station, transmit that data to earth, receive that data, and display the data by conventional methods.

The data to be acquired will be analog in nature. Temperature, pressure, fluid flow, and the like all must be measured. In an application such as a space station, thousands of measurements must be taken regularly and sent to earth for analysis and action. Transducers are used

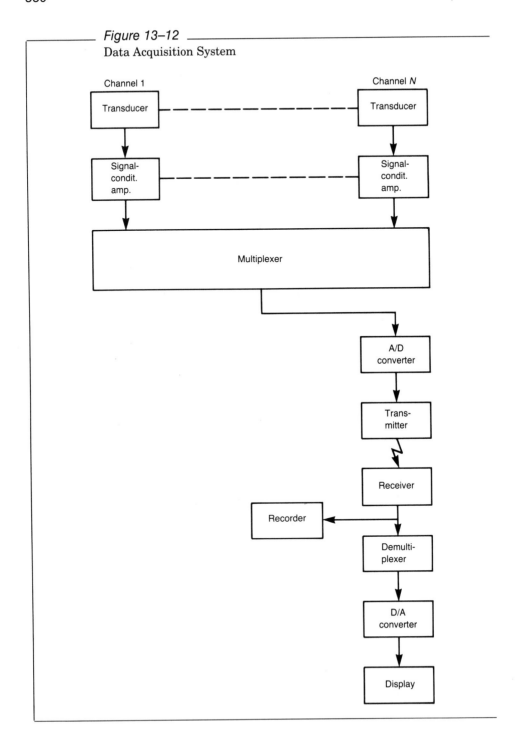

Figure 13–12
Data Acquisition System

to convert the physical measurements into electrical form. However, transducers output voltage and current over a wide range of values. Most A/D converters cannot use such widely ranging voltages and currents, so signal-conditioning amplifiers are used to scale inputs to a usable range. Since it is not cost effective to have a separate transmission path for each measurement, a device called a *multiplexer* is used. A multiplexer samples each "channel," one after the other, and sends the information to the A/D converter. It is not practical to send the analog signals, so they must be converted to digital form for transmission. The digital equivalent of each of the transducer outputs is then transmitted, one after the other, to earth for processing.

On earth, the information from the space station is received and recorded. At the same time that recording is taking place, a *demultiplexer* is performing the opposite function that the multiplexer performed at the space station. Each channel of information is recovered, one after the other. The D/A converter changes the digital information into analog form for display. The converted information may be displayed on conventional instruments such as electrical meters that show temperature, pressure, and fluid flow. Computer operated displays may also be used to show changes in measured parameters from space.

Computers may constantly monitor incoming information and alert operators to changes that may threaten the space station or its occupants.

Many of the functions in Figure 13–12 do not fit into the scope of this book. Let's consider those that do, however. The signal-conditioning amplifiers used to scale the output of transducers to usable ranges are instrumentation amplifiers discussed in Chapter 11. Multiplexers were also discussed in Chapter 11. Both A/D and D/A converters were explained in this chapter. Demultiplexers are merely a reverse form of multiplexers. More than half of the functional blocks in the data acquisition system of Figure 13–12 have been explained in this book. Now you can go on to further studies to learn about transducers, communications, and recording.

_____ *SUMMARY* _____

The inexpensive digital computer has caused a large growth in the use of technology in many applications. First, inexpensive calculation capability made it financially feasible to convert analog measurement to digital form for calculation, then back to analog form for control. As more conversion became necessary, inexpensive A/D and D/A conversion hardware appeared.

The most common technique used to convert digital information to analog form is a resistor network and a summing amplifier. Both weighted resistor and R-$2R$ networks are in use. The R-$2R$ network is easier to use, and less susceptible to temperature and accuracy problems.

A/D conversion uses a number of different techniques. Slow, noise-immune conversion can be accomplished with integrating A/D converters. Speed increases as tracking and successive-approximation A/D converters are used. If extremely high-speed conversion is needed, parallel, or flash, A/D converters are a good choice.

Once again, the availability of inexpensive, easy-to-use integrated circuits has impacted many applications not previously considered as candidates. From outer space to your living room high-fidelity equipment, A/D and D/A converters are making life easier for all of us.

=== QUESTIONS ===

1. Explain, by using an analogy, the difference between analog and digital.

2. What is the relationship between resistors in a D/A converter using a weighted resistor network?

3. What is the relationship between resistors in a D/A converter using an R-$2R$ resistor network?

4. Make a list of relative characteristics of weighted resistor and R-$2R$ networks used in D/A converters.

5. Why is an input register desirable in D/A converters?

6. Why is an 8-bit D/A converter preferable to a 4-bit converter? Explain by showing a numeric example.

7. Make a list of relative characteristics of at least four A/D converter types. Include speed and accuracy characteristics.

8. Draw a functional block diagram of an integrating A/D converter. Explain its principles of operation.

9. Draw a functional block diagram of a counter type A/D converter. Explain its principles of operation.

10. Draw a functional block diagram of a successive-approximation type A/D converter. Explain its principles of operation.

11. Explain the differences between counter A/D converters and successive-approximation A/D converters.

12. Why are sample-and-hold circuits needed with A/D converters?

13. Draw a functional block diagram of a flash type A/D converter. Explain its principles of operation.

14. What is a signal-conditioning amplifier? Why is it necessary in a data acquisition system?

15. What is a multiplexer? Why is it necessary in a data acquisition system?

══ PROBLEMS ═══════════════

1. Using the generalized equation for V_o, verify Table 13–1.

2. Using the generalized equation for V_o, verify Table 13–2.

3. The MSB resistor in an 8-bit weighted resistor network is 5 kΩ. What are the other resistor values?

14

Phase-Locked Loops

OBJECTIVES After reading Chapter 14, you will be able to

1. Define phase-locked loop (PLL).
2. Draw or recognize a block diagram of a phase-locked loop and explain its principles of operation.
3. Explain how a phase detector operates.
4. Explain the principles of operation of a voltage-controlled or current-controlled oscillator.
5. Draw or recognize the block diagram of a common phase-locked loop chip and explain the purpose of each of the sub-blocks.
6. Draw or recognize the block diagram of a frequency-shift keying circuit and explain how it converts two different audio frequencies to logic levels.
7. Explain how frequency modulated information can be recovered from a radio frequency carrier using a phase-locked loop.
8. Draw or recognize the block diagram of a tone decoder circuit used to detect touch-tone dialing tones and explain its principles of operation.
9. Draw or recognize the block diagram of a phase-locked loop used as a frequency synthesizer, and explain how many different stable frequencies can be obtained from the circuit.

INTRODUCTION

A **phase-locked loop (PLL)** is a combination of simple electronic circuits that can perform many functions. It can be used to decode the tones used on your touch-tone phone. Communications equipment such as CB radios use PLLs to generate the frequencies used to tune separate channels. Television sets can use PLLs to maintain a steady picture. FM radios recover the sound from the carrier wave with PLLs. Computers use PLLs to decode the digital information arriving via telephone lines. The uses of PLLs are almost endless.

The concept of phase-locked loops was originally presented in the 1930s. Only recently, however, has technology advanced enough to make PLLs economically feasible. Integrated circuits have allowed hundreds of thousands of circuit components to be placed on a single chip. PLLs can now be used in many of the everyday applications just mentioned.

A PLL is usually an integrated circuit with one input and two outputs, although variations are common. The primary purpose of a PLL is to supply an output that is "locked" to the frequency and phase of the input. Once the PLL is "locked on," any variation in input frequency and/or phase is detected, and the output follows.

The block diagram of Figure 14–1 shows the one input, f_i and the two outputs f_o and E_o. f_o has a fixed phase relationship with and is the same frequency as f_i when the PLL is locked on. f_o is used in automatic frequency control and frequency synthesizing applications. E_o varies as the difference between f_i and f_o occurs. E_o is used in decoding and demodulating applications.

The PLL has three functional sections, as shown in Figure 14–2. They operate together in the following manner. When power is initially applied, the voltage-controlled oscillator (VCO) operates at a "free-running" frequency determined by an RC or LC circuit. VCO operation is explained later in this chapter. A VCO is an oscillator that changes frequency in response to a controlling voltage. It is assumed that the input control voltage to the VCO is zero volts. As the input control voltage changes, the output frequency of the VCO changes. Note that the output of the VCO is also called f_o. Let's assume that the input signal f_i is not

Figure 14–1

Phase-Locked Loop Block Diagram

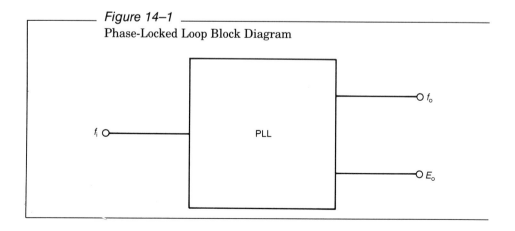

Figure 14–2
PLL Functional Block Diagram

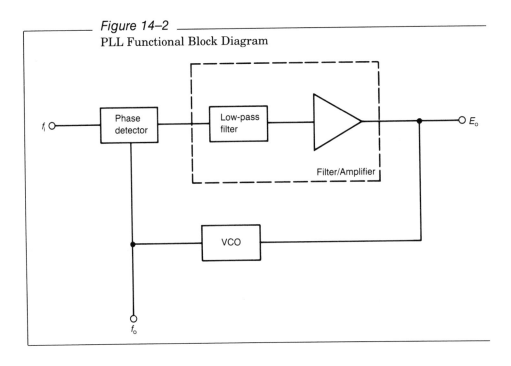

the same frequency as f_o. The phase detector compares f_i and f_o, and develops an error signal proportional to the frequency and phase differences between f_i and f_o. The relationship between frequency and phase is discussed when detailed operation of phase detectors is investigated. A low-pass filter (perhaps with an amplifier included) removes high-frequency components of the error signal. The filtered error signal is called E_o, and is applied as a control voltage to the VCO. Amplitude and polarity of E_o is such that the output of the VCO changes so as to cause f_o to move closer to f_i. When f_i and f_o are the same frequency and phase, the error signal becomes zero volts, and the VCO no longer changes frequency. The PLL is locked on. Any further change in f_i will be accompanied by a change in E_o and a change in f_o.

A PLL has three separate states. In the **free-running state,** f_o is determined by external components only. During the **capture state,** the VCO is changing frequency in response to changes in E_o. When $f_o = f_i$, the PLL is in the **phase-locked state.** Two frequency ranges are mentioned when discussing PLL operation. The **capture range** is the bandwidth over which capture is possible, that is, the frequency range over which the VCO can change and lock on to f_i. The **lock range** is the frequency range over which f_o can follow f_i. Capture range is limited by the low-pass filter, as is the tracking speed. Tracking speed is similar to slew rate in operational amplifiers.

———— THE PHASE DETECTOR ————

A **phase detector** or phase comparator is a circuit that provides an output voltage whose amplitude is proportional to the amount of phase difference between two input signals and whose polarity is dependent on whether a leading or a lagging phase angle exists. Let's review some fundamental facts about frequency and phase. Frequency is defined in terms of the number of cycles per second that occur for an AC signal. Each cycle goes through a full 360°, as you learned when you first studied AC fundamentals. Let's examine one cycle of two AC signals, as shown in Figure 14–3. Note that the period of time it takes for a complete cycle to occur is the same for both signals. That means both signals are the same frequency. Note also that the maximum positive value of signal B occurs *before* the maximum positive value of signal A. Although both signals are the same frequency, signal B *leads* signal A by a phase angle of 90°. We could also say that signal A *lags* signal B by 90°.

Phase difference is usually measured only when two signals are the same frequency. However, when we examine Figure 14–3, we see that phase differences exist between signals of different frequencies. Signal D is twice the frequency of signal C. Note that two cycles of signal D occur for every cycle of signal C. Except for the short intervals when both signals cross the zero voltage line at the same time, a phase difference will always occur. So don't worry about f_i and f_o being different frequencies. A phase difference will occur, and will result in a phase detector output as the frequencies come closer together.

When the two input signals are in phase, the output voltage of a phase detector is zero (or constant at some voltage offset from zero). When a phase difference exists, the polarity of the output voltage is designed to force the frequency of a VCO in a PLL toward the input frequency.

The output voltage of a phase detector has many frequency components, just like a mixer. Both sum and difference frequencies, and the two input frequencies exist. The low-pass filter used in a PLL removes the two input frequency and the sum frequency components.

We now need to consider how a phase detector works. A very simplified functional diagram of a phase detector is shown in Figure 14–4. Functionally the phase detector is merely two operational amplifiers in series. The output of the bottom op amp is connected in series with the top op amp. When the top op amp is "turned on," the output signal from the bottom op amp is routed through the top op amp and becomes the phase detector output (V_o). The bottom op amp is a dual differential amplifier (see Chapters 1 and 11), and the top op amp is a full-wave switch. The waveforms in Figure 14–4B will help explain circuit operation. The VCO input signal performs the switching function, operating

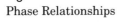

Figure 14–3
Phase Relationships

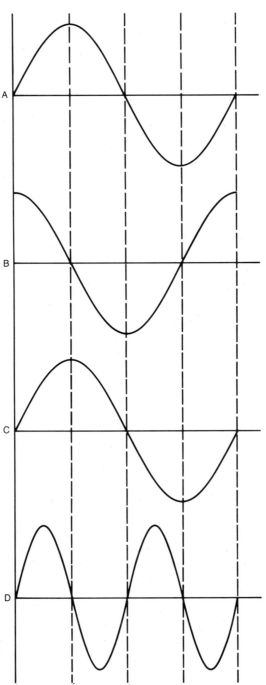

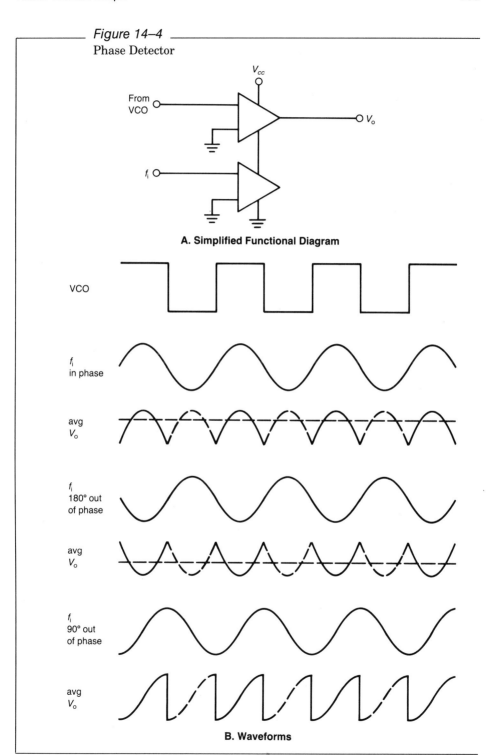

Figure 14–4

Phase Detector

A. Simplified Functional Diagram

VCO

f_i
in phase

avg
V_o

f_i
180° out
of phase

avg
V_o

f_i
90° out
of phase

avg
V_o

B. Waveforms

similar to a full-wave rectifier. That is, both half-cycles are used in the output signal. Note the three conditions of f_i. When f_i is in phase with the VCO input, the phase detector output becomes a series of positive half-cycles. (The low-pass filter that follows the phase detector will filter and smooth the output.) When f_i is 180° out of phase with the VCO input, the phase detector output becomes a series of negative half-cycles. Therefore, when f_i and the VCO output are in phase, a positive output voltage is developed. Likewise, when out of phase, a negative output voltage occurs. It is interesting to note that when a 90° phase difference exists, the phase detector output has equal positive and negative outputs, and the actual output becomes zero. As a result, f_i and VCO output (f_o) are really 90° out of phase when the PLL is locked on! It really doesn't matter that a phase difference exists, as long as the phase difference remains constant as tracking takes place.

In some applications, the signals used in PLLs are not pure sine waves. The VCO output, for example, may be a square wave or a rectangular wave. The input signal may be the square wave output of a stable crystal-controlled oscillator. One of the easiest ways to look at phase detector operation is to consider that both input signals are rectangular waves. Phase relationships also exist with rectangular waves, as shown in Figure 14–5. Both signals A and B are the same frequency, because their periods are 1 s. However, signal B does not go from a low to a high level until 0.2 s after signal A. Therefore signal B *lags* signal A by 0.2 s. In terms of degrees, the 1 s period is equal to 360°. The 0.2 s delay is 0.2 × 360, or 72°. Signal B *lags* signal A by 72°.

Figure 14–5

Digital Phase Relationship

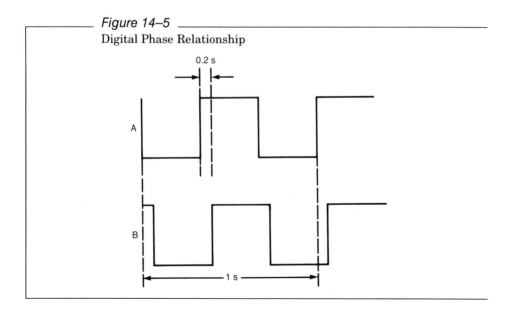

The amplitudes of the rectangular wave signals can be limited to common logic levels, such as 0 V (LOW) and +5 V (HIGH). You were introduced to these concepts when you investigated digital techniques. At that time you also were introduced to a digital circuit called an **EX-CLUSIVE-OR** gate. This circuit produces a HIGH output *only* when its two inputs are different values. That is, when the inputs are the same (either both LOW or both HIGH), the output will be LOW, or 0 V. When the inputs are different, the output will be HIGH, or +5 V. Figure 14–6A shows the input and output waveforms for an EXCLUSIVE-OR gate used as a phase detector.

But we said that the output of a phase detector was a voltage whose amplitude and polarity represented the phase difference between the two input signals. It looks like the output of the EXCLUSIVE-OR phase detector is a series of pulses, whose width is determined by the phase difference between the inputs. Going back to basics, we would find that the *average* voltage of a pulse is equal to the maximum value of the pulse times the duty cycle. The duty cycle (D) is the percentage of the time the pulse is HIGH compared to the full cycle period. That is,

$$V_o = V_{max} \times D \qquad\qquad (14\text{--}1)$$

_____ *Example 14–1* _____

A square wave varies between 0 V and +10 V. What is the average voltage?

Solution

A square wave is a rectangular wave with equal off and on times. Thus the duty cycle is 50%. Using Equation 14–1,

$$V_o = 10 \text{ V} \times .5 = 5 \text{ V}$$

_____ *Example 14–2* _____

A rectangular wave varies from 0 V to +5 V. It is at +5 V 20% of the time. What is the average voltage?

Solution

Using Equation 14–1,

$$V_o = 5 \text{ V} \times .2 = 1 \text{ V}$$

Thus the output voltage varies from zero, when both signals are in phase, to a maximum positive value when 180° out of phase. We do have the amplitude varying with changes of phase difference. Output polarity

Figure 14–6
Digital Phase Detector

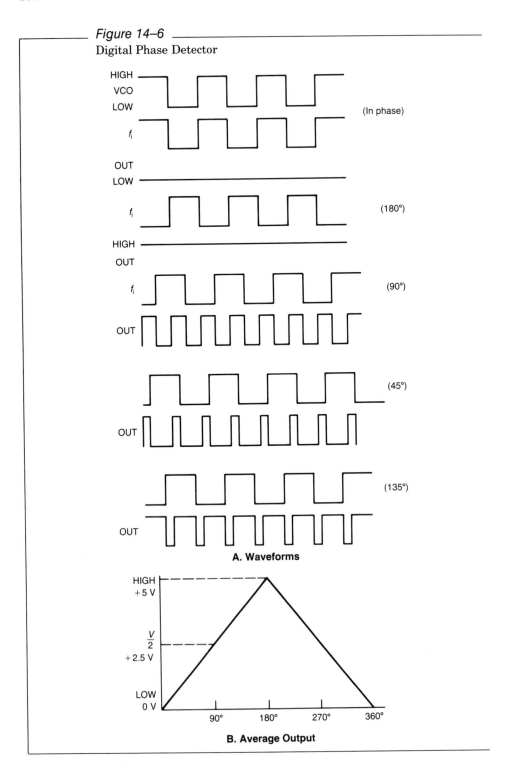

A. Waveforms

B. Average Output

does not change, but we can arbitrarily set 90° phase difference as the locked-on condition. That should result in a 50% duty cycle. If V_{max} is 5 V, then the phase detector output at lock-on is 2.5 V. Between 0° and 89° phase difference, the phase detector output is then *less than* 2.5 V. From 91° to 180°, the phase detector is *greater than* 2.5 V. We now have an arbitrary polarity change, centered around 2.5 V instead of 0 V. See Figure 14–6B.

In this section we have examined phase detectors in enough detail that you can understand how they operate. There may be many different ways of performing the phase detection process, but they all will provide the same function. They will compare the phase of two input signals and derive a control voltage that will cause one of the input signals to become the same frequency and phase as the other. If we can understand the *function* of a circuit, we can use that function to perform even more complex operations. Let's investigate the other functional components of a PLL circuit.

AMPLIFIERS AND LOW-PASS FILTERS

Low-pass filters and amplifiers used in PLLs are much the same as those discussed in earlier chapters. The filters are usually simple *RC* networks that are connected external to the PLL integrated circuit. Calculation of component values is shown later when typical PLL applications are explained. Filter characteristics, such as frequency and phase response, affect the capture range, the speed at which capture can occur, the tracking speed of the PLL, and the stability of the system. The derivation of the formulas for such parameters is beyond the scope of this book. Just follow the guidance provided by the PLL manufacturer, and your PLL will operate properly. Most PLL specification sheets supply formulas and tables to help you get maximum use from their product.

Often the filtered output of the phase comparator is not in the voltage range to operate the VCO. An op amp is used in most PLLs to provide the correct range and polarity for VCO control. The electronic thermometer shown in Chapter 3 demonstrates how an op amp can be used to *shift* the output voltage level to the desired range. Polarity can be changed by using either the inverting or the noninverting amplifier configuration.

VOLTAGE-CONTROLLED OSCILLATORS

A VCO supplies an output signal (commonly a square wave or a triangular wave) whose frequency can be controlled by a DC voltage. Many modern PLL ICs contain their VCO as part of the PLL chip. We

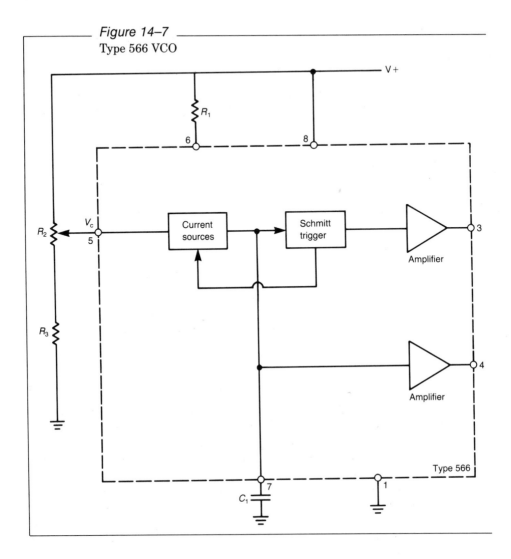

Figure 14–7
Type 566 VCO

can learn much about VCO operation, however, by investigating the
type 566 VCO chip. See Figure 14–7.

The 566 VCO contains a *Schmitt trigger* (remember those from
your digital studies?), current source circuits for charging and discharging the timing capacitor, and buffer amplifiers. As you may recall, the
output of a Schmitt trigger circuit changes state rapidly when the input
signal exceeds a predetermined upper threshold. The output remains in
the new state until the input signal decreases below the upper threshold
and reaches a lower threshold value. Then the Schmitt trigger output
reverses state. Schmitt triggers are often used to convert sine waves to
square waves.

The input signal to the Schmitt trigger in the 566 VCO is the voltage developed across the timing capacitor. The current sources are used to maintain a constant charge and discharge current through the capacitor. Do you remember what happens to the voltage across a capacitor when a constant current flows? A linearly increasing voltage appears under constant current conditions. As the voltage increases across the timing capacitor, the upper threshold of the Schmitt trigger is eventually reached. The Schmitt trigger changes output state, and the capacitor discharges linearly. When the lower threshold is reached, the Schmitt trigger again changes state, and the capacitor voltage again increases. Thus the input to the Schmitt trigger is a linearly increasing and decreasing signal (a triangular wave). Buffer amplifiers isolate the triangular and square waves from the output loads.

Controlling voltage applied to the input of the 566 PLL IC adjusts the current sources to increase or decrease the available charge and discharge currents for the timing capacitor. The result is shorter or longer charging and discharging times, which cause the frequency to increase or decrease. The requirements for a VCO have been met. A DC voltage applied to the input of the VCO causes a change in output frequency.

The output frequency of the 566 VCO can be calculated from

$$f_o = \left(\frac{2}{R_1 C_1}\right)\left(\frac{V_+ - V_c}{V_+}\right)$$

Proper operation is assured by using the following guidelines:

R_1 must range between 2 kΩ and 20 kΩ

V_c must range between V_+ and 0.75 V_+

f_o should be less than 1 MHz

V_+ must range between 10 V and 24 V

If these guidelines are followed, the output frequency will vary over a 10-to-1 range. Examples 14–3 and 14–4 show typical 566 VCO calculations. Use Figure 14–7 for the examples.

_____ *Example 14–3* _____

R_1 is 10 kΩ and C_1 is 1000 pF. V_+ is +12 V. Calculate the lowest and highest output frequency that can be achieved. Use the guidelines just listed, assuming that R_2 varies V_c from 9 V to 11.75 V.

Solution

$$f_o = \left(\frac{2}{R_1 C_1}\right)\left(\frac{V_+ - V_c}{V_+}\right)$$

continued

(*Example 14–3 continued*)

$$f_o = \left(\frac{2}{(10 \times 10^3)(1000 \times 10^{-12})}\right)\left(\frac{12 - 9}{12}\right)$$

$$= \left(\frac{2}{1 \times 10^{-5}}\right)(0.25) = 50 \text{ kHz}$$

and

$$f_o = \left(\frac{2}{(10 \times 10^3)(1000 \times 10^{-12})}\right)\left(\frac{12 - 11.75}{12}\right)$$

$$= \left(\frac{2}{1 \times 10^{-5}}\right)(0.0208) = 4160 \text{ Hz}$$

_____ Example 14–4 _____

Repeat Example 14–3 with $R_1 = 4.7 \text{ k}\Omega$, $C_1 = 560 \text{ pF}$, and $V_+ = +20$ V. V_c varies from 15 V to 19.5 V.

Solution

$$f_o = \left(\frac{2}{(4.7 \times 10^3)(560 \times 10^{-12})}\right)\left(\frac{20 - 15}{20}\right)$$

$$= \left(\frac{2}{2.632 \times 10^{-6}}\right)(0.25) = 190 \text{ kHz}$$

and

$$f_o = \left(\frac{2}{(4.7 \times 10^3)(560 \times 10^{-12})}\right)\left(\frac{20 - 19.5}{20}\right)$$

$$\left(\frac{2}{(2.632 \times 10^{-6})}\right)(0.0125) = 9500 \text{ Hz}$$

Although the PLL IC chip may not use the same type of VCO, the final result will be the same. The output frequency of the VCO is determined by the external RC values and the control voltage developed from the filtered output of the phase detector.

_____ A TYPICAL PLL _____

General concepts and principles of actual PLL operation can best be learned using simple PLL circuits as examples. The 565 PLL, Figure 14–8, is typical. It has been in use since the early 1970s. More modern PLL circuits, such as the 564 and 4046 and their equivalents, are merely higher-frequency versions of the earlier circuits. Many of today's applications, however, can still be performed by the 565.

The signal to be "tracked" is applied to pin 2. The analog phase detector output is directly amplified by the built-in op amp. Note that a

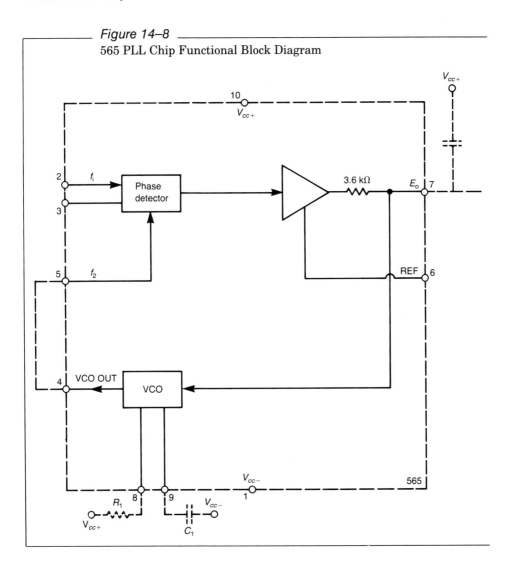

Figure 14–8
565 PLL Chip Functional Block Diagram

reference voltage output is available on pin 6. The reference voltage is used with external comparator circuits. An internal 3.6 kΩ resistor is used with an external capacitor for the low-pass filter. Filtered phase detector output connects internally to control the VCO frequency. VCO resting frequency is set by an external resistor and capacitor. Note that the VCO output is not internally connected to the phase detector input. Separate VCO output is necessary in applications to be discussed shortly.

Calculations for the 565 PLL are relatively simple. The VCO resting frequency can be approximated with the formula $f_o = 1.2/4R_1C_1$.

R_1 should be between 2 kΩ and 20 kΩ to maintain VCO linearity. The only other major external component is C_2, which is used with the internal 3.6 kΩ resistor to form the low-pass filter. Lock and capture ranges are directly related to the low-pass filter characteristics. Example 14–5 illustrates a typical frequency calculation. Additional calculations are shown in the following section as PLL applications are investigated.

Example 14–5

In the circuit of Figure 14–8, R_1 = 10 kΩ and C_1 = 820 pF. Calculate the resting frequency.

Solution

$$f_o = \frac{1.2}{4R_1C_1}$$

$$= \frac{1.2}{(4)(10 \times 10^3)(820 \times 10^{-12})}$$

$$= 36.585 \text{ kHz}$$

APPLICATIONS

Frequency-Shift Keying

When digital information is sent over relatively long distances, it is not practical to use the conventional two-level DC signal. A long-established standard (RS-232-C) has defined a **mark** (logic 1) as −5 V and a **space** (logic 0) as +14 V. One method used to send marks and spaces over long distances is to transmit a 1270 Hz tone for a mark and a 1070 Hz tone for a space. This method of transmission is called **frequency-shift keying (FSK).**

A 565 PLL chip used in conjunction with a comparator can decode the two tones and supply a two-level RS-232-C output. Figure 14–9 shows the 565 PLL chip connected as a FSK decoder. The input frequency will be either 1070 Hz or 1270 Hz, and the loop locks to the input frequency. As the input frequency varies, the PLL tracks the changes. A DC shift results at the PLL output as the frequency varies between 1070 Hz and 1270 Hz.

The VCO frequency is set so that the demodulator output is slightly positive with respect to the reference voltage with the input frequency set to 1070 Hz. The reference voltage is obtained from an internal voltage divider on the PLL IC. An input frequency of 1070 Hz causes the demodulated output to be more positive than the reference voltage.

Figure 14-9
FSK Decoder

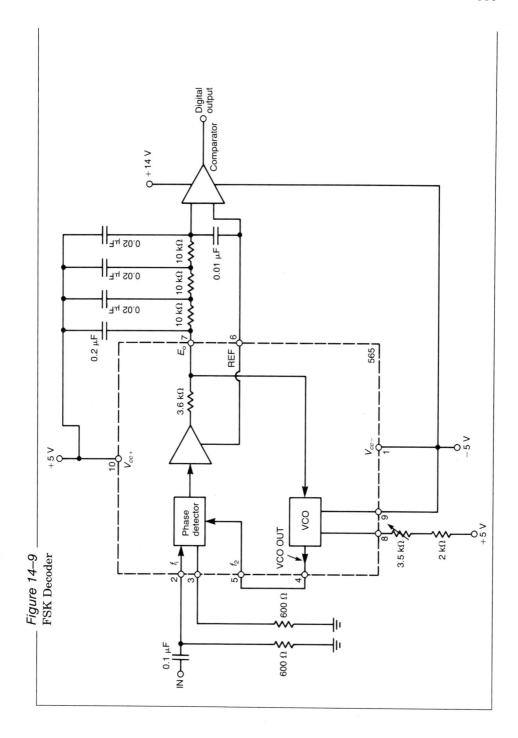

The demodulated output becomes less positive than the reference voltage when an input frequency of 1270 Hz is applied. As noted in Chapter 11, if the voltage at the noninverting input of a comparator is more positive than the voltage at the inverting input, the output is $+V_{cc}$. If the voltage at the inverting input is less positive than the voltage at the inverting input, the output is $-V_{cc}$. Thus the comparator output switches from $+V_{cc}$ at 1070 Hz to $-V_{cc}$ at 1270 Hz. By applying $+14$ V and -5 V to the power inputs of the comparator, the output of the FSK decoder is either $+14$ V or -5 V, converting changes in frequency to RS-232 marks and spaces.

Two interesting features can be seen in Figure 14–9. Note first the 600 Ω resistors connected from pins 2 and 3 to ground. The 600 Ω resistor connected to pin 2 is used to match the low impedance line normally used with digital data transmission. The 600 Ω resistor connected to pin 3 helps to improve the common mode rejection ratio and other errors of the differential amplifier in the phase detector. See Chapters 1 and 11 for information about differential amplifiers.

The second feature to be noted in Figure 14–9 is the filter circuit between pin 7 and the comparator. The internal 3.6 kΩ resistor and the external C_2 form the first part of the filter. A three-section RC filter provides additional filtering to assure that all high-frequency components are removed from the comparator input. Chapter 7 discusses multisection RC filters.

_____ *Example 14–6* _____

Using the values given in Figure 14–9, calculate the resting frequency of the VCO. Assume that R_1 is set to 3500 Ω. The required formula was discussed when the 565 PLL IC was investigated.

$$f_o = \frac{1.2}{4R_1C_1}$$

$$= \frac{1.2}{(4)(5.5 \times 10^3)(0.05 \times 10^{-6})}$$

$$= 1090 \text{ Hz}$$

Troubleshooting: The frequency-shift keying decoder of Figure 14–9 is considered in the troubleshooting example for this chapter. As noted in the text, the frequency-shift decoder output is -5 V when a 1270 Hz tone is received, and it is $+14$ V when a 1070 Hz tone is received. For the troubleshooting example, we wish to determine why the output remains at $+14$ V.

The frequency-shift decoder performs two functions: (1) it recognizes the difference between 1070 Hz and 1270 Hz and (2) it converts the differences in frequency to different DC levels. To troubleshoot, we need to check each function. Let's try the tone-decoding function first.

A change in input tone should result in a changing E_o at pin 7 of the 565 IC. If this check fails, the malfunction is most likely associated with the 565 IC circuit. Assume the check failed.

Apply 1070 Hz at the input to the frequency-shift keying decoder. Check the frequency at the VCO output (pin 4 of the 565 IC). The VCO output frequency should be near 1070 Hz. Now repeat the check at 1270 Hz. Assume that the VCO output frequency does not change.

The VCO is not "following" the input frequency. Before changing the IC, substitute a signal generator at pin 5 of the 565 IC and measure E_o. If E_o changes as the input frequency changes, then all parts of the IC, with the exception of the VCO, are good. In any case, replace the 565 IC because the VCO cannot be changed separately. The circuit should now operate correctly.

FM Demodulation

Phase-locked loops can be used to recover the modulation information from a frequency modulated signal. A typical use of frequency modulation is the FM band on a radio. A radio frequency carrier has its frequency changed at a rate determined by the frequency of the modulating information and by an amount determined by the strength of the modulating information. For example, if a 1 kHz tone is to be transmitted, the frequency of the carrier varies at a 1 kHz rate. The amount the frequency varies—that is, how much above and below the carrier frequency—is determined by the loudness of the 1 kHz tone. Thus in order to recover the 1 kHz tone from the radio frequency carrier, we must be able to determine the frequency of the modulating information, and how far the carrier frequency deviates.

Let's assume a PLL with a center frequency the same as the carrier frequency of the FM carrier. That is, with no modulation present, the VCO of the PLL is locked on to the carrier frequency, and the output voltage of the PLL is zero. If the input frequency (carrier) changes, the output voltage will change and cause the VCO to track the input frequency. Changing the carrier frequency at a 1 kHz rate will thus cause the output voltage of the PLL to change at a 1 kHz rate. We have recovered the frequency of the modulating signal. The amount of carrier frequency change—that is, the variation in carrier frequency—is determined by the "loudness" of the modulating signal. The louder the modulating signal, the more the carrier changes frequency. The PLL is tracking the carrier frequency, and as it changes frequency, the output voltage changes. In fact, the greater the carrier frequency change, the greater will be the amplitude of the output voltage. We have now re-covered the amplitude of the modulating signal, and demodulation of the FM carrier is complete.

When a PLL is used to demodulate an FM signal, f_o is not used. The error voltage E_o is the primary output. Figure 14–10 shows a 565 PLL connected to function as an FM demodulator. A carrier frequency of 67 kHz is assumed. (67 kHz is the carrier frequency used for commercial background music transmission by many FM stations.) The VCO center frequency is set to approximately 67 kHz by selection of R_1 and C_1 using the familiar formula $f_o = 1.2/4R_1C_1$. Input pins 2 and 3 are biased using the 4.7 kΩ resistors network. The capacitors associated with the input biasing network form a high-pass filter to both isolate DC from the 565 PLL input and to attenuate the regular FM channel signal. PLL output is passed through a three-section low-pass filter that reduces noise and adjusts the audio response of the demodulator.

Tone Detectors

A special PLL has been designed for telephone dialing tone decoding and remote control applications. Figure 14–11 is a functional diagram of the 567 tone decoder PLL IC. In addition to the conventional phase detector, VCO (it's a current-controlled oscillator in the 567), and filter/amplifier, a second phase detector has been added. The quadrature phase detector is designed to give maximum output when the phase difference between the oscillator and input signal is 90°. Since the PLL portion of the circuit maintains tracking with a 90° phase difference, the quadrature phase detector can be used to indicate lock-on.

The current-controlled oscillator (CCO) operates at a center frequency determined by R_1 and C_1. Center frequency is determined by the formula

$$f_o = \frac{1.1}{R_1C_1}$$

Detection bandwidth is also adjustable (from 0% to 14% of f_o) by selecting the appropriate value for C_2. Specification sheets for the 567 provide a graph to determine the value of C_2, but the following formula will calculate an approximate value:

$$C_2 = \frac{n}{f_o}$$

where

$n = 13,000$ for detection bandwidth of 14%

$n = 62,000$ for detection bandwidth of 2%

Figure 14–10   FM Demodulator

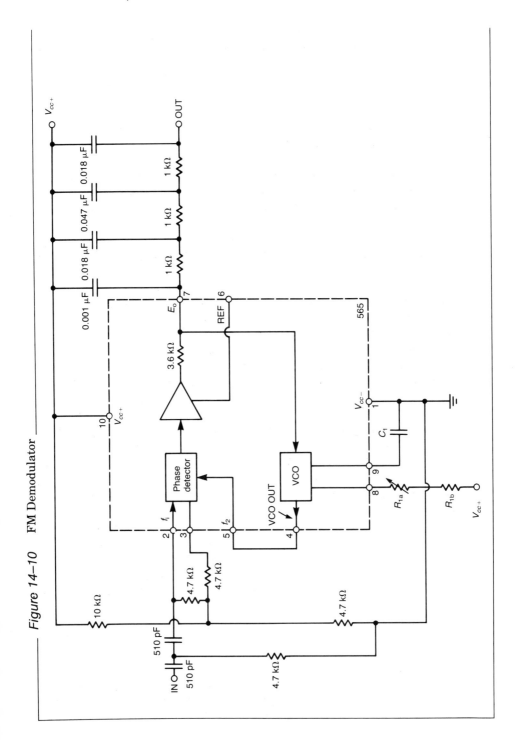

Figure 14–11

567 Tone Decoder

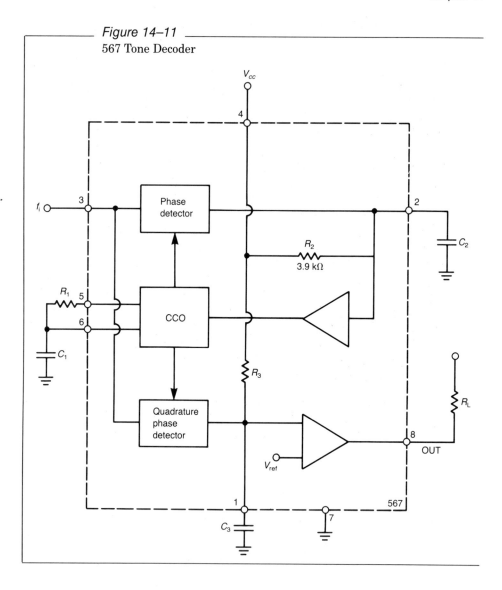

The output capacitor C_3 removes frequency components outside the detection bandwidth. Capacity is not critical, and is usually about twice the value of C_2.

Examples 14–7 and 14–8 show typical calculations for use of the 567 tone decoder PLL.

Example 14–7

A 567 PLL is to be used to detect a 697 Hz tone. The bandwidth will be 14%. Using a value of 0.1 µF for C_1, calculate values for R_1, C_2, and C_3.

$$R_1 = \frac{1.1}{fC_1} \qquad\qquad C_2 = \frac{n}{f} \qquad\qquad C_3 = 2C_2$$

$$= \frac{1.1}{(697)(0.1 \times 10^{-6})} \qquad = \frac{13,000}{697} \qquad = (2)(18.65)$$

$$= 15.78 \text{ k}\Omega \qquad\qquad = 18.65 \text{ µF} \qquad = 37.65 \text{ µF}$$

Example 14–8

Repeat Example 14–7 for 1336 Hz and a bandwidth of 14%.

$$R_1 = \frac{1.1}{fC_1} \qquad\qquad C_2 = \frac{n}{f} \qquad\qquad C_3 = 2C_2$$

$$= \frac{1.1}{(1336)(0.1 \times 10^{-6})} \qquad = \frac{13,000}{1336} \qquad = (2)(9.4)$$

$$= 8.23 \text{ k}\Omega \qquad\qquad = 9.4 \text{ µF} \qquad = 18.8 \text{ µF}$$

Modern telephone systems use a combination of tones to represent the digits 0 through 9 (and the symbols # and *). The digit 1 is represented by a combination of 697 Hz and 1209 Hz tones. The digit 2 uses 697 Hz and 1336 Hz, and so on. Figure 14–12 is a functional diagram of a decoder that detects the digit 2. The decoders for 697 Hz and 1336 Hz were designed in the earlier examples. It is only necessary to combine the decoder outputs in a NOR gate to detect the tones that represent the digit 2. If both tones representing the digit 2 are applied to the input, both decoders will produce a LOW output. The NOR gate output goes HIGH. For any other combination of tones, at least one of the decoders will produce a HIGH output. The NOR gate output will be LOW.

The 567 tone decoder PLL is a versatile and easy-to-use IC. Many variations have been produced, with multiple decoders on the same chip commonly available.

Frequency Synthesis

As mentioned earlier, the output frequency of a PLL has the same frequency and is in a fixed phase relationship with the input frequency. Any variation in input frequency is accompanied by an equivalent change in output frequency. Many radio frequency applications require

Figure 14–12

Dual Tone Decoder

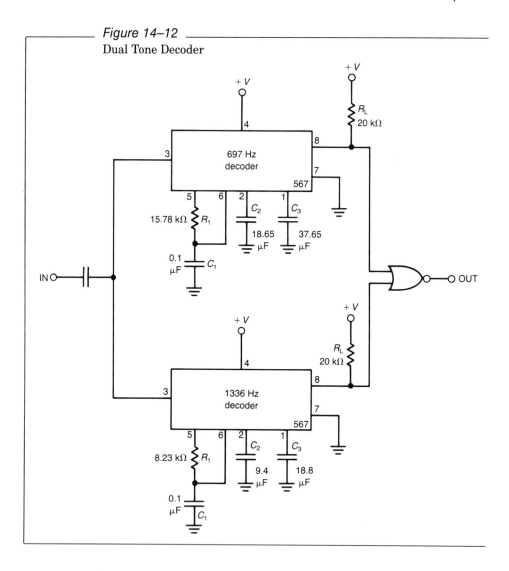

stable frequencies for correct operation. If a stable piezoelectric crystal oscillator is used as the input frequency to a PLL, then the output frequency will be equally stable.

Now let's look at how a frequency that is a multiple of the input frequency, and equally stable, can be obtained. A divider inserted between the VCO output and the phase detector input will do the trick. See Figure 14–13. Assume that the VCO operates at 10 kHz, and that the input frequency to the phase detector is 1 kHz. Inserting a divide-by-ten divider between the VCO output and the phase detector input will provide a 1 kHz VCO input to the phase detector that will be com-

Figure 14–13
Frequency Synthesizer

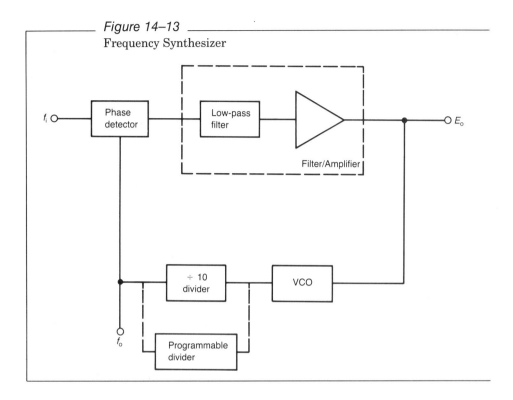

pared with the 1 kHz reference frequency. The PLL doesn't know the difference, even though the output frequency is ten times the reference frequency! In fact, if we can control the division ratio of the divider, we can obtain many different output frequencies, all with the stability of the reference frequency. If the divider is programmed from 1 to 10, then frequencies from 1 kHz to 10 kHz, in 1 kHz steps, may be obtained just by selecting the division ratio. The dotted lines in Figure 14–13 show a simplified diagram of a frequency synthesizer using a PLL and a programmable digital divider.

What happens if the divider is programmed from 100 to 110? With an input frequency of 1 kHz, output frequencies of 100 kHz to 110 kHz, in 1 kHz steps, can be selected. Are you beginning to get the picture? Almost any frequency within the range of the PLL can be obtained just by selecting the desired division ratio. The spacing of the output frequencies, however, is determined by the input reference frequency.

Let's try another trick! Insert a programmable divider between the reference frequency and the input to the PLL. Set the new divider to divide by two. Now the input frequency to the PLL is half the original frequency. If the original input frequency is 1 kHz, the divided input to the PLL is 500 Hz. Output frequency spacing becomes 500 Hz, rather than 1 kHz. Dividing the reference frequency by ten provides 100 Hz spacing, and so on. A complete **synthesized frequency signal generator,** its stability determined by the stability of the reference frequency, is possible because of the PLL.

Frequency synthesizers are also used in communications transmitters and receivers. If you have not studied communications applications, the detailed techniques associated with frequency synthesizers may be a bit complex. Let's look more at what PLLs have made possible in communications, rather than how they work.

When citizen's band (CB) communications equipment first appeared, 23 separate channels were available. Conventional transmitting and receiving techniques required 2 frequency-control crystals and each channel—a total of 46 crystals! Using mixer circuits, however, allowed 4 frequencies to be developed. Proper choice of crystal frequencies and mixer circuits reduced the crystal requirement to only 12. Then 40 channels were assigned to CB use. PLLs to the rescue! Using PLLs, programmable dividers, and mixer circuits, all 40 channels could be obtained with just a few crystals. Large-scale integration has allowed the PLL, dividers, and reference oscillator circuits to be placed on a single chip. We've come a long way from 46 crystals!

_____ SUMMARY _____

Chapter 14 has shown how very complex functions can easily be performed using modern integrated circuits. The PLL, until recently too complex to be used in everyday applications, is now used in radio, television, entertainment, and communications devices.

The PLL accepts an incoming frequency, locks on to the input signal, and provides output that allows the loop to faithfully track any changes in phase or frequency. A phase detector compares the incoming frequency with an internally generated frequency. If both inputs to the phase detector are not in phase, an error signal is generated that causes the internally generated signal to approach the input signal's frequency. When lock-on occurs, any change in input frequency is immediately detected and the internally generated signal is changed.

PLLs can be used to convert audio tones to logic levels, such as in frequency-shift keying and tone decoder applications. FM radio frequency carriers can be demodulated by PLLs, and the intelligence recovered. PLLs can be the heart of the frequency-determining portion of radio, television, and communications devices when used as frequency synthesizers. The applications are almost endless, limited only by the creativity of the designers.

QUESTIONS

1. Draw a block diagram of a PLL, showing how the functional sub-blocks are connected. Explain the purpose of each sub-block, and how the sub-blocks work together.

2. Explain the difference between the free-running, the capture, and the phase-locked states of a PLL.

3. What is the difference between capture range and lock range?

4. Using waveform drawings, show the output of a phase comparator when the internal VCO and the input signal are (a) in phase, (b) 180° out of phase, and (c) 90° out of phase.

5. When would analog phase detectors be used in preference to digital phase detectors?

6. What is the purpose of the low-pass filter in a PLL?

7. What is the purpose of the buffer amplifier in a PLL?

8. Draw a block diagram of a VCO and explain the purpose of each of the sub-blocks.

9. What is frequency-shift keying?

10. How is a PLL used to recover frequency-shift keyed information? Explain the principles of operation.

11. Explain how a PLL can recover frequency-modulated information from a radio frequency carrier.

12. Draw a block diagram of a tone decoder that will detect the digit 1 in a touch-tone telephone system. Determine component values.

13. Draw a block diagram of a frequency synthesizer that uses an input frequency of 1 kHz and provides outputs at 1 kHz steps from 50 kHz to 60 kHz.

14. Why are frequency synthesizers used in communications radios such as citizen's band transceivers?

PROBLEMS

1. In the 566 VCO circuit of Figure 14–7, R_1 = 9.1 kΩ and C_1 = 1300 pF. V_+ = 16 V. Calculate the lowest and highest output frequency, assuming that V_c ranges from +12 V to +15.5 V.

2. In the PLL circuit of Figure 14–8, R_1 = 12 kΩ and C_1 = 1500 pF. Calculate the resting frequency.

3. A 567 PLL is to be used to detect a 1209 Hz tone. Bandwidth is to be 14%. C_1 = 0.1 μF. Calculate R_1, C_2, and C_3.

Applications

INTRODUCTION

Operational amplifier applications are practically endless. Chapter 15 selects seven typical applications that span the range from simple DC applications to complex waveform generation circuits. The op-amp-based thermometer is an example of DC application of operational amplifiers, whereas the tone detector shows AC operation. FET-input op amps are demonstrated in the level sensor circuit, and voltage and current control of operational amplifier characteristics receive coverage in the oscillator discussion.

The function generator section of Chapter 15 shows application of almost all of the basic op amp circuits. Both AC and DC amplifications are used, along with the mathematical function of integration. Conversion from nonsinusoidal to sinusoidal waveform using logarithmic amplifiers or multiple-diode feedback shows yet another op amp application.

An op-amp-related LSI assembly, the analog signal-processing subsystem, is applied to obtain the absolute-value, or precision full-wave rectifier, function. Troubleshooting techniques are scattered throughout Chapter 15. The valuable experience gained by applying these techniques serves to integrate the chapter.

THERMOMETER

Many of the principles of op amp operation are combined in the thermometer circuit of Figure 15–1. As shown in Figure 15–1A, the tem-

Figure 15–1
Electronic Thermometer

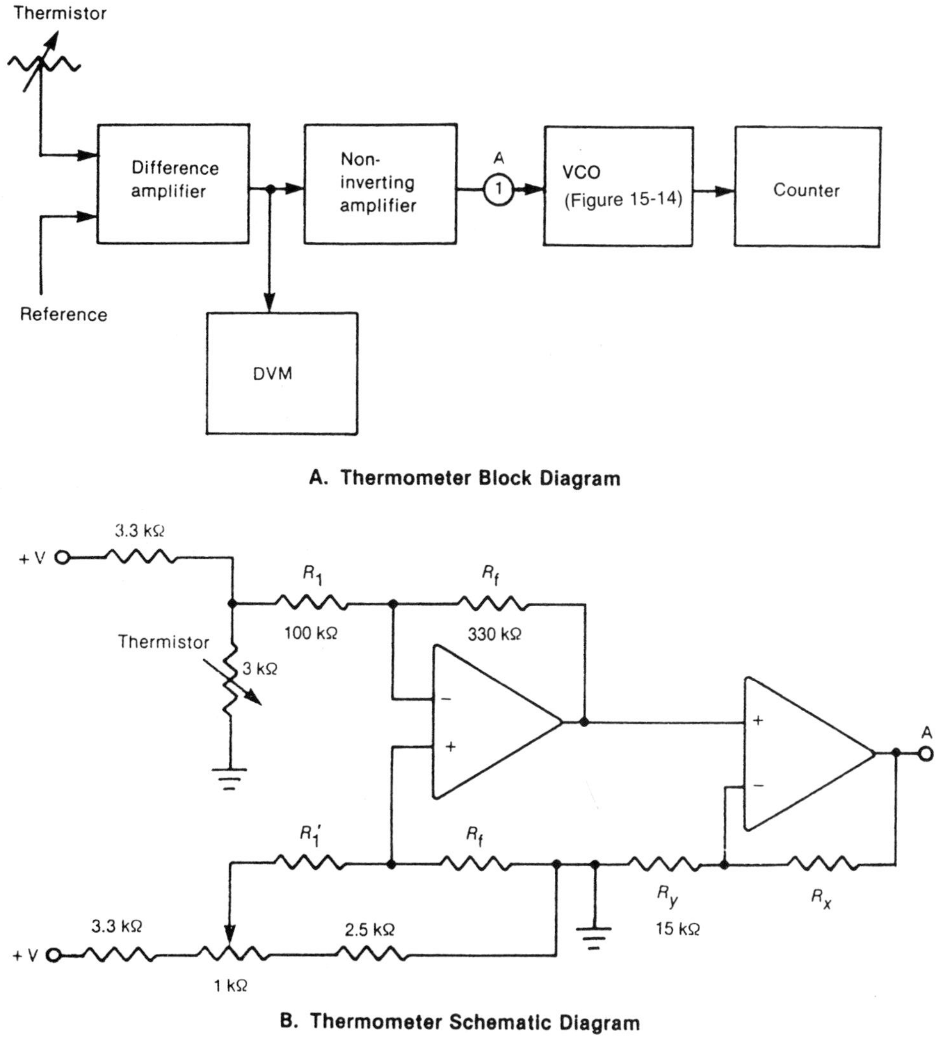

A. Thermometer Block Diagram

B. Thermometer Schematic Diagram

perature-sensing element is compared with a reference in a difference amplifier. The change is further amplified and used to control the frequency of a voltage-controlled oscillator (VCO). Temperature may be displayed as a voltage on a digital voltmeter (DVM) or as the output frequency of the VCO on a frequency counter. (Only the difference amplifier and the noninverting amplifier are diagrammed in Figure 15–1B.)

The temperature-sensing element is a negative temperature-coefficient thermistor, whose resistance decreases as temperature increases. A bridge circuit with the thermistor in one leg is used to supply inputs to the difference amplifier. The inverting input voltage is a function of the voltage drop across the thermistor, which varies with temperature change. The noninverting input voltage is supplied by a voltage divider in the other leg of the bridge. An adjustment is provided to balance the bridge at a known reference temperature.

The difference amplifier combines the two input voltages and provides an output voltage that is a function of the difference between the inputs and the gain of the amplifier. As with any inverting amplifier, gain is a function of the ratio between R_f and R_1. An appropriate gain is selected to be compatible with the thermistor characteristics. A digital voltmeter may then be connected at the output of the difference amplifier, and the voltage will be a direct function of temperature. For example, the bridge may be balanced at 0°C so that the digital voltmeter will show 0 V. Considering a linear thermistor characteristic, 10°C should read 10 mV, 20°C should read 20 mV, and so on. Selection of the proper ratio of R_f to R_1 will accomplish this.

Using the varying voltage output of the difference amplifier to control the frequency of a VCO will allow the use of a frequency counter to display temperature. Unfortunately, the output of the difference amplifier does not have the range required for wide variation of oscillator frequency. The inclusion of a noninverting amplifier will step up the difference amplifier voltage to the necessary value. Once again, the feedback ratio determines the gain of the noninverting amplifier. R_x and R_y are selected to amplify the output of the difference amplifier to the proper range. It is merely necessary to know the range of the difference amplifier output and the required range of VCO input to determine required gain. Any VCO may be used—a circuit such as that discussed in Figure 15–4, for example.

The most common difficulties encountered with this type of circuit are associated with component drift. As components age, the critical gain values may vary. Output offsets may change, and adjustments may be necessary. This type of circuit does, however, have much to offer. Using a single-quad IC, it requires but a few external components to implement both the amplifiers and VCO. The circuit is simple and easy to use but can be highly accurate when properly calibrated. It is yet another example of the many things that op amps can do for us.

_____ TONE DETECTOR _____

The circuit diagrammed in Figure 15–2 will indicate that the input frequency is approximately 600 Hz. It is basically a tone detector that can be used in many signaling and communications applications. Let's consider some possible troubleshooting situations for this type of circuit.

_____ *Figure 15–2* _____

600 Hz Tone Detector Circuit

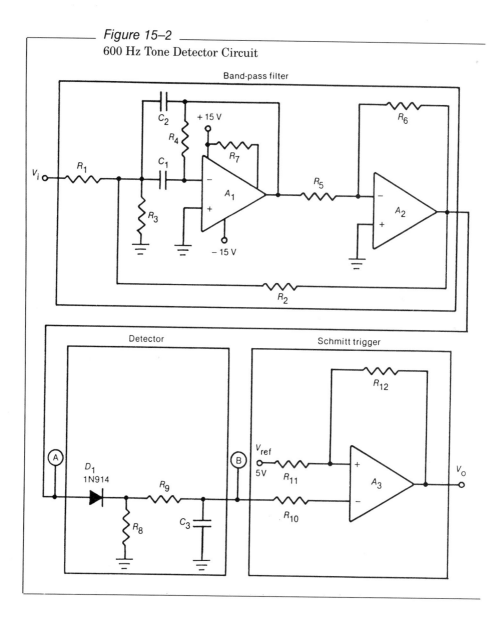

Tone Detector Circuit Operation

First, however, circuit operation must be understood. If the circuit must respond only to a 600 Hz input, some type of band-pass filter must be present. If the A_1-A_2 combination is examined, it may be recognized as a version of the multiple-feedback band-pass filter discussed in Chapter 8. A_1 and its associated components resemble the multiple-feedback band-pass filter of Chapter 8. The addition of A_2 and its associated components allows greater gain and filter quality to be obtained while still maintaining stability. R_1, C_1, R_4, and C_2 generally control the center frequency of the filter. R_2, R_5, and R_6 affect the gain and bandwidth. The component values that follow provide a filter bandwidth of approximately 50 Hz centered at 600 Hz. Filter voltage gain is approximately 20, with a Q of 12. The values are as follows:

$R_1 = 68$ kΩ	$R_6 = 390$ kΩ	$R_{11} = 1$ kΩ
$R_2 = 200$ kΩ	$R_7 = 3$ MΩ	$R_{12} = 100$ kΩ
$R_3 = 470$ kΩ	$R_8 = 300$ kΩ	$C_1 = C_2 = 0.047$ μF
$R_4 = 68$ kΩ	$R_9 = 30$ kΩ	$C_3 = 1$ μF
$R_5 = 68$ kΩ	$R_{10} = 10$ kΩ	

The output of A_2 is rectified by D_1 and filtered by R_8, R_9, and C_3 to supply a DC voltage proportional to the amplitude of the AC input to the filter. C_3 actually serves as an integrating capacitor, charging when A_2 output is positive. When A_2 output is negative, C_3 discharges, but at a much slower rate than it charged. Therefore, C_3 will accumulate a charge over a period of time if the input to the detector is of sufficient amplitude. Detector output supplies the inverting input to A_3. The positive feedback via R_{12} is summed with a reference voltage at the noninverting input to A_3 to form a **Schmitt trigger** with hysteresis. Thus, when the output of the detector exceeds the reference voltage, the output of the Schmitt trigger circuit will switch. The switching points may be determined in the same manner as discussed in Chapter 9. With V_{ref} = 5 V, and assuming that the output of A_3 will change from $+14$ V to -14 V and vice versa, the switching points are approximately 5.1 V and 4.8 V. If the circuit is operating properly, the output should switch from approximately $+14$ V to -14 V only when a small band of frequencies centered around 600 Hz, and with an amplitude of about 1 V, is applied to the filter input.

Troubleshooting the Tone Detector

Now for a troubleshooting problem. Assume that the output remains at $+14$ V with the required 1 V, 600 Hz input to the filter. Changing either frequency or amplitude of the input signal does not affect the output. What must be done to isolate the problem? Let's pick a point about half-way through the circuit and check operation. This so-called **half-splitting** approach is one of the most efficient methods of troubleshooting. Instead of randomly making measurements, at least half of the circuit is verified by the half-splitting method. If operation is satisfactory from input to halfway through the circuit, then the problem must be in the last half. Otherwise, the first half of the circuit is defective. The defective half may then be split again, using the same technique.

If we pick test point A (Figure 15–2) as the halfway point, circuit operation may be verified by observing the AC waveform while varying input amplitude and frequency. A sine wave should be present, increasing to a maximum at about 600 Hz. The amplitude of the sine wave at point A should be greater than at the input, perhaps becoming distorted as the input voltage is increased well above its rated 1 V value. If test point A is correct, the defective portion of the circuit is in the last half. Splitting the last half of the circuit by observing test point B will further isolate malfunctioning components. Point B should show an increasing DC voltage as the input frequency approaches 600 Hz, becoming maximum at 600 Hz, and then decreasing as the frequency continues to be varied. Furthermore, the magnitude of the DC voltage at point B should increase as the input voltage is increased, and vice versa.

If the DC voltage at point B does not change, the problem has been isolated between points A and B. Assuming such a malfunction, the next check should be to isolate the *most probable* defective component. Of the four components connected between points A and B, diode D_1 is the most likely to fail. Capacitors do short but usually not in low-voltage circuits such as the detector. Resistors do open-circuit but not as often as diodes fail. The diode may be checked by measuring forward and reverse resistance. Assuming a diode failure, replacement would return the circuit to normal operation.

We have discussed only one of many possible failures that could occur in the tone detector of Figure 15–2. Most important, we have learned to use a troubleshooting method that is guaranteed to reduce troubleshooting time. The half-splitting method of troubleshooting, along with a good knowledge of circuit operation, is an unbeatable combination.

LEVEL SENSOR

A circuit that demonstrates the application of both FET op amps and comparators is shown in Figure 15–3. The circuit is used to indicate that the level of a liquid—water, for example—in a tank is not within limits. A warning lamp lights when the water is either above the level

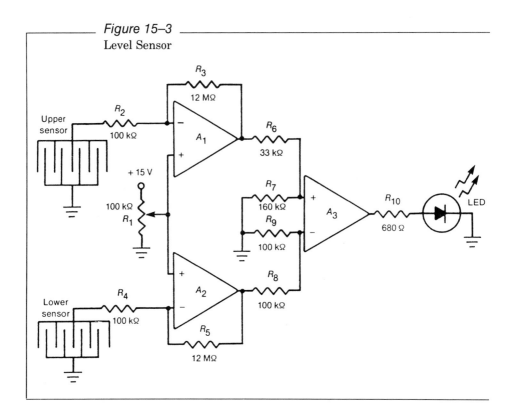

Figure 15–3
Level Sensor

of the top sensor or below the level of the bottom sensor. Between the two levels, the lamp is extinguished. Both op amps operate in the same manner, and their outputs are combined in the comparator. Operation of the sensor circuits requires the use of FET op amps. Low offset and bias currents are a must in this high input impedance circuit, and conventional op amps may not be able to meet the requirement.

Level Sensor Circuit Operation

The noninverting input of each of the op amps (Figure 15–3) is set at a reference voltage that provides adequate sensitivity for the level-sensing circuit. Potentiometer R_1 acts as an adjustable voltage divider to provide the required bias. The inverting input, with its high resistance feedback path, connects to the actual level sensor via an isolation resistor. A_1, for example, uses R_3 as its feedback resistor and R_2 as its isolation resistor. The operating principles of op amps will cause the inverting input to drive the output of the op amp so that there is 0 V differential between inputs. With a 0.5 V reference, for example, at the noninverting input, an equal 0.5 V will appear at the inverting input. Negligible current flows in the input circuits of op amps, so the output voltage will also be 0.5 V. Since both A_1 and A_2 have identical components, both outputs will be the same.

Note the difference in the output voltage dividers, however. Let's determine the inputs to the comparator as a result of the voltage dividers, assuming that both op amps have a 0.5 V output. The noninverting input of the comparator is 0.41 V, calculated as follows:

$$V_{i+} = A_{1_o} \times \frac{R_7}{R_6 + R_7} = 0.5 \times \frac{160}{160 + 33} = 0.41 \text{ V}$$

The inverting input of the comparator is 0.25 V, calculated as follows:

$$V_{i-} = A_{2_o} \times \frac{R_9}{R_8 + R_9} = 0.5 \times \frac{100}{100 + 100} = 0.25 \text{ V}$$

Since the noninverting input is more positive than the inverting input, the output is driven to V_{cc}, or about $+15$ V. The light-emitting diode is turned on, indicating an out-of-limits condition. In this case, the liquid is below the bottom sensor. It is, therefore, also below the top sensor, and both op amps have the same inputs.

The liquid sensor is nothing more than a grid of conducting wires or printed circuit conductors that are alternately connected to ground and an op amp input via an isolation resistor. See Figure 15–3. Most liquids contain enough **ions** so that they are not perfect insulators. When the liquid covers the sensor, a small amount of current flows due to these ions. Consider the sensor connected to the inverting input of A_2. When the liquid rises to cover the sensor, the resulting current flow causes a voltage drop across R_4. The inverting input of A_2 drops, causing a positive shift at the output of A_2. The actual shift will be determined by the ion concentration in the liquid. Let's consider that the A_2 output shifts to $+10$ V. Voltage divider R_8-R_9 causes the inverting input of the comparator to rise to $+5$ V, and the comparator output shifts to 0 V. The LED is extinguished, indicating that the liquid is within limits.

When the liquid rises to cover the top sensor, the output of A_1 also shifts toward the positive direction. Again, let's assume that it shifts to $+10$ V. Voltage divider R_4-R_5 causes the noninverting input of the comparator to rise to $+8.3$ V. The noninverting input is now more positive than the inverting input, and the output shifts back to V_{cc}. Since the liquid level is above the top sensor, it is out of tolerance, and the LED is illuminated.

As noted earlier, it is necessary to use op amps with very high input impedance and minimal offset current ratings. Since the inverting inputs to each of the op amps are effectively "open," even a few nanoam-peres of leakage will cause sufficient input change to give false output indications. The problem may be somewhat compensated by adjusting sensitivity, but there is no substitute for FET-input op amps in this application.

Troubleshooting the Level Sensor

Now let's try a troubleshooting problem concerned with the level-sen-sing circuit. Assume that the tank has been pumped "dry," without any indication of an out-of-limits condition. In other words, the liquid fell below the lower sensor, and the light did not illuminate. The clues would imply a problem in the low-level sensing circuit, and it would be good practice to start troubleshooting in this area. Employing the half-split-ting method, a voltage check at the output of A_2 would be advisable. With no liquid in the tank, A_2 output should be approximately $+0.5$ V. Assume that, instead, it is approximately $+10$ V, which is incorrect. The problem has been isolated to the input part of the circuit, not the com-parator. By half-splitting again, A_2 inputs are checked. If the bias at the noninverting input is correct, the inverting input is checked. One more assumption—the inverting input is less than $+0.5$ V. The problem has now been isolated to either the op amp or the sensor and isolation resis-tor R_4. Op amps do not often fail, so it would be advisable to disconnect the sensor. At this point, the LED illuminates. Examination of the sen-sor shows that the grid has become shorted because of chemical deposits from the liquid. A path for current flow was thus established through the sensor, giving an indication that it was still covered by the liquid. Replacement of the sensor restores operation to normal.

In this example of troubleshooting, many of the basic principles of op amp operation were used. Note also that the half-splitting method of troubleshooting saved considerable time in isolating the fault. The use of previous experience should also have been mentioned here. An inexperienced troubleshooter probably would have proceeded as men-tioned above. Experience probably would have led the troubleshooter to check the sensor *first*. Op amps seldom fail. Devices exposed to corrosive materials often fail. Once again, a successful troubleshooter must apply many different techniques. Nothing, however, substitutes for critical analysis of circuit operation *before* beginning the actual troubleshooting.

VOLTAGE-CONTROLLED OSCILLATOR

In many oscillator applications, it is preferable to control fre-quency of oscillation by varying a voltage rather than by varying com-

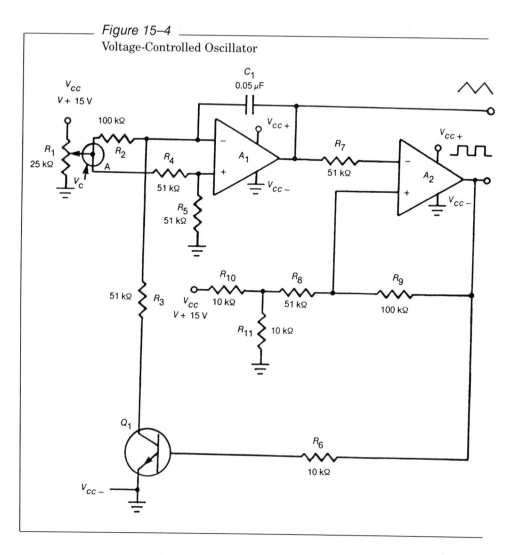

Figure 15–4

Voltage-Controlled Oscillator

ponent values. Many of the principles of op amp circuits are incorporated in the voltage-controlled oscillator (VCO) shown in Figure 15–4. Let's practice analysis and troubleshooting with the VCO diagram.

VCO Circuit Operation

Recognition of circuit functions is one of the primary requirements during analysis and troubleshooting of electronic devices. Closely related to this requirement is a knowledge of the characteristics of the active devices being used. A common and inexpensive op amp, type 741, is used as an example. The type 741 op amp has been discussed at length in this book and some of its typical characteristics are shown in Appendix A. These characteristics should be reviewed before proceeding further.

With the operational amplifier characteristics in mind, only one more active device remains to be considered. Q_1 is a conventional NPN transistor. The waveforms shown on the diagram (Figure 15–4) indicate nonsinusoidal outputs, so we are not interested in the linear characteristics of the transistor. In the switching mode, most transistors are considered to be a very low resistance from collector to emitter when the base-emitter junction is forward biased. When reverse biased at the base-emitter junction, the collector-to-emitter resistance is very high. For our purposes, these switching characteristics are all that is necessary.

One of the first points to investigate on a schematic diagram is the power distribution. Note that $+15$ V is used to power the op amps. The V_{cc-} is grounded. Since the type 741 op amp normally requires both $+$ and $-$ 15 V power, the output of the circuit will be limited to 0 V at the low end and $+15$ V at the high end. If a symmetrical output is required, one of each of the op amp inputs must be biased such that the no-signal output is about halfway between 0 V and $+15$ V. This little bit of knowledge immediately explains the purpose of resistor pairs R_4-R_5 and R_{10}-R_{11}. R_4-R_5 places the noninverting input of A_1 midway between ground and the oscillator control voltage V_c. R_{10}-R_{11} biases the noninverting input of A_2 to $1/2V_{cc}$. Symmetrical output around a reference is thus established.

Let's now investigate the rest of the circuitry associated with A_2. The positive feedback via R_9 and R_8 may be recognized as the conventional feedback used with comparator circuits. R_7 provides an inverting input resistance equal to the noninverting input resistance to reduce input offset errors. A_2 and its associated circuitry thus appear to be a comparator operating "centered" around $V_{cc}/2$. The output of A_2 should be a square wave varying from near 0 V to near $+15$ V. Square wave generators previously discussed used a similar technique.

Disregarding Q_1 and its associated resistors for the moment, consider the circuitry associated with A_1. The circuit is seen to be an integrator. When power is first applied, the capacitor charges through R_2, forming a **linear ramp output voltage.** Without Q_1 and its associated resistors, the output of A_1 would decrease linearly from V_{cc+} to 0 V. If a discharge path were provided, however, the ramp voltage could then both decrease and increase, forming a triangular wave. The triangular wave output of A_1 could then supply an input to comparator A_2 to form a square wave. As the ramp output of A_1 decreases, it causes the output of A_2 to switch. The $+$ output of A_2 forward biases Q_1, causing it to turn on. The low resistance of the collector-emitter path of Q_1 connects R_3 to ground, providing a discharge path for C_1. As C_1 discharges, the positive-going ramp output of A_1 causes comparator A_2 to switch to ground. Q_1 is turned off, and C_1 is allowed to recharge. The cycle repeats, supplying a triangular wave output from A_1 and a square wave output from A_2. Output frequency is determined by the RC time constant of R_2 and C_1 and the control voltage V_c at point A. If V_c is any positive voltage greater than 0 V, it will take less time for C_1 to charge to its switching point. Hence, the output frequency will increase. A simple potentiometer, therefore, can be used to vary the output frequency of the triangular/square wave generator.

Troubleshooting a VCO

Troubleshooting a VCO such as that shown in Figure 15–4 requires the type of analysis just performed. Knowing *what* the circuit does and *how* it does it is very important to the troubleshooting task. A **closed-loop system** such as the triangular/square wave generator is especially difficult to troubleshoot because of interaction of the many components. But let's try a simple troubleshooting problem. Assume that the circuit does not function. Neither triangular nor square waves are seen at either output when using an oscilloscope for troubleshooting. It is noted, however, that a transient condition occurs when power is first applied. The oscilloscope shows approximately 0 V at the output of A_1, whereas the output of A_2 is approximately $+15$ V. No output changes occur after the initial startup transient. Circuit analysis indicates that C_1 has charged and caused A_1 to go to negative saturation. A_2 output is at positive saturation because of the 0 V input from A_1. Apparently, C_1 is not being discharged. But the $+15$ V from A_2 should definitely forward bias Q_1 and discharge C_1 through R_3. Measurement indicates that Q_1 is forward biased but that a voltage greater than 0 V is present at its collector. Thus, Q_1 is apparently defective. Replacement of Q_1 should restore normal operation of the circuit.

The analysis and troubleshooting steps used to discuss the VCO are relatively standard for any troubleshooting situation. It is imperative that circuit operation and component characteristics be understood in order to effectively analyze and troubleshoot. Removal and replacement of components until operation is restored is one method but may not be possible with modern equipment. All too many modern electronic devices have components permanently soldered to printed circuit boards. Isolation of the problem to the most probable defective component is, therefore, a must. Random removal and replacement is both time consuming and destructive to modern electronic circuit boards. Learn to analyze—it saves much time, effort, and money.

CURRENT-CONTROLLED OSCILLATOR

An interesting application for programmable op amps is that of the current-controlled oscillator. Programmable op amps, remember, have an external connection that allows control of the amplifier's characteristics. Power dissipation, bandwidth, slew rate, and gain all are adjustable by merely controlling a set current. The current-controlled oscillator takes advantage of the variable slew rate to provide square waves in a wide frequency range.

In Figure 15–5, A_1 is the programmable op amp, and A_2 is a comparator. Note that the comparator is functioning as a zero-crossing detector with hysteresis. The switching voltage is determined by the following equation:

$$V_{ref} = V_o \times \frac{R_3}{R_3 + R_4}$$

where $V_o = V_{cc}$. Assuming that V_o is equal to both V_{cc+} and V_{cc-}, the reference voltages are calculated as follows:

$$V_{ref} = +15 \times \frac{10}{14.7} = +10.2 \text{ V}$$

and

$$V_{ref} = -15 \times \frac{10}{14.7} = -10.2 \text{ V}$$

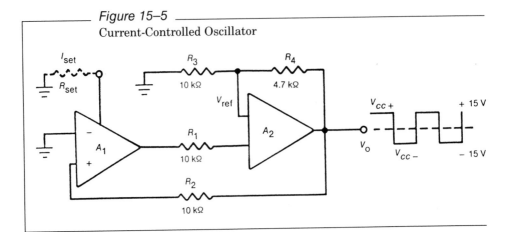

Figure 15–5

Current-Controlled Oscillator

Thus, the comparator output will change from $+15$ V to -15 V (and vice versa) as soon as the input voltage to the inverting input exceeds the reference voltage.

Assume that the comparator output has just switched from $+15$ V to -15 V. At this time, the reference voltage changes polarity and the output of the programmable op amp starts changing in the negative direction. The rate of change of output (slew rate), however, is determined by the set current. The input to A_1 has just changed almost instantly from $+15$ V to -15 V, but the output can change only as quickly as the slew rate allows. When A_1's output exceeds V_{ref}, A_2 switches back from -15 V to $+15$ V. The reference voltage again changes polarity and A_1 begins slewing in the opposite direction. The cycle continues as long as power is applied to the circuit. If the set current is changed, the slewing rate changes. An increasing current, for example, increases the slew rate. The output of A_1 can then change faster, and A_2 switches faster. Thus, a higher frequency of oscillation occurs.

Set current may be supplied by any current source. A simple resistor connected to ground will allow current to flow. The value for R_{set} is found from the following equation:

$$R_{set} = \frac{V_{cc+} - 0.7}{I_{set}}$$

Either bipolar or field effect transistors may be used in place of R_{set} so that I_{set} may be varied by an external circuit. Using an FET, for example, allows a complete range of I_{set} from less than 1 nA to near 100 μA, with a control voltage change of as little as 0.5 V.

FUNCTION GENERATORS

Waveform generators that supply more than one type of output waveform are called **function generators.** In the past, separate generators were used for sine waves, square waves, pulses, and so on. Today, most of these waveforms are supplied by a single generator. The concepts of function generators may be illustrated by showing a combination square wave and triangular wave circuit. Other variations will then be shown as pulse, sine, and sawtooth wave outputs are developed.

Function Generator Block Diagram

A common approach to waveform generation is to start with the square wave generator (or an equivalent) discussed earlier. The square wave output is supplied to an *integrator* to form a triangular wave of the same

Figure 15–6
Waveform Generator Block Diagram

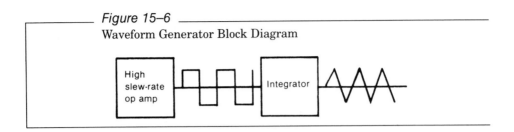

frequency. Figure 15–6 is a block diagram of such a waveform generator and the associated waveforms. As shown, a triangular wave is a periodic wave that rises linearly to a given positive voltage, then changes direction and falls linearly to a chosen negative voltage before repeating its linear rise. The rising portion of the waveform is called a **positive ramp,** and the falling portion is called a **negative ramp.** A triangular wave is said to be made up of equal positive and negative ramps.

When a square wave is used as the input to an integrator, the output is a triangular wave. An integrator performs the mathematical operation of integration, which effectively provides the area under the curve defined by the input function. But our interest here is more in how circuits function. Let's look at an integrator circuit and determine how it can convert a square wave input into a triangular wave.

Integrator Operation

Figure 15–7A is a schematic diagram of a simple integrator. Note that it very much resembles a common inverter amplifier, except that the feedback component is a capacitor instead of a resistor. Let's review the operation of an integrator, as was similarly discussed in Chapter 10. Operation of the integrator circuit can be explained by establishing some initial conditions. As with any basic op amp circuit, it is assumed that the voltage differential between the inverting and noninverting inputs is 0 with no input signal. Furthermore, no current flows in either the inverting or noninverting input circuits of the op amp. Under these circumstances, there is no input to the op amp, and, consequently, there is no output. With no input and no output, there is no voltage differential between input and output, and no voltage exists across capacitor C_f. The capacitor is, therefore, in a discharged state.

Now let's cause the input to the integrator to change instantaneously from 0 V to some positive voltage, as shown at initial waveform transition in Figure 15–7B. Application of the input voltage will cause current to flow in R_i. Since no current can flow in the op amp input circuit, the current must flow through the capacitor. The capacitive current must equal the current through the resistor to maintain op amp input current at 0. Since the input voltage is constant, the current

Figure 15–7

Integrator Operation

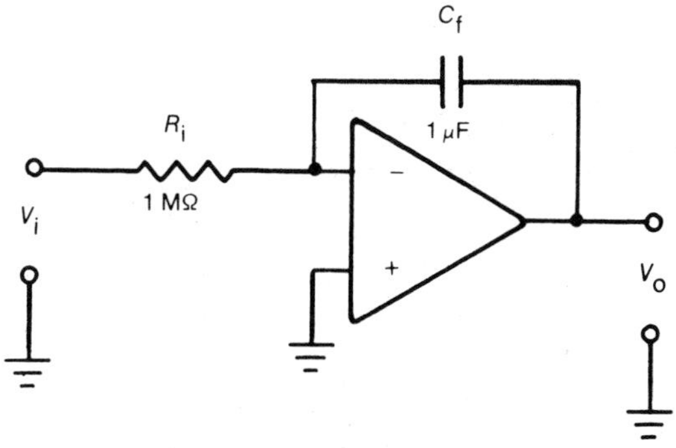

A. Schematic Diagram

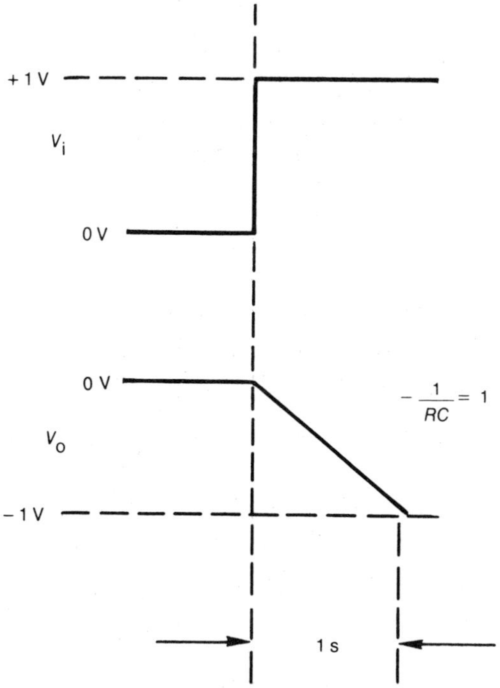

B. Waveforms

through the resistor is constant. The matching current through the capacitor must also be constant. A constant current applied through a capacitor causes the voltage across the capacitor to change linearly. Therefore, in order to maintain a constant current through the capacitor as it charges, the voltage at the output of the op amp must change linearly.

As long as the input voltage remains positive, the op amp output voltage will fall linearly within the range of the op amp and its supply voltage. In other words, the negative ramp cannot continue forever.

When the input to the integrator goes from a positive voltage to a negative voltage, the opposite condition exists. The capacitor must now try to charge in the opposite direction, and the output voltage becomes a positive-going ramp. Integrator output must be defined in terms of both voltage and time. The change in integrator output voltage is a function of the time constant formed by R_i and C_f. An actual example will be shown shortly.

Another way of looking at the operation of the integrator is to realize that one end of the capacitor is at the output of the op amp, while the other end is at ground potential. Remember, if the noninverting input of an op amp is grounded, then the inverting input must also be at a virtual ground to maintain the input differential voltage at 0. If it were not for C_f, the output voltage would try to be very large. In fact, it would *try* to reach a value equal to the open-loop gain of the op amp times the input voltage. Even though it cannot go that high, the integrating capacitor C_f will be trying to charge to that voltage. Since it will only be able to charge to a very small fraction of the fictitious very-high voltage, only a very small part at the beginning of the time constant curve is used. The beginning portion of the time constant curve is linear, and the resulting output of the integrator is thus quite linear.

Square and Triangular Wave Output

Figure 15–8 is a diagram of a simple square wave and triangular wave generator. The square wave generator, consisting of A_1 and its associated components, is identical to circuits discussed earlier. A square wave output of $+15$ V to -15 V is assumed. As with square wave circuits discussed earlier, the output frequency is determined by the formula $f = 1/2RC$ (within 10%) when the positive feedback divider resistors are equal in value. For the square wave oscillator in Figure 15–8, then, the output frequency is calculated as follows:

$$f = \frac{1}{2RC} = \frac{1}{2 \times 1000\ \Omega \times 0.01\ \mu F} = \frac{1}{0.000020} = 50{,}000\ \text{Hz}$$

Integrator output is a triangular wave of the same frequency and period as the square wave. The amplitude of the triangular wave is generally dependent on the input voltage and frequency and on the time constant of the integrator. For linear triangular output of reasonable amplitude, the integrator time constant is usually selected to be at least equal to the period of the input waveform.

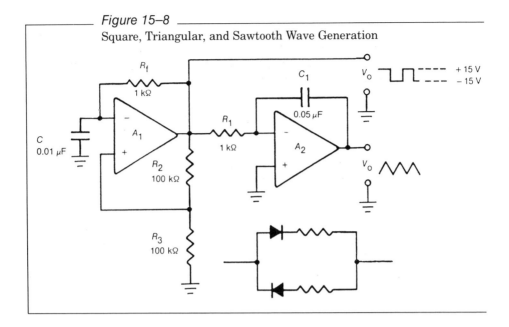

Figure 15–8
Square, Triangular, and Sawtooth Wave Generation

Sawtooth Wave Output

A sawtooth wave is merely a triangular wave with a shorter negative ramp time than its positive ramp time. Such waveforms are used in oscilloscopes to deflect the electron beam at a known and linear rate. With minor modification, the triangular wave generator of Figure 15–8 may also be used to generate sawtooth waves. It is merely necessary to change the resistor (R_1) in the integrator time constant circuit. The time constant during the negative ramp generation is made much shorter than the time constant during the positive ramp generation. This is accomplished by using a much smaller integrator time constant resistor during negative ramp generation. Which resistor is to be used is automatically determined by forward biasing of the appropriate diode in Figure 15–8.

Pulse and Sine Wave Output

Pulse output is simple using the square wave generator portion of Figure 15–8. It is only necessary to add a one-shot that uses the square wave generator output as a trigger. Sine wave output may also be obtained using the triangular wave output of the function generator. A number of different methods may be employed. One approach uses a complex mathematical operation with a circuit called a four-quadrant multiplier. This method is beyond the scope of our discussion. Another approach takes advantage of the nonlinear logarithmic transfer characteristic of transistors connected in the differential amplifier configuration. Once again, this is not directly related to op amp applications. Both of the methods yield relatively pure sine waves with less than 1% distortion when correctly adjusted.

Triangular-to-Sine Wave Conversion

A simple op amp circuit (Figure 15–9) may also be used to convert triangular waves to sine waves. Although distortion may be on the order of 3%, the simplicity of the circuit sometimes makes it applicable. A conventional inverting amplifier configuration with feedback is used. Note, however, that more than one feedback path is provided. When the amplitude of the input triangular wave is small, the circuit gain is controlled by the feedback-resistor/input-resistor ratio. As the amplitude of the input signal increases, germanium diodes D_1 and D_2 conduct, connecting the second feedback resistor in parallel with the first. The equivalent resistance is now lower, more feedback exists, and gain is reduced.

Figure 15–9

Triangular-to-Sine Wave Converter

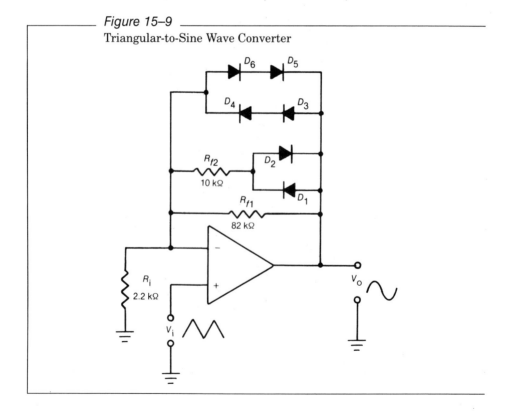

At even higher input signal amplitudes, the remaining germanium diodes (D_3, D_4, D_5, and D_6) conduct, placing their forward resistance in parallel with both feedback resistors. Even more feedback results, and gain is lowered further. Thus, as the amplitude of the triangular wave increases, gain is reduced. The peaks of the triangular wave are rounded off to approximate a sine wave. Judicious selection of component values will result in a relatively good sine wave over a reasonable range of frequencies. With a 2 V peak-to-peak triangular wave input and the values shown in Figure 15–9, the output of the op amp is a usable sine wave from about 100 Hz to 5 kHz. It should be noted that Figure 15–9 is shown merely as an example of op amp application. Modern sine wave shaping circuits tend to use the more complex multiplier and differential amplifier configurations.

LSI Function Generator

Although not specifically related to op amps, another method of waveform generation should be shown. Numerous manufacturers now provide a single IC that generates many of the basic waveforms. Figure 15–10 is a functional block diagram of a function generator IC. It does not represent any specific IC but does show what functions must be provided. The basic oscillator supplies the square wave output. It may be the op amp type of square wave generator discussed earlier or any of a

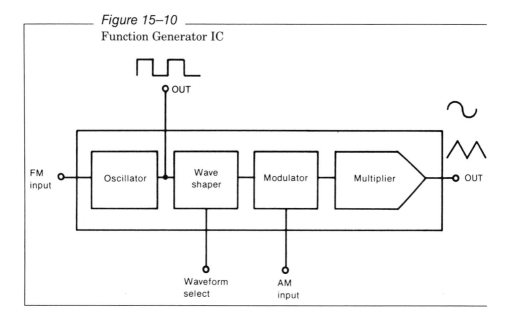

Figure 15–10

Function Generator IC

number of other configurations. Most function generators have an input that allows the frequency of the basic oscillator to be varied by applying an external voltage. **Frequency modulation,** or sweeping of the oscillator, may thus be accomplished. The square wave output is supplied to a group of wave-shaping circuits. External switches govern whether the triangular wave, pulse, sawtooth, or sine wave shaping circuit is selected.

The selected waveform may be changed in amplitude by an external voltage (amplitude modulated). Actual output from the function generator IC is via an op amp that provides a low-impedance waveform to the desired external circuit. Therefore, on one IC, all the waveform generation functions described in this section have been provided. The growth of large-scale integration is supplying more and more multiple functions in single ICs. Circuits formerly requiring many op amps and external components can now be implemented with single ICs and fewer external components.

ABSOLUTE-VALUE CIRCUIT

One final application of operational amplifiers is shown to point out the direction in which integrated circuit engineering is going. The analog signal-processing subsystem was discussed in Chapter 11. Figure 11–16 showed that the analog signal processor consisted of two gated transconductance amplifiers, a unity gain buffer amplifier, and a comparator all on one chip. A rather unusual application of this versatile IC is shown in Figure 15–11A.

The absolute-value, or precision full-wave rectifier, circuit was discussed in Chapter 12. It was implemented by summing the output of a precision half-wave rectifier and the original input. The technique required five matched resistors, two diodes, and two op amps. Implementation of the circuit in Figure 15–11 requires only two matched resistors and the analog signal-processing subsystem IC, plus a few noncritical components.

The two gated transconductance amplifiers allow a *selectable* signal path with a gain of either +1 or −1. A zero-crossing detector is formed with the on-chip comparator, which monitors the input signal polarity and selects the desired signal path. Comparator output, which is a full-wave rectified signal, is amplified by the NPN transistor and applied to the gated transconductance amplifiers via an EXCLUSIVE-OR digital IC. Polarity switching is under digital control by EXCLU-SIVE-ORing the comparator output with a polarity selection signal. See Figure 15–11B for typical waveforms. Output polarity selection normally requires either a programmable-gain op amp or physical switching of diodes.

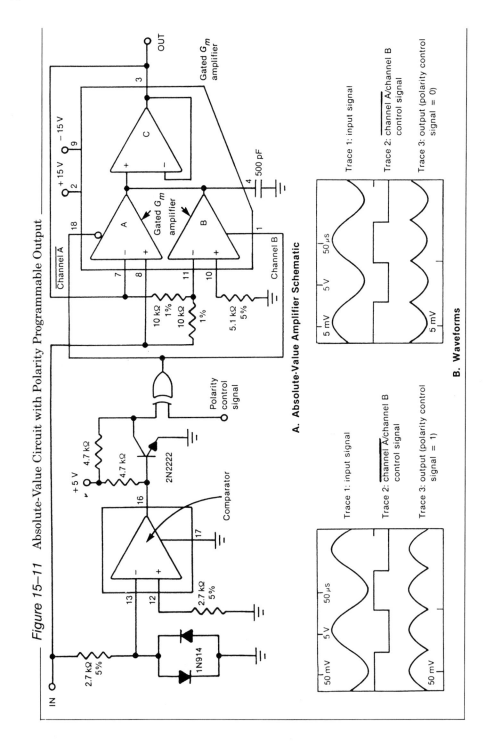

Figure 15–11 Absolute-Value Circuit with Polarity Programmable Output

A. Absolute-Value Amplifier Schematic

B. Waveforms

Very little distortion is added to the signal path when the analog signal-processing subsystem is used to form the absolute-value circuit. The parts count is not necessarily less than for the conventional absolute-value circuit, but the performance is far superior. Many other applications will be found for this versatile integrated circuit.

DIGITAL AUDIO

The compact disc (CD) is one of the newest additions to the high-fidelity audio scene. The CD uses digital audio and optical laser techniques. Many of the circuits we've worked with are used in CD technology.

Why digital audio? We hear music, for example, as amplitude changes in time. Everything in the reproduction chain, from the microphones and amplifiers at the recording end to the amplifiers and speakers at the reproducing end adds its own distortion and noise. The output is very seldom an exact replica of the input.

With digital audio, music, for example, is converted into a stream of binary data (numbers). The analog information is carried through the reproduction chain in digital form, and noise does not affect digital information. Faithful reproduction results.

Simply stated, in digital audio the audio signal amplitude is sampled at a high rate (about 44,000 times a second). Each sample's amplitude is converted to a binary number by an A/D converter. The binary numbers are assembled into words, control information is added, and the combination encoded for recording. In the case of the CD medium, small "pits" are burned into the CD for a binary 1, while the absence of a pit represents a binary 0.

Music is recovered from the CD using a laser optical pickup. Laser light illuminates the CD, and the reflected light is detected. When the light strikes an area between two pits, almost all of the light is reflected and detected. If the light strikes a pit, the result is almost no reflected light. Thus binary information can be recovered from the CD.

The reverse of the recording process takes place during playback. Recovered binary information is decoded back into "words." The words are processed by an error detection and correction circuit. Control information is removed and used to position the optical pickup and control disc drive speed. Corrected words are changed back to analog form by the D/A converter.

A simplified block diagram of the digital recording process is shown in Figure 15–12. Note the low-pass filters at the input of the recording system. They are needed to limit high frequencies. Similar filters are used at the output of the reproducing system to remove high-

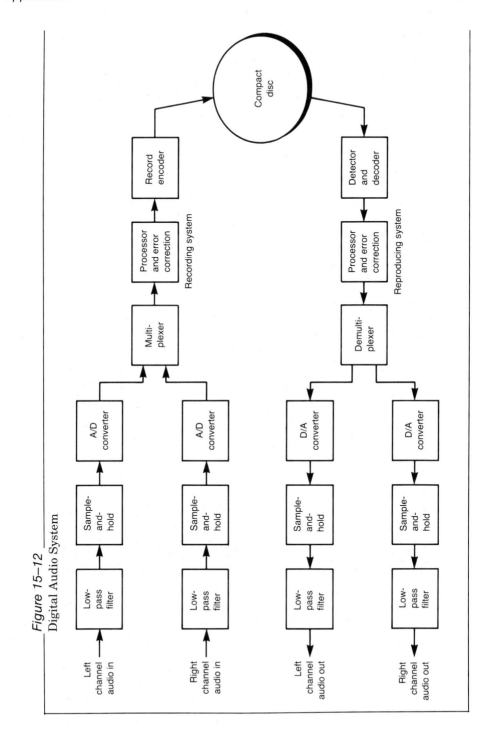

Figure 15–12
Digital Audio System

frequency components generated by the decoding process. Also note the parallel input and output channels required for stereo reproduction.

Because of the large numbers of functions necessary in digital audio systems, special large-scale integrated circuits are used in place of separate ICs. Troubleshooting is limited to replacement of entire circuit boards in many cases. Even though you may not be able to replace the circuits, let's examine some of the blocks in Figure 15–12 to see what functions would be performed.

The low-pass filters are often high-order active filters such as those discussed in Chapter 8. Sample-and-hold circuits, shown in Chapter 11, perform the sampling of the analog signal. Chapter 13 discussed the A/D converters used in the recording system and the D/A converters used in the reproducing system. Multiplexers combine stereo channels during recording and demultiplexers separate the channels during reproduction. See Chapter 11 for multiplexer and demultiplexer explanations. Processing and error correction is primarily a digital function and is beyond the scope of this book. Op amps and comparators abound in all of the analog circuits.

Digital audio is in its infancy. The techniques perfected with digital audio have far-reaching impact in television and information storage. The best is yet to come!

—————— SUMMARY ——————————————————————————————

Chapter 15 has provided a fitting end to our study of operational amplifiers. From the basic concepts to complex circuits, it has been shown that op amps have changed the field of electronics. The physical size of devices have been reduced because of op amps. Electronic devices formerly costing thousands of dollars are now available for only tens of dollars, and many consumer-related electronic devices not even previously envisioned are commonplace today because of op amps.

Just a few basic facts have allowed us to understand the many applications of op amps. In Chapter 1, we reviewed amplification from a systems viewpoint. The details of what was happening inside the amplifier were shown to be relatively unimportant. Only the input/output details are needed for circuit analysis. Chapter 2 provided discussion of DC specifications and the three basic circuit configurations for op amps. The basic circuit configurations were then used in DC applications (Chapter 3) such as typical amplifiers and voltage regulators.

Chapter 4 expanded our knowledge to AC specifications and circuits so that more complex applications could be investigated. Audio amplifiers were discussed in Chapter 5, and high-frequency amplifiers in Chapter 6. Chapters 7 and 8 were devoted to explanations of filters.

Chapter 7 provided the basics and showed how op amps could improve simple filters. Advanced active filters were explained in Chapter 8.

Waveform generation circuits based on op amps were the subject of Chapter 9. Both sinusoidal and nonsinusoidal oscillators were shown, with many variations developed to demonstrate the versatility of the op amp. Chapter 10 went back to the original purpose for op amps by investigating mathematical operations using op amps. Special-purpose op amps and their applications were detailed in Chapter 11. Comparators, instrumentation amplifiers, current difference amplifiers, and the like were mentioned as they related to the subject of op amps.

Chapter 12 showed how op amps could improve the characteristics of semiconductor devices such as diodes and transistors. It was also shown that transistors and other semiconductor devices could be used for control of op amps and for extension of their capabilities. Chapter 13 showed how the analog and digital worlds interface using linear integrated circuits. Phase-locked loops, one of the miracles of modern technology, were explained in Chapter 14. Last, but surely not least, Chapter 15 provided a further look at the applications of various types of op amps. These applications are typical and provide an overview of the world of operational amplifiers.

One of the best ways to determine if you have really gained capability in understanding and applying op amps is to evaluate possible malfunctions in circuits. Determining the effect of component changes also tests your knowledge of operational amplifiers.

═══ QUESTIONS ═══

1. At 10°C, the output of the difference amplifier in Figure 15–1 is 15 mV. What is the most likely cause of malfunction?

2. At 10°C, the output of the difference amplifier in Figure 15–1 is 10 mV. A VCO and counter connected at point A indicates 15°C. What is the most likely cause of malfunction?

3. Using Figure 15–2, consider that the same problem discussed in the text exists in the circuit. The problem is isolated between points A and B, but the diode tests satisfactorily. What is the *next* most probable cause of malfunction?

4. The output frequency of the VCO in Figure 15–4 suddenly shifts to a higher frequency. V_c remains constant. What is the most likely cause of malfunction?

5. The square wave output of the circuit in Figure 15–8 is satisfactory, but the triangular wave is distorted such that the positive and negative peaks are flattened. What is the most probable cause of malfunction?

6. Triangular wave input to the sine wave converter of Figure 15–9 is correct, but the sine wave output is distorted at the positive and negative peaks. Discuss the most probable cause of malfunction and how to remedy the problem.

7. Changing the polarity control signal input to the circuit of Figure 15–11 does not reverse the output waveform. Discuss how you would locate the cause of malfunction.

8. The output of the circuit in Figure 15–11 is half-wave instead of full-wave. What is the most probable cause of malfunction, and how would you isolate the problem?

═══ PROBLEMS ═══

1. For the circuit in Figure 15–1, determine the proper value for R_i' and R_i' to obtain 10 mV output at 10°C.

2. The center frequency of the circuit of Figure 15–2 must be changed to 500 Hz. Determine the necessary component values.

Appendix A
Data Sheets

— Type 741 Frequency-Compensated Operational Amplifier*

— Type LF353 Wide Bandwidth Dual JFET Input Operational Amplifiers*

— Type LF111/LF211/LF311 Voltage Comparators*

— Type LM565/LM565C Phase Locked Loop*

— Type LM555/LM555C Timer*

— Type LM109/LM309 5-Volt Regulator*

— Type LM1877 Dual Power Audio Amplifier*

— Type AD568 12-Bit Ultrahigh-Speed Monolithic D/A Converter**

USING IC DATA SHEETS

Introduction

IC data sheets contain information for a broad range of users. Experimenters, technicians, engineers, and scientists will all find useful and valuable information for their work. Although IC data sheets are primarily for those designing equipment using ICs, the information provides much insight into circuit performance and operation.

Most IC data sheets contain the following types of information: (1) general description of the IC, (2) pin configurations, (3) internal equivalent circuit schematic, (4) absolute maximum ratings, (5) electrical characteristics, (6) typical performance curves. Much of the information on IC data sheets has been discussed in previous chapters. It is collected in this appendix for your convenience.

*Reprinted in this appendix with permission of National Semiconductor Corp.

**Reprinted in this appendix with permission of Analog Devices.

The manufacturers, publisher, and author hold no responsibility for the circuitry described in this appendix.

General Description of the IC

The general description of the IC usually appears on the first page of the data or specification sheet. It is used to get a preliminary idea about what the IC does. The IC's good points and features are highlighted. In some cases, the manufacturing process is described if the manufacturer thinks it adds to the usefulness of the IC specification sheet.

Pin Configurations

Pin configuration information is used to determine power, input, output, and special-purpose connections. Op amps, for example, may require the connection of external components to tailor the frequency response to a specific circuit's needs. Other ICs may require external jumpers to cause the IC to perform specific functions.

Many ICs may be obtained in more than one type of package. The IC data sheet includes the pin configurations for all available packages.

Internal Equivalent Circuit Schematic

Most IC data sheets include an internal equivalent circuit schematic on the first page. This information may be used to analyze internal IC circuit operation. Characteristics not shown on the data sheet may also be determined by using the internal equivalent circuit schematic. It should be noted that the circuit is only an equivalent circuit and may not necessarily represent the actual components as they appear on the IC chip.

Absolute-Maximum Ratings

The absolute-maximum ratings, often shown on the first page of the IC data sheet, are the values that cannot be exceeded without damage to the IC. Often, the damage is destructive if the absolute-maximum ratings are exceeded. The values are typical for the IC shown. Some of the parameters that appear in the absolute-maximum ratings section of an IC data sheet are listed next.

> *Supply voltage*: The maximum ± supply voltages that may be applied to the IC. Although the IC may be designed for a specific supply voltage, it will usually operate over a wide range of supply voltages as long as the maximum is not exceeded.

> *Internal power dissipation*: The maximum power that the IC can dissipate without destruction. A specified temperature is provided, as is a derating formula to determine allowable dissipation at higher temperatures. The type of package also affects dissipation.

Differential input voltage: The maximum voltage that can be applied between the + and the − inputs of an op amp.

Input voltage: The maximum voltage that can be applied to the inputs of an op amp with inputs connected together. This is often called the maximum common-mode input voltage.

Operating temperature: The range of temperatures over which the IC may be safely operated. Military-rated ICs operate between −55°C and +125°C. Industrial-rated ICs operate between −25°C and +85°C. Commercial-grade ICs operate between 0°C and +70°C.

Output short-circuit duration: The maximum time that the output terminal can be shorted to ground or supply voltage without damage to the IC.

Lead temperature: The maximum temperature that may be applied to the IC leads during soldering. It is usually 300°C for a duration of 60 seconds.

Electrical Characteristics

Detailed performance information, defining the range of performance, may be found in the electrical characteristics section of the IC data sheet. The information is usually used for design purposes. Characteristics are generally provided at a specified temperature and supply voltage. Minimums, typical values, and maximums are provided.

Input characteristics include the following items:

Offset voltage: The voltage that must be applied between the input terminals of an op amp to obtain 0 V output. A null adjustment is often provided.

Offset current: The difference in input terminal currents when the output is 0 V.

Bias current: The average of the two input currents in an op amp.

Voltage range: The range of voltages acceptable at the input terminals that will allow in-specification operation. This characteristic is sometimes called the common-mode input voltage range.

Resistance: The resistance "seen" when looking into an input terminal of an IC. When you are determining op amp input resistance, the unused input terminal is grounded.

Output characteristics include the following items:

Resistance: The resistance "seen" when looking into the IC's output terminal.

Short-circuit current: The maximum current available with the output terminal shorted to ground or supply voltage.

Voltage swing: The peak output voltage swing that can be obtained without saturation or clipping.

Dynamic characteristics include the following parameters:

Open-loop voltage gain: The ratio of output voltage to input voltage without feedback.

Large-signal voltage gain: The ratio of maximum output voltage to input voltage. The maximum output voltage is usually specified, such as ± 10 V.

Slew rate: The maximum rate of change of the output voltage of an op amp, in volts per microsecond. This characteristic is considered a large-signal characteristic.

Rise time: The 10% to 90% closed-loop, step-function response time of an IC. This characteristic is usually a small-signal characteristic.

Gain-bandwidth product: A "figure-of-merit" of an op amp. It is the product of available open-loop gain and bandwidth at a specified frequency.

Other electrical characteristics noted on the IC data sheet include the following:

Supply current: The current that the op amp will draw from the power supply under no-signal conditions.

Common-mode rejection ratio (CMRR): The ability of an op amp to reject signals simultaneously present on both inputs.

Performance Curves

Numerous performance curves are provided in IC specification sheets. Some typical curves are discussed here.

Open-loop voltage gain versus frequency: Discussed in detail throughout this text.

Open-loop phase versus frequency: Discussed in detail in previous chapters.

Output voltage swing versus supply voltage: This curve tells you what output voltages can be expected with different supply voltages. It is convenient when you are examining the supply voltage options in designing circuits.

Output voltage swing versus load resistance: This curve tells you what output voltages can be expected with different load resistances. It is convenient when you are examining the effects of load resistance variations.

Each IC has a different set of performance curves. Reference to these curves will help you determine how a circuit operates and will make troubleshooting easier. Use performance curves and IC data sheets often to make your job easier.

Type 741 Frequency-Compensated Operational Amplifier

GENERAL DESCRIPTION — The μA741 is a high performance monolithic Operational Amplifier constructed using the Fairchild Planar* epitaxial process. It is intended for a wide range of analog applications. High common mode voltage range and absence of "latch-up" tendencies make the μA741 ideal for use as a voltage follower. The high gain and wide range of operating voltage provides superior performance in integrator, summing amplifier, and general feedback applications.

- **NO FREQUENCY COMPENSATION REQUIRED**
- **SHORT CIRCUIT PROTECTION**
- **OFFSET VOLTAGE NULL CAPABILITY**
- **LARGE COMMON-MODE AND DIFFERENTIAL VOLTAGE RANGES**

- **LOW POWER CONSUMPTION**
- **NO LATCH UP**

ABSOLUTE MAXIMUM RATINGS

Supply Voltage			Storage Temperature Range	
Military (741)	±22 V		Metal Can, DIP, and Flatpak	−65°C to +150°C
Commercial (741C)	±18 V		Mini DIP	−55°C to +125°C
Internal Power Dissipation (Note 1)			Operating Temperature Range	
Metal Can	500 mW		Military (741)	−55°C to +125°C
DIP	670 mW		Commercial (741C)	0°C to +70°C
Mini DIP	310 mW		Lead Temperature (Soldering)	
Flatpak	570 mW		Metal Can, DIP, and Flatpak (60 seconds)	300°C
Differential Input Voltage	±30 V		Mini DIP (10 seconds)	260°C
Input Voltage (Note 2)	±15 V		Output Short Circuit Duration (Note 3)	Indefinite

EQUIVALENT CIRCUIT

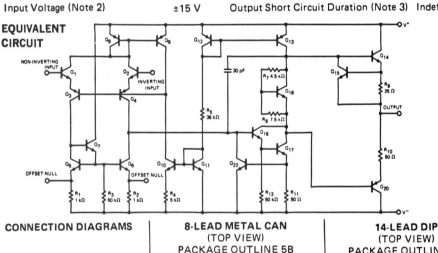

CONNECTION DIAGRAMS

8-LEAD MINI DIP
(TOP VIEW)
PACKAGE OUTLINE 9T

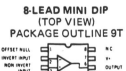

8-LEAD METAL CAN
(TOP VIEW)
PACKAGE OUTLINE 5B

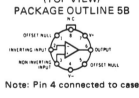

Note: Pin 4 connected to case

14-LEAD DIP
(TOP VIEW)
PACKAGE OUTLINE 6A

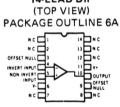

741C

ELECTRICAL CHARACTERISTICS ($V_S = \pm 15$ V, $T_A = 25°$C unless otherwise specified)

PARAMETERS (see definitions)		CONDITIONS	MIN.	TYP.	MAX.	UNITS
Input Offset Voltage		$R_S \leqslant 10$ kΩ		2.0	6.0	mV
Input Offset Current				20	200	nA
Input Bias Current				80	500	nA
Input Resistance			0.3	2.0		MΩ
Input Capacitance				1.4		pF
Offset Voltage Adjustment Range				±15		mV
Input Voltage Range			±12	±13		V
Common Mode Rejection Ratio		$R_S \leqslant 10$ kΩ	70	90		dB
Supply Voltage Rejection Ratio		$R_S \leqslant 10$ kΩ		30	150	μV/V
Large Signal Voltage Gain		$R_L \geqslant 2$ kΩ, $V_{OUT} = \pm 10$ V	20,000	200,000		
Output Voltage Swing		$R_L \geqslant 10$ kΩ	±12	±14		V
		$R_L \geqslant 2$ kΩ	±10	±13		V
Output Resistance				75		Ω
Output Short Circuit Current				25		mA
Supply Current				1.7	2.8	mA
Power Consumption				50	85	mW
Transient Response (Unity Gain)	Risetime	$V_{IN} = 20$ mV, $R_L = 2$ kΩ, $C_L \leqslant 100$ pF		0.3		μs
	Overshoot			5.0		%
Slew Rate		$R_L \geqslant 2$ kΩ		0.5		V/μs

The following specifications apply for $0°$C $\leqslant T_A \leqslant +70°$C:

	CONDITIONS	MIN.	TYP.	MAX.	UNITS
Input Offset Voltage				7.5	mV
Input Offset Current				300	nA
Input Bias Current				800	nA
Large Signal Voltage Gain	$R_L \geqslant 2$ kΩ, $V_{OUT} = \pm 10$ V	15,000			
Output Voltage Swing	$R_L \geqslant 2$ kΩ	±10	±13		V

TYPICAL PERFORMANCE CURVES FOR 741C

OUTPUT VOLTAGE SWING AS A FUNCTION OF SUPPLY VOLTAGE

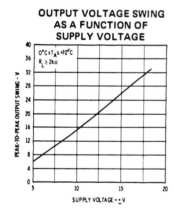

INPUT COMMON MODE VOLTAGE RANGE AS A FUNCTION OF SUPPLY VOLTAGE

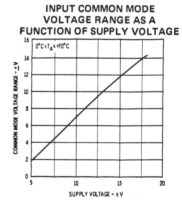

NOTES:
1. Rating applies to ambient temperatures up to 70°C. Above 70°C ambient derate linearly at 6.3 mW/°C for the Metal Can, 8.3 mW/°C for the DIP, 5.6 mW/°C for the Mini DIP and 7.1 mW/°C for the Flatpak.
2. For supply voltages less than ±15 V, the absolute maximum input voltage is equal to the supply voltage.
3. Short circuit may be to ground or either supply. Rating applies to +125°C case temperature or 75°C ambient temperature.

TYPICAL PERFORMANCE CURVES FOR 741C

INPUT BIAS CURRENT AS A FUNCTION OF AMBIENT TEMPERATURE

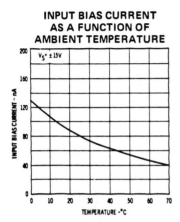

INPUT OFFSET CURRENT AS A FUNCTION OF AMBIENT TEMPERATURE

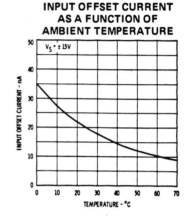

POWER CONSUMPTION AS A FUNCTION OF SUPPLY VOLTAGE

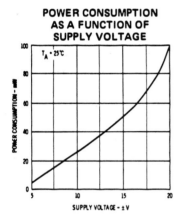

OPEN LOOP VOLTAGE GAIN AS A FUNCTION OF FREQUENCY

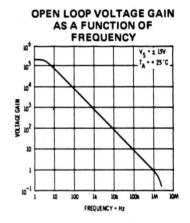

OPEN LOOP PHASE RESPONSE AS A FUNCTION OF FREQUENCY

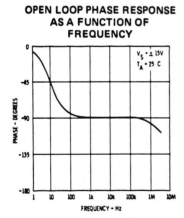

INPUT RESISTANCE AND INPUT CAPACITANCE AS A FUNCTION OF FREQUENCY

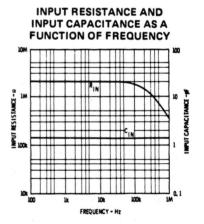

OUTPUT VOLTAGE SWING AS A FUNCTION OF LOAD RESISTANCE

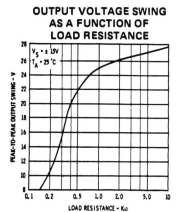

OUTPUT VOLTAGE SWING AS A FUNCTION OF FREQUENCY

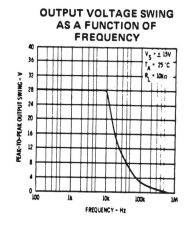

INPUT NOISE VOLTAGE AS A FUNCTION OF FREQUENCY

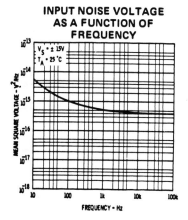

TRANSIENT RESPONSE

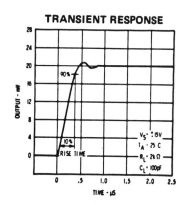

VOLTAGE OFFSET NULL CIRCUIT

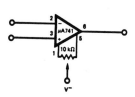

VOLTAGE FOLLOWER LARGE-SIGNAL PULSE RESPONSE

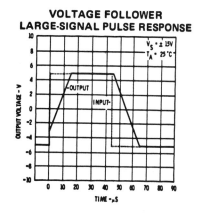

Type LF353 Wide Bandwidth Dual JFET Input Operational Amplifiers

General Description

These devices are low cost, high speed, dual JFET input operational amplifiers with an internally trimmed input offset voltage (BI-FET II™ technology). They require low supply current yet maintain a large gain bandwidth product and fast slew rate. In addition, well matched high voltage JFET input devices provide very low input bias and offset currents. The LF353 is pin compatible with the standard LM1558 allowing designers to immediately upgrade the overall performance of existing LM1558 and LM358 designs.

These amplifiers may be used in applications such as high speed integrators, fast D/A converters, sample and hold circuits and many other circuits requiring low input offset voltage, low input bias current, high input impedance, high slew rate and wide bandwidth. The devices also exhibit low noise and offset voltage drift.

Features

- Internally trimmed offset voltage   2 mV
- Low input bias current   50 pA
- Low input noise voltage $16 \, nV/\sqrt{Hz}$
- Low input noise current $0.01 \, pA/\sqrt{Hz}$
- Wide gain bandwidth   4 MHz
- High slew rate $13 \, V/\mu s$
- Low supply current   3.6 mA
- High input impedance $10^{12} \Omega$
- Low total harmonic distortion $A_V = 10$, $<0.02\%$
  $R_L = 10k$, $V_O = 20 \, Vp-p$, $BW = 20 \, Hz\text{-}20 \, kHz$
- Low 1/f noise corner   50 Hz
- Fast settling time to 0.01% $2 \, \mu s$

Typical Connection

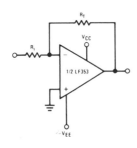

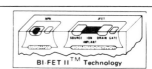

BI-FET II™ Technology

Connection Diagrams

LF353H Metal Can Package (Top View)

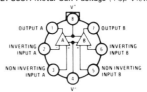

Simplified Schematic

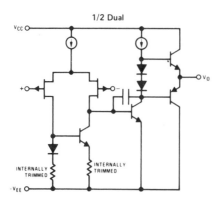

LF353N Dual-In-Line Package (Top View)

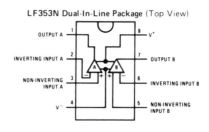

Absolute Maximum Ratings

Supply Voltage	± 18V
Power Dissipation (Note 1)	500 mW
Operating Temperature Range	0 °C to + 70 °C
T_j(MAX)	115 °C
Differential Input Voltage	± 30V
Input Voltage Range (Note 2)	± 15V
Output Short Circuit Duration	Continuous
Storage Temperature Range	− 65 °C to + 150 °C
Lead Temperature (Soldering, 10 seconds)	300 °C

AC Electrical Characteristics (Note 4)

SYMBOL	PARAMETER	CONDITIONS	LF353A MIN	LF353A TYP	LF353A MAX	LF353B MIN	LF353B TYP	LF353B MAX	LF353 MIN	LF353 TYP	LF353 MAX	UNITS
	Amplifier to Amplifier Coupling	T_A = 25 °C, f = 1 Hz–20 kHz (Input Referred)		− 120			− 120			− 120		dB
SR	Slew Rate	V_S = ± 15V, T_A = 25 °C		13			13			13		V/µs
GBW	Gain Bandwidth Product	V_S = ± 15V, T_A = 25 °C		4			4			4		MHz
e_n	Equivalent Input Noise Voltage	T_A = 25 °C, R_S = 100Ω, f = 1000 Hz		16			16			16		nV/√Hz
i_n	Equivalent Input Noise Current	T_j = 25 °C, f = 1000 Hz		0.01			0.01			0.01		pA/√Hz

Note 1: For operating at elevated temperature, the device must be derated based on a thermal resistance of 160 °C/W junction to ambient for the N package, and 150 °C/W junction to ambient for the H package.
Note 2: Unless otherwise specified the absolute maximum negative input voltage is equal to the negative power supply voltage.
Note 3: The power dissipation limit, however, cannot be exceeded.
Note 4: These specifications apply for V_S = ± 15V and 0 °C ⩽ T_A ⩽ + 70 °C. V_{OS}, I_B and I_{OS} are measured at V_{CM} = 0.
Note 5: The input bias currents are junction leakage currents which approximately double for every 10 °C increase in the junction temperature, T_j. Due to the limited production test time, the input bias currents measured are correlated to junction temperature. In normal operation the junction temperature rises above the ambient temperature as a result of internal power dissipation, P_D. T_j = T_A + Θ_{jA} P_D where Θ_{jA} is the thermal resistance from junction to ambient. Use of a heat sink is recommended if input bias current is to be kept to a minimum.
Note 6.: Supply voltage rejection ratio is measured for both supply magnitudes increasing or decreasing simultaneously in accordance with common practice.

DC Electrical Characteristics (Note 4)

SYMBOL	PARAMETER	CONDITIONS	LF353A MIN	LF353A TYP	LF353A MAX	LF353B and LF353B-1 MIN	LF353B and LF353B-1 TYP	LF353B and LF353B-1 MAX	LF353 MIN	LF353 TYP	LF353 MAX	UNITS
V_{OS}	Input Offset Voltage	R_S = 10kΩ, T_A = 25 °C		1	2		3	5		5	10	mV
		Over Temperature			4			7			13	mV
$\Delta V_{OS}/\Delta T$	Average TC of Input Offset Voltage	R_S = 10kΩ		10			10			10		µV/°C
	LF351B-1							30				µV/°C
I_{OS}	Input Offset Current	T_j = 25 °C, (Notes 4, 5)		25	100		25	100		25	100	pA
		T_j ⩽ 70 °C			2			4			4	nA
I_B	Input Bias Current	T_j = 25 °C, (Notes 4, 5)		50	200		50	200		50	200	pA
		T_j ⩽ 70 °C			4			8			8	nA
R_{IN}	Input Resistance	T_j = 25 °C		10^{12}			10^{12}			10^{12}		Ω
A_{VOL}	Large Signal Voltage Gain	V_S = ± 15V, T_A = 25 °C, V_O = ± 10V, R_L = 2kΩ	50	100		50	100		25	100		V/mV
		Over Temperature	25			25			15			V/mV
V_O	Output Voltage Swing	V_S = ± 15V, R_L = 10kΩ	± 12	± 13.5		± 12	± 13.5		± 12	± 13.5		V
V_{CM}	Input Common-Mode Voltage Range	V_S = ± 15V	± 11	+ 15		± 11	+ 15		± 11	+ 15		V
				− 12			− 12			− 12		V
CMRR	Common-Mode Rejection Ratio	R_S ⩽ 10kΩ	80	100		80	100		70	100		dB
PSRR	Supply Voltage Rejection Ratio	(Note 6)	80	100		80	100		70	100		dB
I_S	Supply Current			3.6	5.6		3.6	5.6		3.6	6.5	mA

Typical Performance Characteristics

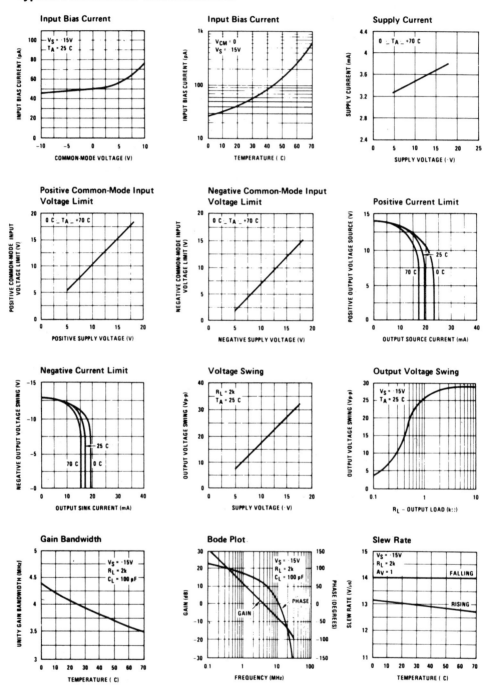

Typical Performance Characteristics (Continued)

Distortion vs Frequency

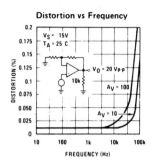

Undistorted Output Voltage Swing

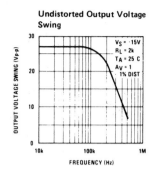

Open Loop Frequency Response

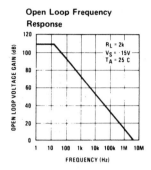

Common-Mode Rejection Ratio

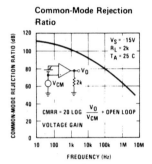

Power Supply Rejection Ratio

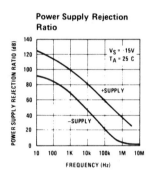

Equivalent Input Noise Voltage

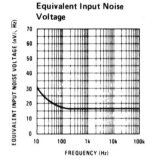

Open Loop Voltage Gain (V/V)

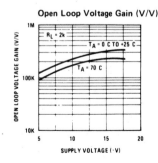

Output Impedance

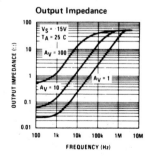

Inverter Settling Time

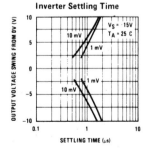

LF111/LF211/LF311 Voltage Comparators

General Description

The LF111, LF211 and LF311 are FET input voltage comparators that virtually eliminate input current errors. Designed to operate over a 5.0V to ±15V range the LF111 can be used in the most critical applications.

The extremely low input currents of the LF111 allows the use of a simple comparator in applications usually requiring input current buffering. Leakage testing, long time delay circuits, charge measurements, and high source impedance voltage comparisons are easily done.

Further, the LF111 can be used in place of the LM111 eliminating errors due to input currents. See the "application hints" of the LM311 for application help.

Features

■ Eliminates input current errors
■ Interchangeable with LM111
■ No need for input current buffering

Schematic Diagram

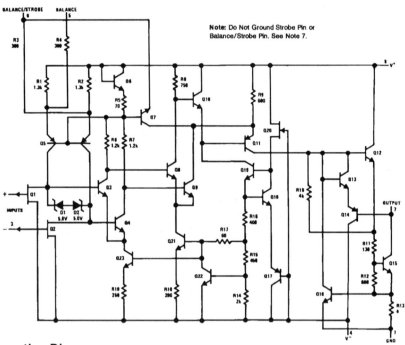

Note: Do Not Ground Strobe Pin or
Balance/Strobe Pin. See Note 7.

Connection Diagram

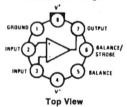

Metal Can Package

Top View

Absolute Maximum Ratings

If Military/Aerospace specified devices are required, contact the National Semiconductor Sales Office/Distributors for availability and specifications. (Note 8)

	LF111/LF211	LF311
Total Supply Voltage (V_{84})	36V	36V
Output to Negative Supply Voltage (V_{74})	50V	40V
Ground to Negative Supply Voltage (V_{14})	30V	30V
Differential Input Voltage	±30V	±30V
Input Voltage (Note 1)	±15V	±15V
Power Dissipation (Note 2)	500 mW	500 mW
Output Short Circuit Duration	10 seconds	10 seconds

	LF111/LF211	LF311
Operating Temp. Range		
LF111	−55°C to +125°C	
LF211	−25°C to +85°C	
LF311		0°C to +70°C
Storage Temp. Range	−65°C to +150°C	−65°C to +150°C
Lead Temp. (Soldering, 10 seconds)	300°C	300°C
ESD rating to be determined.		

Electrical Characteristics (LF111/LF211) (Note 3)

Parameter	Conditions	Min	Typ	Max	Units
Input Offset Voltage (Note 4)	$T_A = 25°C$, $R_S \leq 50k$		0.7	4.0	mV
Input Offset Current (Note 4)	$T_A = 25°C$, $V_{CM} = 0$ (Note 6)		5.0	25	pA
Input Bias Current	$T_A = 25°C$, $V_{CM} = 0$ (Note 6)		20	50	pA
Voltage Gain	$T_A = 25°C$	40	200		V/mV
Response Time (Note 5)	$T_A = 25°C$		200		ns
Saturation Voltage	$V_{IN} \leq -5.0$ mV, $I_{OUT} = 50$ mA, $T_A = 25°C$		0.75	1.5	V
Strobe On Current	$T_A = 25°C$		3.0		mA
Output Leakage Current	$V_{IN} \leq 5.0$ mV, $V_{OUT} = 35V$, $T_A = 25°C$		0.2	10	nA
Input Offset Voltage (Note 4)	$R_S \leq 50k$			6.0	mV
Input Offset Current (Note 4)	$V_S = ±15V$, $V_{CM} = 0$ (Note 6)		2.0	3.0	nA
Input Bias Current	$V_S = ±15V$, $V_{CM} = 0$ (Note 6)		5.0	7.0	nA
Input Voltage Range		−13.5	±14	13.0	V
Saturation Voltage	$V^+ \geq 4.5V$, $V^- = 0$ $V_{IN} \leq -6.0$ mV, $I_{SINK} \leq 8.0$ mA		0.23	0.4	V
Output Leakage Current	$V_{IN} \geq 5.0$ mV, $V_{OUT} = 35V$		0.1	0.5	μA
Positive Supply Current	$T_A = 25°C$		5.1	6.0	mA
Negative Supply Current	$T_A = 25°C$		4.1	5.0	mA

Note 1: This rating applies for ±15V supplies. The positive input voltage limit is 30V above the negative supply. The negative input voltage limit is equal to the negative supply voltage or 30V below the positive supply, whichever is less.

Note 2: The maximum junction temperature of the LF111 is +150°C, the LF211 is +110°C and the LF311 is +85°C. For operating at elevated temperatures, devices in the TO-5 package must be derated based on a thermal resistance of +74°C/W junction to ambient (in 400 linear feet/min air flow), +225°C/W junction to ambient (in static air), or +23°C/W junction to case.

Note 3: These specifications apply for $V_S = ±15V$, and the Ground pin at ground, and −55°C ≤ T_A ≤ +125°C for the LF111, unless otherwise stated. With the LF211, however, all temperature specifications are limited to −25°C ≤ T_A ≤ ±85°C and for the LF311 0°C ≤ T_A ≤ +70°C. The offset voltage, offset current and bias current specifications apply for any supply voltage from a single 5.0V supply up to ±15V supplies.

Note 4: The offset voltages and offset currents given are the maximum values required to drive the output within a volt of either supply with a 1.0 mA load. Thus, these parameters define an error band and take into account the worst case effects of voltage gain and input impedance.

Note 5: The response time specified (see definitions) is for a 100 mV input step with 5.0 mV overdrive.

Note 6: For input voltages greater than 15V above the negative supply the bias and offset currents will increase—see typical performance curves.

Note 7: Do not short the strobe pin to ground; it should be current driven at 3 to 5 mA.

Note 8: Refer to RETSF111X for LF111H military specifications.

Electrical Characteristics (LF311) (Note 3)

Parameter	Conditions	Min	Typ	Max	Units
Input Offset Voltage (Note 4)	$T_A = 25°C$, $R_S \leq 50k$		2.0	10	mV
Input Offset Current (Note 4)	$T_A = 25°C$, $V_{CM} = 0$ (Note 6)		5.0	75	pA
Input Bias Current	$T_A = 25°C$, $V_{CM} = 0$ (Note 6)		25	150	pA
Voltage Gain	$T_A = 25°C$		200		V/mV
Response Time (Note 5)	$T_A = 25°C$		200		ns
Saturation Voltage	$V_{IN} \leq -10$ mV, $I_{OUT} = 50$ mA, $T_A = 25°C$		0.75	1.5	V
Strobe On Current	$T_A = 25°C$		3.0		mA
Output Leakage Current	$V_{IN} \geq 10$mV, $V_{OUT} = 35V$, $T_A = 25°C$		0.2	10	nA
Input Offset Voltage (Note 4)	$R_S \leq 50k$			15	mV
Input Offset Current (Note 4)	$V_S = \pm 15V$, $V_{CM} = 0$ (Note 6)		1.0		nA
Input Bias Current	$V_S = 15V$, $V_{CM} = 0$ (Note 6)		3.0		nA
Input Voltage Range			+14		V
			−13.5		V
Saturation Voltage	$V^+ \geq 4.5V$, $V^- = 0$ $V_{IN} \leq -10$ mV, $I_{SINK} \leq 8.0$ mA		0.23	0.4	V
Positive Supply Current	$T_A = 25°C$		5.1	7.5	mA
Negative Supply Current	$T_A = 25°C$		4.1	5.0	mA

Note 1: This rating applies for ± 15V supplies. The positive input voltage limit is 30V above the negative supply. The negative input voltage limit is equal to the negative supply voltage or 30V below the positive supply, whichever is less.

Note 2: The maximum junction temperature of the LF111 is +150°C, the LF211 is +110°C and the LF311 is +85°C. For operating at elevated temperatures, devices in the TO-5 package must be derated based on a thermal resistance of + 150°C/W, junction to ambient, or +45°C/W, junction to case.

Note 3: These specifications apply for $V_S = \pm 15V$ and $-55°C \leq T_A \leq +125°C$ for the LF111, unless otherwise stated. With the LF211, however, all temperature specifications are limited to $-25°C \leq T_A \leq +85°C$ and for the LF311 $0°C \leq T_A \leq +70°C$. The offset voltage, offset current and bias current specifications apply for any supply voltage from a single 5.0 mV supply up to ±15V supplies.

Note 4: The offset voltages and offset currents given are the maximum values required to drive the output within a volt of either supply with a 1.0 mA load. Thus, these parameters define an error band and take into account the worst case effects of voltage gain and input impedance.

Note 5: The response time specified (see definitions) is for a 100 mV input step with 5.0 mV overdrive.

Note 6: For input voltages greater than 15V above the negative supply the bias and offset currents will increase—see typical performance curves.

Note 7: Do not short the strobe pin to ground; it should be current driven at 3 to 5 mA.

Auxiliary Circuits

Offset Balancing

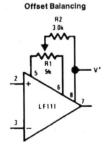

Strobing

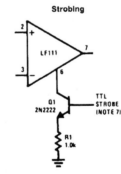

Increasing Input Stage Current*

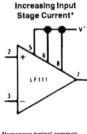

*Increases typical common mode slew from 7.0V/μs to 18V/μs

Typical Performance Characteristics

Input Bias Current vs Common Mode

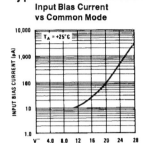

Input Bias Current vs Temperature

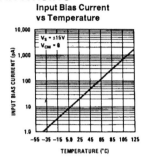

Transfer Function

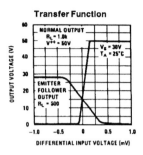

Response Time for Various Input Overdrives

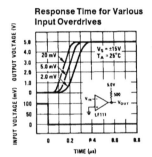

Response Time for Various Input Overdrives

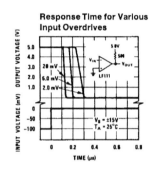

Output Saturation Voltage

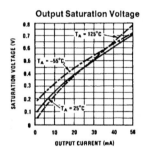

Response Time for Various Input Overdrives

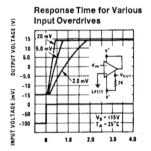

Response Time for Various Input Overdrives

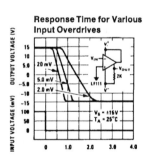

Supply Current

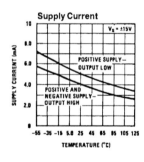

Output Limiting Characteristics

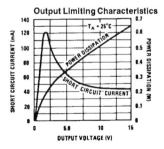

Supply Current

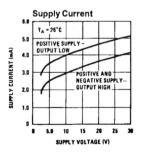

Leakage Currents

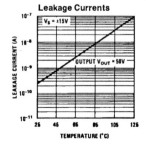

LM565/LM565C Phase Locked Loop

General Description

The LM565 and LM565C are general purpose phase locked loops containing a stable, highly linear voltage controlled oscillator for low distortion FM demodulation, and a double balanced phase detector with good carrier suppression. The VCO frequency is set with an external resistor and capacitor, and a tuning range of 10:1 can be obtained with the same capacitor. The characteristics of the closed loop system—bandwidth, response speed, capture and pull in range—may be adjusted over a wide range with an external resistor and capacitor. The loop may be broken between the VCO and the phase detector for insertion of a diital frequency divider to obtain frequency multiplication.

The LM565H is specified for operation over the −55°C to +125°C military temperature range. The LM565CH and LM565CN are specified for operation over the 0°C to +70°C temperature range.

Features

- 200 ppm/°C frequency stability of the VCO
- Power supply range of ±5 to ±12 volts with 100 ppm/% typical
- 0.2% linearity of demodulated output

- Linear triangle wave with in phase zero crossings available
- TTL and DTL compatible phase detector input and square wave output
- Adjustable hold in range from ±1% to > ±60%

Applications

- Data and tape synchronization
- Modems
- FSK demodulation
- FM demodulation
- Frequency synthesizer
- Tone decoding
- Frequency multiplication and division
- SCA demodulators
- Telemetry receivers
- Signal regeneration
- Coherent demodulators

Connection Diagrams

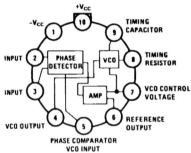

Metal Can Package

Dual-In-Line Package

Absolute Maximum Ratings

If Military/Aerospace specified devices are required, contact the National Semiconductor Sales Office/ Distributors for availability and specifications.

Supply Voltage	±12V
Power Dissipation (Note 1)	1400 mW
Differential Input Voltage	±1V

Operating Temperature Range	
LM565H	−55°C to +125°C
LM565CH, LM565CN	0°C to +70°C
Storage Temperature Range	−65°C to +150°C
Lead Temperature (Soldering, 10 sec.)	260°C

Electrical Characteristics AC Test Circuit, T_A = 25°C, V_{CC} = ±6V

Parameter	Conditions	LM565			LM565C			Units
		Min	Typ	Max	Min	Typ	Max	
Power Supply Current			8.0	12.5		8.0	12.5	mA
Input Impedance (Pins 2, 3)	−4V < V_2, V_3 < 0V	7	10			5		kΩ
VCO Maximum Operating Frequency	C_o = 2.7 pF	300	500		250	500		kHz
VCO Free-Running Frequency	C_o = 1.5 nF R_o = 20 kΩ f_o = 10 kHz	−10	0	+10	−30	0	+30	%
Operating Frequency Temperature Coefficient			−100			−200		ppm/°C
Frequency Drift with Supply Voltage			0.1	1.0		0.2	1.5	%/V
Triangle Wave Output Voltage		2	2.4	3	2	2.4	3	V_{p-p}
Triangle Wave Output Linearity			0.2			0.5		%
Square Wave Output Level		4.7	5.4		4.7	5.4		V_{p-p}
Output Impedance (Pin 4)			5			5		kΩ
Square Wave Duty Cycle		45	50	55	40	50	60	%
Square Wave Rise Time			20			20		ns
Square Wave Fall Time			50			50		ns
Output Current Sink (Pin 4)		0.6	1		0.6	1		mA
VCO Sensitivity	f_o = 10 kHz		6600			6600		Hz/V
Demodulated Output Voltage (Pin 7)	±10% Frequency Deviation	250	300	400	200	300	450	mV_{p-p}
Total Harmonic Distortion	±10% Frequency Deviation		0.2	0.75		0.2	1.5	%
Output Impedance (Pin 7)			3.5			3.5		kΩ
DC Level (Pin 7)		4.25	4.5	4.75	4.0	4.5	5.0	V
Output Offset Voltage $\mid V_7 − V_6 \mid$			30	100		50	200	mV
Temperature Drift of $\mid V_7 − V_6 \mid$			500			500		μV/°C
AM Rejection		30	40			40		dB
Phase Detector Sensitivity K_D			.68			.68		V/radian

Note 1: The maximum junction temperature of the LM565 and LM565C is +150°C. For operation at elevated temperatures, devices in the TO-5 package must be derated based on a thermal resistance of +150°C/W junction to ambient or +45°C/W junction to case. Thermal resistance of the dual-in-line package is +85°C/W.

Typical Performance Characteristics

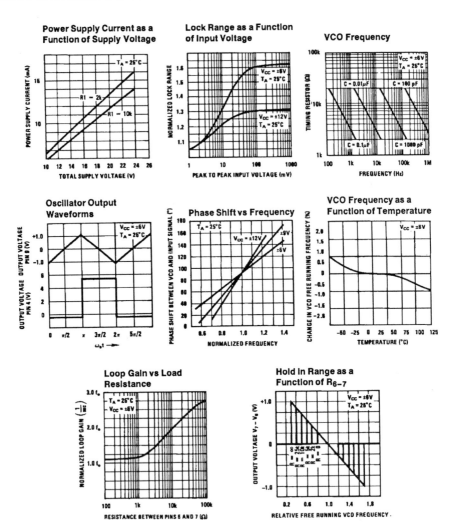

Schematic Diagram

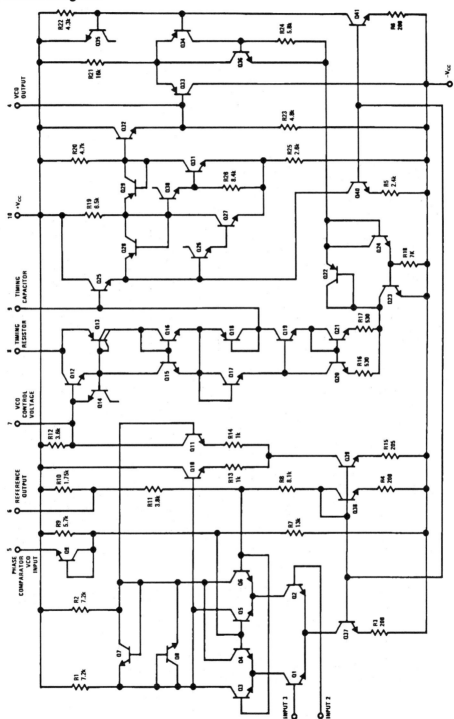

AC Test Circuit

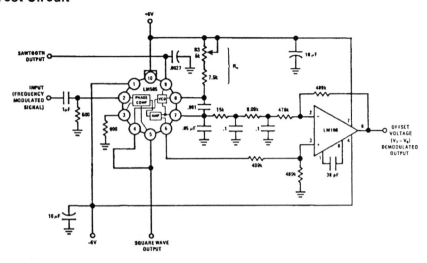

Note: S_1 open for output offset voltage $(V_7 - V_6)$ measurement.

Typical Applications

2400 Hz Synchronous AM Demodulator

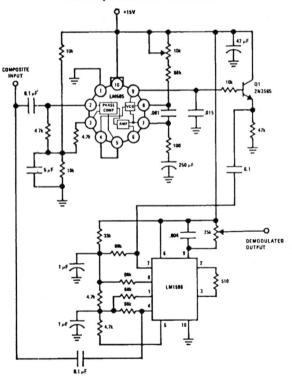

LM555/LM555C Timer

General Description

The LM555 is a highly stable device for generating accurate time delays or oscillation. Additional terminals are provided for triggering or resetting if desired. In the time delay mode of operation, the time is precisely controlled by one external resistor and capacitor. For astable operation as an oscillator, the free running frequency and duty cycle are accurately controlled with two external resistors and one capacitor. The circuit may be triggered and reset on falling waveforms, and the output circuit can source or sink up to 200 mA or drive TTL circuits.

Features

■ Direct replacement for SE555/NE555
■ Timing from microseconds through hours
■ Operates in both astable and monostable modes

■ Adjustable duty cycle
■ Output can source or sink 200 mA
■ Output and supply TTL compatible
■ Temperature stability better than 0.005% per °C
■ Normally on and normally off output

Applications

■ Precision timing
■ Pulse generation
■ Sequential timing
■ Time delay generation
■ Pulse width modulation
■ Pulse position modulation
■ Linear ramp generator

Schematic Diagram

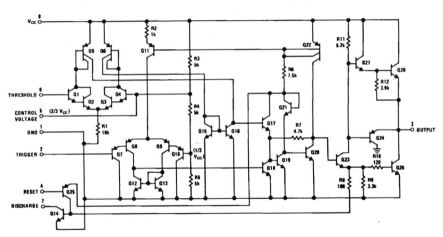

Absolute Maximum Ratings

If Military/Aerospace specified devices are required, contact the National Semiconductor Sales Office/ Distributors for availability and specifications.

Supply Voltage	+ 18V
Power Dissipation (Note 1) LM555H, LM555CH	760 mW
Operating Temperature Ranges	
LM555N, LM555CN	1180 mW
LM555C	0°C to +70°C
LM555	−55°C to + 125°C
Storage Temperature Range	−65°C to + 150°C

Soldering Information
Dual-In-Line Package
Soldering (10 Seconds)   260°C
Small Outline Package
Vapor Phase (60 Seconds)   215°C
Infrared (15 Seconds)   220°C
See AN-450 "Surface Mounting Methods and Their Effect on Product Reliability" for other methods of soldring sur- face mount devices.

Electrical Characteristics (T_A = 25°C, V_{CC} = +5V to + 15V, unless othewise specified)

Parameter	Conditions	Limits						Units
		LM555			LM555C			
		Min	Typ	Max	Min	Typ	Max	
Supply Voltage		4.5		18	4.5		16	V
Supply Current	V_{CC} = 5V, R_L = ∞		3	5		3	6	mA
	V_{CC} = 5V, R_L = ∞ (Low State) (Note 2)		10	12		10	15	mA
Timing Error, Monostable								
Initial Accuracy			0.5			1		%
Drift with Temperature	R_A, R_B = 1k to 100 k,		30			50		ppm/°C
Accuracy over Temperature	C = 0.1 μF, (Note 3)		1.5			1.5		%
Drift with Supply			0.05			0.1		%/V
Timing Error, Astable								
Initial Accuracy			1.5			2.25		%
Drift with Temperature			90			150		ppm/°C
Accuracy over Temperature			2.5			3.0		%
Drift with Supply			0.15			0.30		%/V
Threshold Voltage			0.667			0.667		x V_{CC}
Trigger Voltage	V_{CC} = 15V	4.8	5	5.2		5		V
	V_{CC} = 5V	1.45	1.67	1.9		1.67		V
Trigger Current			0.01	0.5		0.5	0.9	μA
Reset Voltage		0.4	0.5	1	0.4	0.5	1	V
Reset Current			0.1	0.4		0.1	0.4	mA
Threshold Current	(Note 4)		0.1	0.25		0.1	0.25	μA
Control Voltage Level	V_{CC} = 15V	9.6	10	10.4	9	10	11	V
	V_{CC} = 5V	2.9	3.33	3.8	2.6	3.33	4	V
Pin 7 Leakage Output High			1	100		1	100	nA
Pin 7 Sat (Note 5)								
Output Low	V_{CC} = 15V, I_7 = 15 mA		150			180		mV
Output Low	V_{CC} = 4.5V, I_7 = 4.5 mA		70	100		80	200	mV

Electrical Characteristics T_A = 25°C, V_{CC} = +5V to +15V, (unless othewise specified) (Continued)

Parameter	Conditions	Limits						Units
		LM555			LM555C			
		Min	Typ	Max	Min	Typ	Max	
Output Voltage Drop (Low)	V_{CC} = 15V							
	I_{SINK} = 10 mA		0.1	0.15		0.1	0.25	V
	I_{SINK} = 50 mA		0.4	0.5		0.4	0.75	V
	I_{SINK} = 100 mA		2	2.2		2	2.5	V
	I_{SINK} = 200 mA		2.5			2.5		V
	V_{CC} = 5V							
	I_{SINK} = 8 mA		0.1	0.25				V
	I_{SINK} = 5 mA					0.25	0.35	V
Output Voltage Drop (High)	I_{SOURCE} = 200 mA, V_{CC} = 15V		12.5			12.5		V
	I_{SOURCE} = 100 mA, V_{CC} = 15V	13	13.3		12.75	13.3		V
	V_{CC} = 5V	3	3.3		2.75	3.3		V
Rise Time of Output			100			100		ns
Fall Time of Output			100			100		ns

Note 1: For operating at elevated temperatures the device must be derated above 25°C based on a +150°C maximum junction temperature and a thermal resistance of 164°c/w (TO-5), 106°c/w (DIP) and 170°c/w (S0-8) junction to ambient.

Note 2: Supply current when output high typically 1 mA less at V_{CC} = 5V.

Note 3: Tested at V_{CC} = 5V and V_{CC} = 15V.

Note 4: This will determine the maximum value of R_A + R_B for 15V operation. The maximum total (R_A + R_B) is 20 MΩ.

Note 5: No protection against excessive pin 7 current is necessary providing the package dissipation rating will not be exceeded.

Note 6: Refer to RETS555X drawing of military LM555H and LM555J versions for specifications.

Connection Diagrams

Metal Can Package

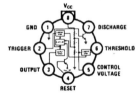

Top View

Dual-In-Line and Small Outline Packages

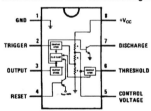

Top View

Typical Performance Characteristics

Minimum Pulse Width Required for Triggering

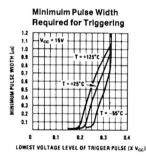

Supply Current vs Supply Voltage

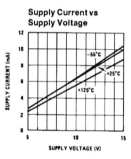

High Output Voltage vs Output Source Current

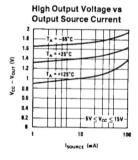

Low Output Voltage vs Output Sink Current

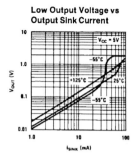

Low Output Voltage vs Output Sink Current

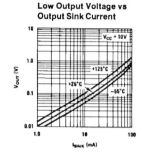

Low Output Voltage vs Output Sink Current

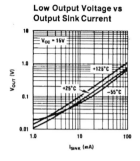

Output Propagation Delay vs Voltage Level of Trigger Pulse

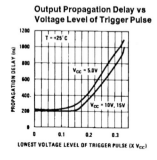

Output Propagation Delay vs Voltage Level of Trigger Pulse

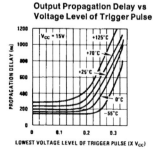

Discharge Transistor (Pin 7) Voltage vs Sink Current

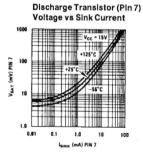

Discharge Transistor (Pin 7) Voltage vs Sink Current

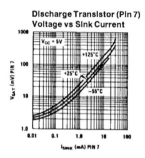

Application Information

MONOSTABLE OPERATION

In this mode of operation, the timer functions as a one-shot *(Figure 1)*. The external capacitor is initially held discharged by a transistor inside the timer. Upon application of a negative trigger pulse of less than 1/3 V_{CC} to pin 2, the flip-flop is set which both releases the short circuit across the capacitor and drives the output high.

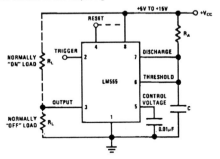

FIGURE 1. Monostable

The voltage across the capacitor then increases exponentially for a period of t = 1.1 R_A C, at the end of which time the voltage equals 2/3 V_{CC}. The comparator then resets the flip-flop which in turn discharges the capacitor and drives the output to its low state. *Figure 2* shows the waveforms generated in this mode of operation. Since the charge and the threshold level of the comparator are both directly proportional to supply voltage, the timing internal is independent of supply.

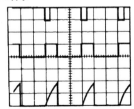

V_{CC} = 5V   Top Trace: Input 5V/Div.
TIME = 0.1 ms/DIV. Middle Trace: Output 5V/Div.
R_A = 9.1 kΩ   Bottom Trace: Capacitor Voltage 2V/Div.
C = 0.01 μF

FIGURE 2. Monostable Waveforms

During the timing cycle when the output is high, the further application of a trigger pulse will not effect the circuit. However the circuit can be reset during this time by the application of a negative pulse to the reset terminal (pin 4). The output will then remain in the low state until a trigger pulse is again applied.

When the reset function is not in use, it is recommended that it be connected to V_{CC} to avoid any possibility of false triggering.

Figure 3 is a nomograph for easy determination of R, C values for various time delays.

NOTE: In monostable operation, the trigger should be driven high before the end of timing cycle.

ASTABLE OPERATION

If the circuit is connected as shown in *Figure 4* (pins 2 and 6 connected) it will trigger itself and free run as a

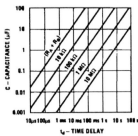

FIGURE 3. Time Delay

multivibrator. The external capacitor charges through R_A + R_B and discharges through R_B. Thus the duty cycle may be precisely set by the ratio of these two resistors.

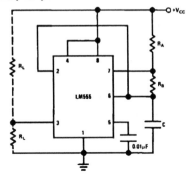

FIGURE 4. Astable

In this mode of operation, the capacitor charges and discharges between 1/3 V_{CC} and 2/3 V_{CC}. As in the triggered mode, the charge and discharge times, and therefore the frequency are independent of the supply voltage.

Applications Information (Continued)

Figure 5 shows the waveforms generated in this mode of operation.

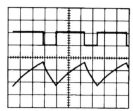

$V_{CC} = 5V$ Top Trace: Output 5V/Div.
TIME = 20 μs/DIV.   Bottom Trace: Capacitor Voltage 1V/Div.
R_A = 3.9 kΩ
R_B = 3 kΩ
C = 0.01 μF

FIGURE 5. Astable Waveforms

The charge time (output high) is given by:

$$t_1 = 0.693 (R_A + R_B) C$$

And the discharge time (output low) by:

$$t_2 = 0.693 (R_B) C$$

Thus the total period is:

$$T = t_1 + t_2 = 0.693 (R_A + 2R_B) C$$

The frequency of oscillation is:

$$f = \frac{1}{T} = \frac{1.44}{(R_A + 2 R_B) C}$$

Figure 6 may be used for quick determination of these RC values.

The duty cycle is: $D = \dfrac{R_B}{R_A + 2R_B}$

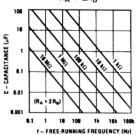

FIGURE 6. Free Running Frequency

FREQUENCY DIVIDER

The monostable circuit of *Figure 1* can be used as a frequency divider by adjusting the length of the timing cycle. *Figure 7* shows the waveforms generated in a divide by three circuit.

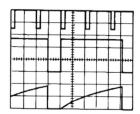

$V_{CC} = 5V$ Top Trace: Input 4V/Div.
TIME = 20 μs/DIV. Middle Trace: Output 2V/Div.
R_A = 9.1 kΩ Bottom Trace: Capacitor 2V/Div.
C = 0.01 μF

FIGURE 7. Frequency Divider

PULSE WIDTH MODULATOR

When the timer is connected in the monostable mode and triggered with a continuous pulse train, the output pulse width can be modulated by a signal applied to pin 5. *Figure 8* shows the circuit, and in *Figure 9* are some waveform examples.

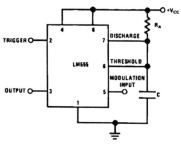

FIGURE 8. Pulse Width Modulator

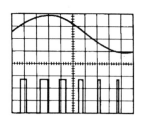

$V_{CC} = 5V$ Top Trace: Modulation 1V/Div.
TIME = 0.2 ms/DIV. Bottom Trace: Capacitor Voltage 2V/Div.
R_A = 9.1 kΩ
C = 0.01 μF

FIGURE 9. Pulse Width Modulator

PULSE POSITION MODULATOR

This application uses the timer connected for astable operation, as in *Figure 10*, with a modulating signal again applied to the control voltage terminal. The pulse position varies with the modulating signal, since the threshold voltage and hence the time delay is varied. *Figure 11* shows the waveforms generated for a triangle wave modulation signal.

Applications Information (Continued)

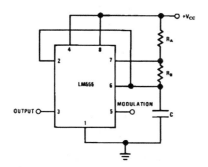

FIGURE 10. Pulse Position Modulator

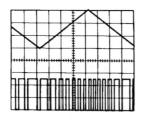

V_{CC} = 5V   Top Trace: Modulation Input 1V/Div.
TIME = 0.1 ms/Div.   Bottom Trace: Output 2V/Div.
R_A = 3.9 kΩ
R_B = 3 kΩ
C = 0.01 µF

FIGURE 11. Pulse Position Modulator

LINEAR RAMP

When the pullup resistor, R_A, in the monostable circuit is replaced by a constant current source, a linear ramp is generated. *Figure 12* shows a circuit configuration that will perform this function.

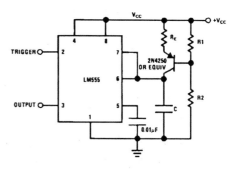

FIGURE 12

Figure 13 shows waveforms generated by the linear ramp. The time interval is given by:

$$T = \frac{2/3\, V_{CC}\, R_E\, (R_1 + R_2)\, C}{R_1\, V_{CC} - V_{BE}\, (R_1 + R_2)}$$

$$V_{BE} \cong 0.6V$$

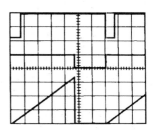

V_{CC} = 5V   Top Trace: Input 3V/Div.
TIME = 20 µs/Div.   Middle Trace: Output 5V/Div.
R_1 = 47 kΩ   Bottom Trace: Capacitor Voltage 1V/Div.
R_2 = 100 kΩ
R_E = 2.7 kΩ
C = 0.01 µF

FIGURE 13. Linear Ramp

50% DUTY CYCLE OSCILLATOR

For a 50% duty cycle, the resistors R_A and R_B may be connected as in *Figure 14*. The time period for the out-

Applications Information (Continued)

put high is the same as previous, $t_1 = 0.693\ R_A\ C$. For the output low it is $t_2 =$

$$\left[(R_A\,R_B)/(R_A + R_B)\right] CLn \left[\frac{R_A - 2R_B}{2R_A - R_B}\right]$$

Thus the frequency of oscillation is $f = \dfrac{1}{t_1 + t_2}$

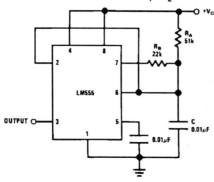

FIGURE 14. 50% Duty Cycle Oscillator

Note that this circuit will not oscillate if R_B is greater than $1/2\ R_A$ because the junction of R_A and R_B cannot bring pin 2 down to $1/3\ V_{CC}$ and trigger the lower comparator.

ADDITIONAL INFORMATION

Adequate power supply bypassing is necessary to protect associated circuitry. Minimum recommended is 0.1 μF in parallel with 1 μF electrolytic.

Lower comparator storage time can be as long as 10 μs when pin 2 is driven fully to ground for triggering. This limits the monostable pulse width to 10 μs minimum.

Delay time reset to output is 0.47 μs typical. Minimum reset pulse width must be 0.3 μs, typical.

Pin 7 current switches within 30 ns of the output (pin 3) voltage.

LM109/LM309 5-Volt Regulator

General Description

The LM109 series are complete 5V regulators fabricated on a single silicon chip. They are designed for local regulation on digital logic cards, eliminating the distribution problems association with single-point regulation. The devices are available in two standard transistor packages. In the solid-kovar TO-5 header, it can deliver output currents in excess of 200 mA, if adequate heat sinking is provided. With the TO-3 power package, the available output current is greater than 1A.

The regulators are essentially blowout proof. Current limiting is included to limit the peak output current to a safe value. In addition, thermal shutdown is provided to keep the IC from overheating. If internal dissipation becomes too great, the regulator will shut down to prevent excessive heating.

Considerable effort was expended to make these devices easy to use and to minimize the number of external components. It is not necessary to bypass the output, although this does improve transient response somewhat. Input bypassing is needed, however, if the regulator is located very far from the filter capacitor of the power supply. Stability is also achieved by methods that provide very good rejection of load or line transients as are usually seen with TTL logic.

Although designed primarily as a fixed-voltage regulator, the output of the LM109 series can be set to voltages above 5V, as shown. It is also possible to use the circuits as the control element in precision regulators, taking advantage of the good current-handling capability and the thermal overload protection.

Features

- Specified to be compatible, worst case, with TTL and DTL
- Output current in excess of 1A
- Internal thermal overload protection
- No external components required

Schematic Diagram

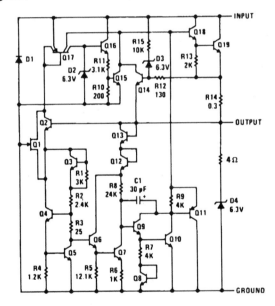

Absolute Maximum Ratings

If Military/Aerospace specified devices are required, contact the National Semiconductor Sales Office/Distributors for availability and specifications.

(Note 3)

Input Voltage	35V
Power Dissipation	Internally Limited

Operating Junction Temperature Range

LM109	$-55°C$ to $+150°C$
LM309	$0°C$ to $+125°C$
Storage Temperature Range	$-65°C$ to $+150°C$
Lead Temperature (Soldering, 10 sec.)	$300°C$

Electrical Characteristics (Note 1)

Parameter	Conditions	LM109			LM309			Units
		Min	Typ	Max	Min	Typ	Max	
Output Voltage	$T_j = 25°C$	4.7	5.05	5.3	4.8	5.05	5.2	V
Line Regulation	$T_j = 25°C$ $7.10V \leq V_{IN} \leq 25V$		4.0	50		4.0	50	mV
Load Regulation	$T_j = 25°C$							
TO-5 Package	$5 mA \leq I_{OUT} \leq 0.5A$		15	50		15	50	mV
TO-3 Package	$5 mA \leq I_{OUT} \leq 1.5A$		15	100		15	100	mV
Output Voltage	$7.40V \leq V_{IN} \leq 25V,$ $5 mA \leq I_{OUT} \leq I_{MAX},$ $P < P_{MAX}$	4.6		5.4	4.75		5.25	V
Quiescent Current	$7.40V \leq V_{IN} \leq 25V$		5.2	10		5.2	10	mA
Quiescent Current Change	$7.40V \leq V_{IN} \leq 25V$ $5 mA \leq I_{OUT} \leq I_{MAX}$			0.5 0.8			0.5 0.8	mA mA
Output Noise Voltage	$T_A = 25°C$ $10 Hz \leq f \leq 100 kHz$		40			40		μV
Long Term Stability			10			20		mV
Ripple Rejection	$T_j = 25°C$	50			50			dB
Thermal Resistance,	(Note 2)							
Junction to Case								
TO-5 Package			15			15		°C/W
TO-3 Package			2.5			2.5		°C/W

Note 1: Unless otherwise specified, these specifications apply $-55°C \leq T_j \leq +150°C$ for the LM109 and $0°C \leq T_j \leq +125°C$ for the LM309; $V_{IN} = 10V$; and $I_{OUT} = 0.1A$ for the TO-39 package or $I_{OUT} = 0.5A$ for the TO-3 package. For the TO-39 package, $I_{MAX} = 0.2A$ and $P_{MAX} = 2.0W$. For the TO-3 package, $I_{MAX} = 1.0A$ and $P_{MAX} = 20W$.

Note 2: Without a heat sink, the thermal resistance of the TO-39 package is about 150°C/W, while that of the TO-3 package is approximately 35°C/W. With a heat sink, the effective thermal resistance can only approach the values specified, depending on the efficiency of the sink.

Note 3: Refer to RETS109H drawing for LM109H or RETS109K drawing for LM109K military specifications.

Connection Diagrams

Metal Can Packages

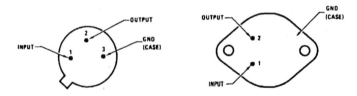

Application Hints

a. Bypass the input of the LM109 to ground with $\geq 0.2\ \mu F$ ceramic or solid tantalum capacitor if main filter capacitor is more than 4 inches away.

b. Use steel package instead of aluminum if more than 5,000 thermal cycles are expected. ($\Delta T \geq 50°C$)

c. Avoid insertion of regulator into "live" socket if input voltage is greater than 10V. The output will rise to within 2V of the unregulated input if the ground pin does not make contact. The LM109 may also be damaged if a large output capacitor is charged up, then discharged through the internal clamp zener when the ground pin makes contact.

d. The output clamp zener is designed to absorb transients only. It will not clamp the output effectively if a failure occurs in the internal power transistor structure. Zener dynamic impedance is $\approx 4\Omega$. Continuous RMS current into the zener should not exceed 0.5A.

e. Paralleling of LM109s for higher output current is not recommended. Current sharing will be almost nonexistent, leading to a current limit mode operation for devices with the highest initial output voltage. The current limit devices may also heat up to the thermal shutdown point ($\approx 175°C$). Long term reliability cannot be guaranteed under these conditions.

f. Preventing latchoff for loads connected to negative voltage:

If the output of the LM109 is pulled negative by a high current supply so that the output pin is more than 0.5V negative with respect to the ground pin, the LM109 can latch off. This can be prevented by clamping the ground pin to the output pin with a germanium or Schottky diode as shown. A silicon diode (1N4001) at the output is also needed to keep the positive output from being pulled too far negative. The 10Ω resistor will raise $+V_{OUT}$ by $\approx 0.05V$.

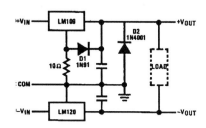

Crowbar Overvoltage Protection

Input Crowbar

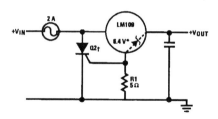

Output Crowbar

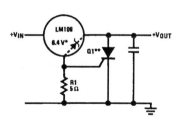

*Zener is internal to LM109.

**Q1 must be able to withstand 7A continuous current if fusing is not used at regulator input. LM109 bond wires will fuse at currents above 7A.

†Q2 is selected for surge capability. Consideration must be given to filter capacitor size, transformer impedance, and fuse blowing time.

††Trip point is $\approx 7.5V$.

Typical Performance Characteristics

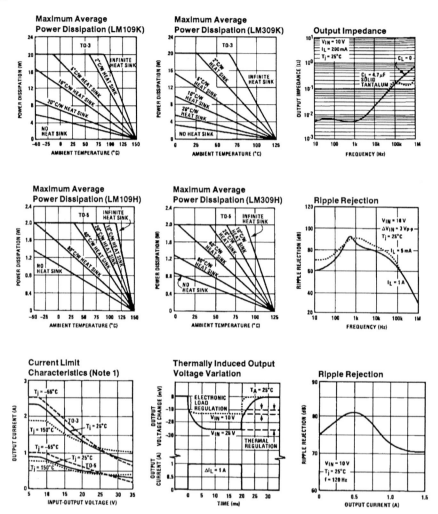

Note 1: Current limiting foldback characteristics
are determined by input output differential, not by output voltage.

Typical Performance Characteristics (Continued)

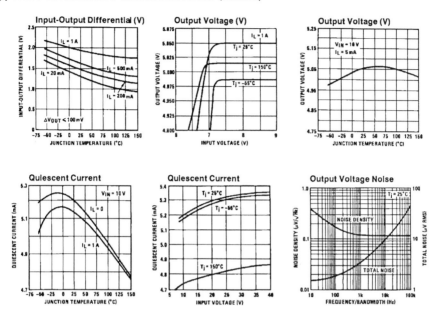

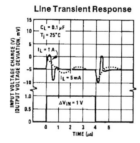

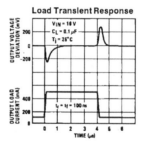

LM1877 Dual Power Audio Amplifier

General Description

The LM1877 is a monolithic dual power amplifier designed to deliver 2W/channel continuous into 8Ω loads. The LM1877 is designed to operate with a low number of external components, and still provide flexibility for use in stereo phonographs, tape recorders and AM-FM stereo receivers, etc. Each power amplifier is biased from a common internal regulator to provide high power supply rejection, and output Q point centering. The LM1877 is internally compensated for all gains greater than 10.

Features

- 2W/channel
- −65 dB ripple rejection, output referred
- −65 dB channel separation, output referred

- Wide supply range, 6V–24V
- Very low cross-over distortion
- Low audio band noise
- AC short circuit protected
- Internal thermal shutdown

Applications

- Multi-channel audio systems
- Stereo phonographs
- Tape recorders and players
- AM-FM radio receivers
- Servo amplifiers
- Intercom systems
- Automotive products

Connection Diagram

Dual-In-Line Package

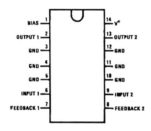

Top View

Equivalent Schematic Diagram

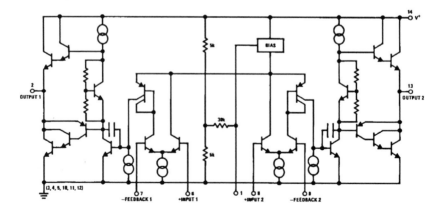

Absolute Maximum Ratings

If Military/Aerospace specified devices are required, contact the National Semiconductor Sales Office/Distributors for availability and specifications.

Supply Voltage	26V
Input Voltage	±0.7V

Operating Temperature	0°C to +70°C
Storage Temprature	−65°C to +150°C
Junction Temperature	150°C
Lead Temperature (Soldering, 10 sec.)	260°C

Electrical Characteristics

V_S = 20V, T_A = 25°C, (See Note 1) R_L = 8Ω, A_V = 50 (34 dB) unless otherwise specified

Parameter	Conditions	Min	Typ	Max	Units
Total Supply Current	P_O = 0W		25	50	mA
Output Power LM1877	THD = 10% V_S = 20V, R_L = 8Ω	2.0			W/Ch
Total Harmonic Distortion LM1877	f = 1 kHz, V_S = 14V				
	P_O = 50 mW/Channel		0.075		%
	P_O = 500 mW/Channel		0.045		%
	P_O = 1 W/Channel		0.055		%
Output Swing	R_L = 8Ω		V_S −6		Vp-p
Channel Separation	C_F = 50 μF, C_{IN} = 0.1 μF, f = 1 kHz, Output Referred				
	V_S = 20V, V_O = 4 Vrms	−50	−70		dB
	V_S = 7V, V_O = 0.5 Vrms		−60		dB
PSRR Power Supply Rejection Ratio	C_F = 50 μF, C_{IN} = 0.1 μF, f = 120 Hz, Output Referred				
	V_S = 20V, V_{RIPPLE} = 1 Vrms	−50	−65		dB
	V_S = 7V, V_{RIPPLE} = 0.5 Vrms		−40		dB
Noise	Equivalent Input Noise				
	R_S = 0, C_{IN} = 0.1 μF, BW = 20 Hz–20 kHz, Output Noise Wideband		2.5		μV
	R_S = 0, C_N = 0.1 μF, A_V 200		0.80		mV
Open Loop Gain	R_S = 0, f = 100 kHz, R_L = 8Ω		70		dB
Input Offset Voltage			15		mV
Input Bias Current			50		nA
Input Impedance	Open Loop		4		MΩ
DC Output Level	V_S = 20V	9	10	11	V
Slew Rate			2.0		V/μs
Power Bandwidth			65		kHz
Current Limit			1.0		A

Note 1: For operation at ambient temperature greater than 25°C, the LM1877 must be derated based on a maximum 150°C junction temperature using a thermal resistance which depends upon device mounting techniques.

Typical Performance Characteristics

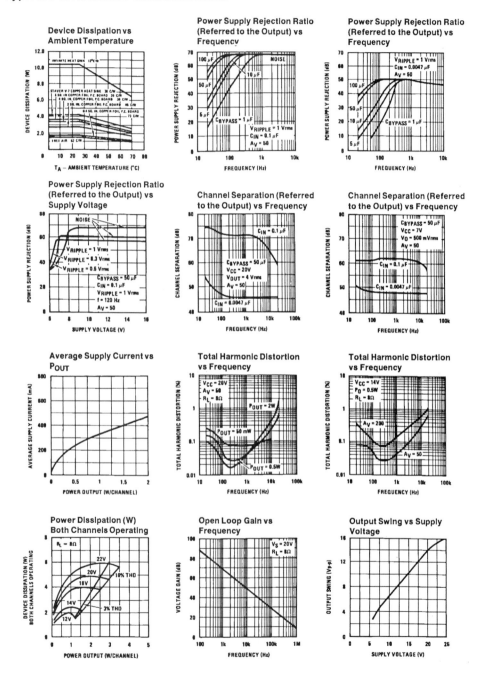

Type AD568 12-Bit Ultrahigh-Speed Monolithic D/A Converter

PRODUCT DESCRIPTION

The AD568 is an ultrahigh-speed, 12-bit digital-to-analog converter (DAC) settling to 0.025% in 35ns. The monolithic device is fabricated using Analog Devices' Complementary Bipolar (CB) Process. This is a proprietary process featuring high-speed NPN and PNP devices on the same chip without the use of dielectric isolation or multichip hybrid techniques. The high speed of the AD568 is maintained by keeping impedance levels low enough to minimize the effects of parasitic circuit capacitances.

The DAC consists of 16 current sources configured to deliver a 10.24mA full-scale current. Multiple matched current sources and thin-film ladder techniques are combined to produce bit weighting. The DAC's output is a 10.24mA full scale (FS) for current output applications or a 1.024V FS unbuffered voltage output. Additionally, a 10.24V FS buffered output may be generated using an onboard 1kΩ span resistor with an external op amp. Bipolar ranges are accomplished by pin strapping.

Laser wafer trimming insures full 12-bit linearity. All grades of the AD568 are guaranteed monotonic over their full operating temperature range. Furthermore, the output resistance of the DAC is trimmed to 100Ω ± 1.0%. The gain temperature coefficient of the voltage output is 30ppm/°C max (K).

The AD568 is available in three performance grades. The AD568JQ and KQ are available in 24-pin cerdip (0.3") packages and are specified for operation from 0 to + 70°C. The AD568SQ features operation from − 55°C to + 125°C and is also packaged in the hermetic 0.3" cerdip.

PRODUCT HIGHLIGHTS

1. The ultrafast settling time of the AD568 allows leading edge performance in waveform generation, graphics display and high-speed A/D conversion applications.

2. Pin strapping provides a variety of voltage and current output ranges for application versatility. Tight control of the absolute output current reduces trim requirements in externally-scaled applications.

3. Matched on-chip resistors can be used for precision scaling in high-speed A/D conversion circuits.

4. The digital inputs are compatible with TTL and + 5V CMOS logic families.

5. Skinny DIP (0.3") packaging minimizes board space requirements and eases layout considerations.

SPECIFICATIONS (@ T_A = + 25°C, V_{CC}, V_{EE} = ± 15V unless otherwise noted)

Model	AD568J			AD568K			AD568S			Units
	Min	Typ	Max	Min	Typ	Max	Min	Typ	Max	
RESOLUTION	12			12			12			Bits
ACCURACY[1]										
Linearity	−1/2		+1/2	−1/4		+1/4	−1/2		+1/2	LSB
T_{min} to T_{max}	−3/4		+3/4	−1/2		+1/2	−3/4		+3/4	LSB
Differential Nonlinearity	−1		+1	−1/2		+1/2	−1		+1	LSB
T_{min} to T_{max}	−1		+1	−1		+1	−1		−1	LSB
Monotonicity				GUARANTEED OVER RATED SPECIFICATION TEMPERATURE RANGE						
Unipolar Offset	−0.2		+0.2	*		*	*		*	% of FSR
Bipolar Offset	−1.0		+1.0	*		*	*		*	% of FSR
Bipolar Zero	−0.2		+0.2	*		*	*		*	% of FSR
Gain Error	−1.0		+1.0	*		*	*		*	% of FSR
TEMPERATURE COEFFICIENTS[2]										
Unipolar Offset	−5		+5	−3		+3	−5		+5	ppm of FSR/°C
Bipolar Offset	−30		+30	−20		+20	−30		+30	ppm of FSR/°C
Bipolar Zero	−15		+15	*		*	*		*	ppm of FSR/°C
Gain Drift	−50		+50	−30		+30	−50		+50	ppm of FSR/°C
Gain Drift (I_{OUT})	−150		+150	*		*	*		*	ppm of FSR/°C
DATA INPUTS										
Logic Levels (T_{min} to T_{max})										
V_{IH}	2.0		7.0	*		*	*		*	V
V_{IL}	0.0		0.8	*		*	*		*	V
Logic Currents (T_{min} to T_{max})										
I_{IH}	−1.0		+1.0	*		*	*		*	μA
I_{IL}	+0.5		+80	*		*	*		*	μA
V_{TH} Pin Voltage		1.4			*			*		V
CODING				BINARY, OFFSET BINARY						
CURRENT OUTPUT RANGES				0 to 10.24, ± 5.12						mA
VOLTAGE OUTPUT RANGES				0 to 1.024, ± 0.512						V
COMPLIANCE VOLTAGE	−2		+1.2	*		*	*		*	V
OUTPUT RESISTANCE										
Exclusive of R_L	160	200	240		*			*		Ω
Inclusive of R_L	99	100	101		*			*		Ω
SETTLING TIME										
Current to										
± 0.025%		35			*			*		ns to 0.025% of FSR
± 0.1%		23			*			*		ns to 0.1% of FSR
Voltage										
50Ω Load[3], 0.512V p-p,										
to 0.025%		37			*			*		ns to 0.025% of FSR
to 0.1%		25			*			*		ns to 0.1% of FSR
to 1%		18								ns to 1% of FSR
75Ω Load[3], 0.768V p-p,										
to 0.025%		40			*			*		ns to 0.025% of FSR
to 0.1%		25			*			*		ns to 0.1% of FSR
to 1%		20								ns to 1% of FSR
100Ω (Internal R_L)[3], 1.024V p-p,										
to 0.025%		50			*			*		ns to 0.025% of FSR
to 0.1%		38			*			*		ns to 0.1% of FSR
to 1%		24								ns to 1% of FSR
Glitch Impulse[4]		350								pV-sec
Peak Amplitude		15								% of FSR
FULL-SCALE TRANSITION[5]										
10% to 90% Rise Time		11			*			*		ns
90% to 10% Fall Time		11			*			*		ns
POWER REQUIREMENTS										
+ 13.5V to + 16.5V		27	32			*			*	mA
− 13.5V to − 16.5V		7	8			*			*	− mA
Power Dissipation		525	625			*			*	mW
PSRR			0.05			*			*	%FSR/V
TEMPERATURE RANGE										
Rated Specification[2]	0		70	0		70	−55		+125	°C
Storage	−65		+150	*		*	*		*	°C

NOTES
*Same as AD568J.
[1]Measured in I_{OUT} mode.
[2]Measured in V_{OUT} mode, unless otherwise specified. See text for further information.
[3]Total Resistance. Refer to Figure 3.

[4]At the major carry, driven by HCMOS logic. See text for further explanation.
[5]Measured in V_{OUT} mode.
Specifications shown in boldface are tested on all production units at final electrical test.
Specifications subject to change without notice.

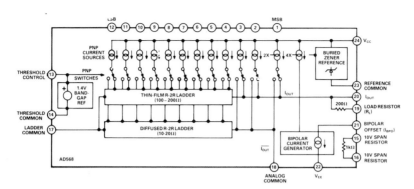

Figure 1. Functional Block Diagram

AD568 PIN CONFIGURATION

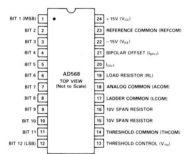

OUTLINE DIMENSIONS

Dimensions shown in inches and (mm).

24-PIN CERDIP (SUFFIX Q)

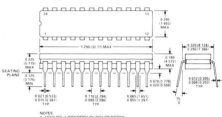

ABSOLUTE MAXIMUM RATINGS*

V_{CC} to RefCOM . . . . 0V to +18V
V_{EE} to RefCOM . . . . 0V to −18V
RefCOM to LCOM . . . . +100mV to −10V
ACOM to LCOM . . . . ±100mV
DigCOM to LCOM . . . . ±500mV
SPANs to LCOM . . . . ±12V
I_{BPO} to LCOM . . . . ±5V
I_{OUT} to LCOM . . . . −5V to V_{TH}
Digital Inputs to THCOM . . . . −500mV to +7.0V
Voltage Across Span Resistor 12V
V_{TH} to THCOM . . . . −0.7V to +1.4V
Logic Threshold Control Input Current 5mA

Power Dissipation 1000mW
Storage Temperature Range
 Q (Cerdip) Package . . . . −65°C to +150°C
Junction Temperature . . . . 175°C
Thermal Resistance
 θ_{ja} . . . . 75°C/W
 θ_{jc} . . . . 25°C/W

*Stresses above those listed under "Absolute Maximum Ratings" may cause permanent damage to the device. This is a stress rating only and functional operation of the device at these or any other conditions above those indicated in the operational sections of this specification is not implied. Exposure to absolute maximum rating conditions for extended periods may affect device reliability.

Appendix B
Basic Formulas

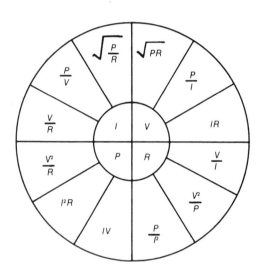

$$\text{Series: } R_T = R_1 + R_2 + R_3 + \cdots$$

$$\text{Parallel: } R_T = \cfrac{1}{\cfrac{1}{R_1} + \cfrac{1}{R_2} + \cfrac{1}{R_3} + \cdots}$$

$$\text{Voltage Divider: } V_1 = V_T \left(\frac{R_1}{R_T} \right)$$

$$\text{Current Divider: } I_1 = I_T \left(\frac{R_2}{R_T} \right)$$

AC

Sinusoidal Voltage and Current

$$\text{effective value} = 0.707 \times \text{peak value}$$
$$\text{average value} = 0.637 \times \text{peak value}$$
$$\text{peak value} = 1.414 \times \text{effective value}$$
$$\text{effective value} = 1.11 \times \text{average value}$$
$$\text{peak value} = 1.57 \times \text{average value}$$
$$\text{average value} = 0.9 \times \text{effective value}$$

AC Circuits

General:

$$X_L = 2\pi f L \qquad X_C = \frac{1}{2\pi f C} \qquad f = \frac{1}{2\pi\sqrt{LC}}$$

$$Q = \frac{X_L}{R} \qquad f_c = \frac{1}{2\pi RC} \text{ (cutoff frequency)}$$

Series:

$$V_T = I_T Z \qquad Z = \sqrt{R^2 + (X_L - X_C)^2} \qquad V_R = IR$$

$$V_L = IX_L \qquad V_c = IX_C \qquad \theta = \tan^{-1}\frac{X}{R}$$

$$C_T = \frac{1}{\dfrac{1}{C_1} + \dfrac{1}{C_2} + \dfrac{1}{C_3} + \cdots} \qquad L_T = L_1 + L_2 + L_3 + \cdots$$

Parallel:

$$Z = \frac{V_T}{I_T} \qquad I_T = \sqrt{I_R^2 + (I_L - I_C)^2} \qquad Z = \frac{RX}{\sqrt{R^2 + X^2}}$$

$$I_R = \frac{V_T}{R} \qquad I_L = \frac{V_T}{X_L} \qquad I_C = \frac{V_T}{X_C}$$

$$\theta = \tan^{-1}\frac{R}{X} \qquad C_T = C_1 + C_2 + C_3 + \cdots$$

$$L_T = \frac{1}{\dfrac{1}{L_1} + \dfrac{1}{L_2} + \dfrac{1}{L_3} + \cdots}$$

Transformers:

$$\frac{N_\mathrm{p}}{N_\mathrm{s}} = \frac{V_\mathrm{p}}{V_\mathrm{s}} = \frac{I_\mathrm{s}}{I_\mathrm{p}} = \sqrt{\frac{Z_\mathrm{p}}{Z_\mathrm{s}}}$$

Decibels

Equal Impedances:

$$\mathrm{dB} = 10 \log \frac{P_1}{P_2} = 20 \log \frac{V_1}{V_2} = 20 \log \frac{I_1}{I_2}$$

Unequal Impedances:

$$\mathrm{dB} = 10 \log \frac{P_1}{P_2} = 20 \log \frac{V_1\sqrt{Z_2}}{V_2\sqrt{Z_1}} = 20 \log \frac{I_1\sqrt{Z_1}}{I_2\sqrt{Z_2}}$$

dB Table			
dB	P ratio	V or I ratio	
0	1.00	1.00	
0.5	1.12	1.06	
1.0	1.26	1.12	
1.5	1.41	1.19	
2.0	1.58	1.26	
3.0	2.00	1.41	. . . Half-power point
4.0	2.51	1.58	
5.0	3.16	1.70	
6.0	3.98	2.00	
7.0	5.01	2.24	
8.0	6.31	2.51	
9.0	7.94	2.82	
10	10.0	3.2	
15	31.6	5.6	
20	100	10	
25	316	18	
30	1,000	32	
40	10,000	100	
50	10^5	316	
60	10^6	1,000	
70	10^7	3,162	
80	10^8	10,000	
90	10^9	31,620	
100	10^{10}	10^5	

Bipolar Transistors

$$I_e = I_c + I_b \qquad \alpha = \frac{\Delta I_c}{\Delta I_e} \text{ (common base current gain)}$$

$$\beta = \frac{\Delta I_c}{\Delta I_b} \text{ (common emitter current gain)} \qquad I_c = \alpha I_e = \beta I_b$$

$$\alpha = \frac{\beta}{1 + \beta} \qquad \text{and} \qquad \beta = \frac{\alpha}{1 - \alpha}$$

Field Effect Transistors

$$g_m = \frac{\Delta I_D}{\Delta V_{gs}} \qquad R_d = \frac{\Delta V_{ds}}{\Delta I_D} \qquad A_V \approx -g_m R_L \text{ (common source)}$$

General Amplification

$$A_V = \frac{V_o}{V_i} \qquad A_I = \frac{I_o}{I_i} \qquad A_P = \frac{P_o}{P_i} \qquad \beta = \frac{R_1}{R_1 + R_f} \text{ (feedback factor)}$$

Appendix C
Sample Computer
Programs

This appendix contains five sample computer programs. They demonstrate the use of computers to help understand operational amplifier and linear integrated circuit applications. BASIC language was used to develop each program.

Since there are many dialects of BASIC, you may need to modify slightly a few of the program lines for your computer. Key in the program and try it! If it doesn't run successfully, locate the lines to be modified and change them. Each program has been tested and performs the desired operations.

- Program 1   Noninverting Amplifier Gain
- Program 2   Inverting Amplifier Gain
- Program 3   Monostable Multivibrator Calculations
- Program 4   Instrumentation Amplifier Gain
- Program 5   555 Timer

PROGRAM 1: NONINVERTING AMPLIFIER GAIN

```
10 PRINT "     THIS PROGRAM CALCULATES THE VALUE OF"
20 PRINT "     FEEDBACK RESISTANCE NEEDED FOR A"
30 PRINT "     SPECIFIED GAIN ASSUMING A SELECTED"
40 PRINT "     VALUE OF R1. (SEE FIG. 2-3.)"
45 PRINT:PRINT
50 INPUT "ENTER GAIN REQUIRED:"; A
60 IF A=0, THEN PRINT "IMPRACTICAL!!":GOTO 50
70 IF A=1, THEN PRINT "CONNECT AMPLIFIER OUTPUT DIRECTLY TO
                       INVERTING INPUT":GOTO 50
80 IF A<0, THEN PRINT "USE INVERTING AMPLIFIER CONFIGURATION"
85 GOTO 50
100 PRINT "NONINVERTING AMPLIFIER CONFIGURATION SELECTED"
110 PRINT
120 INPUT "SELECT TRIAL VALUE FOR RIN IN OHMS:";RIN
```

```
130 PRINT
140 RF = (A-1)*RIN
150 RF = INT(RF)
160 PRINT:PRINT:PRINT
170 PRINT "FOR A GAIN OF";A;" USE:"
180 PRINT:PRINT"RIN = ";RIN;" OHMS"
190 PRINT "RF =";RF;" OHMS"
200 PRINT:PRINT
210 PRINT "PRESS ANY KEY TO CONTINUE"
220 A$=INKEY$:IF A$=""THEN 220
230 PRINT:PRINT
240 PRINT "I'D LIKE TO:"
250 PRINT "     1.  TRY ANOTHER VALUE FOR RIN"
260 PRINT "     2.  TRY ANOTHER VALUE FOR A"
270 PRINT "     3.  TRY ANOTHER VALUE FOR BOTH A AND RIN"
280 PRINT "     4.  QUIT"
290 INPUT "ENTER YOUR CHOICE:",C
300 ON C GOTO 120, 50, 50, 400
400 PRINT:PRINT:PRINT "THANKS FOR USING ME.  TRY AGAIN SOME TIME!"
410 PRINT:PRINT "          'BYE!'"
420 END
```

——— *PROGRAM 2: INVERTING AMPLIFIER GAIN* ——

```
10 PRINT "     THIS PROGRAM CALCULATES THE VALUE OF"
20 PRINT "     FEEDBACK RESISTANCE NEEDED FOR THE"
30 PRINT "     SPECIFIED GAIN OF AN INVERTING AMPLIFIER."
40 PRINT "     YOU MUST ALSO SELECT A VALUE FOR R1."
50 PRINT "     (SEE FIG. 2-4.)  THE INVERTING AMPLIFIER"
60 PRINT "     PRODUCES A 180-DEGREE PHASE REVERSAL."
70 PRINT "     PLEASE ENTER THE REQUIRED GAIN AS A"
80 PRINT "     NEGATIVE (-) NUMBER."
90 PRINT:PRINT
100 INPUT "ENTER GAIN REQUIRED: "; A
110 PRINT:PRINT
120 IF A=0 THEN PRINT "IMPRACTICAL!!":GOTO 100
130 IF A>0 THEN PRINT "USE NONINVERTING AMPLIFIER CONFIGURATION"
135 GOTO 100
140 PRINT
150 INPUT "SELECT TRIAL VALUE FOR R1 IN OHMS: "; R1
160 PRINT:PRINT
170 RF = ABS(A)*R1
180 RF = INT(RF)
190 PRINT "FOR A GAIN OF ";A;" USE:"
200 PRINT:PRINT"R1 = ";R1;" OHMS"
210 PRINT "RF = ";RF;" OHMS"
220 PRINT:PRINT
230 PRINT "PRESS ANY KEY TO CONTINUE"
240 A$=INKEY$:IF A$=""THEN 240
250 PRINT:PRINT
260 PRINT "I'D LIKE TO:"
270 PRINT "     1.  TRY ANOTHER VALUE FOR R1"
```

```
280 PRINT "    2.  TRY ANOTHER VALUE FOR A"
290 PRINT "    3.  TRY ANOTHER VALUE FOR BOTH A AND R1"
300 PRINT "    4.  QUIT"
310 INPUT "ENTER YOUR CHOICE: "; C
320 ON C GOTO 140, 90, 90, 330
330 PRINT:PRINT:PRINT "THANKS FOR USING ME.  TRY AGAIN SOME TIME!"
340 PRINT:PRINT"              'BYE!"
350 END
```

——— PROGRAM 3: MONOSTABLE ——— MULTIVIBRATOR CALCULATIONS

```
5 CLS
10 PRINT "    THIS PROGRAM DETERMINES THE RESISTOR"
20 PRINT "    AND CAPACITOR VALUES FOR THE MONOSTABLE"
30 PRINT "    MULTIVIBRATOR OF FIGURE 9-17."
40 PRINT:PRINT
50 PRINT:INPUT "PULSE DURATION IN MILLISECONDS (MS) "; T
60 T = T/1000
70 PRINT:PRINT
80 INPUT "FIRST TRY FOR C1 IN MICROFARADS (UF) "; C
90 C = C*1E-6
100 R = T/(.693*C)
110 R = INT(R)
120 C = C*1E6
130 T = T*1000
140 PRINT:PRINT
150 PRINT "FOR A PULSE DURATION OF";T;"MILLISECONDS, USE"
160 PRINT "A";R;"OHM RESISTOR FOR RF AND A";C;"UF"
170 PRINT "CAPACITOR FOR C."
180 PRINT:PRINT
190 PRINT "NOW I'D LIKE TO:"
200 PRINT "    1.  TRY SOME OTHER VALUES"
210 PRINT "    2.  QUIT"
220 PRINT:INPUT "ENTER YOUR CHOICE: ";X
230 ON X GOTO 40, 240
240 PRINT:PRINT:PRINT"SEE YOU LATER!"
```

——— PROGRAM 4: INSTRUMENTATION ——— AMPLIFIER GAIN

```
10 CLS:PRINT:PRINT
20 PRINT "    THIS PROGRAM CALCULATES THE VALUE OF"
30 PRINT "    THE GAIN-SETTING RESISTOR R(G) IN THE"
40 PRINT "    INSTRUMENTATION AMPLIFIER OF FIG. 11-7."
50 PRINT:PRINT
60 PRINT:INPUT"ENTER GAIN REQUIRED: "; A
70 IF A<2 THEN GOSUB 500
```

```
80 IF A>1000 THEN GOSUB 500
90 GOSUB 1000
100 R = 40/(A-1)
110 R = R*1000:R = INT(R):R = R/1000
120 PRINT:PRINT
130 PRINT "FOR YOUR SELECTED GAIN OF";A;"USE A";R;"K-OHM RESISTOR
        FOR R(G)."
140 PRINT:PRINT"NOW I'D LIKE TO:"
150 PRINT "  1.    TRY AGAIN"
160 PRINT "  2.    QUIT"
170 PRINT:INPUT "ENTER YOUR CHOICE:";X
180 ON X GOTO 50, 190
190 PRINT:PRINT"SO LONG!":END
500 PRINT "THIS PROGRAM OPERATES WITH VOLTAGE GAINS
510 PRINT "RANGING FROM 2 TO 1000.  TRY AGAIN."
520 GOTO 50
1000 PRINT:PRINT "PRESS ANY KEY TO CONTINUE:"
1010 A$=INKEY$:IF A$=""THEN 1010
1020 RETURN
```

———— *PROGRAM 5: 555 TIMER* ————

```
10 CLS:PRINT:PRINT
20 PRINT "    555 IC TIMER CALCULATIONS"
25 PRINT "         (SEE FIG. 11-17.)"
30 PRINT:PRINT
40 INPUT "<A>STABLE OR <M>ONOSTABLE ";Z$
50 IF Z$<>"A" AND Z$<>"M" THEN 10
60 IF Z$ = "A" THEN 70 ELSE 250
70 CLS:PRINT:PRINT
80 PRINT "    ASTABLE OPERATION"
90 PRINT:PRINT
100 INPUT "OUTPUT FREQUENCY (HZ) "; F
110 IF F>200E3 THEN PRINT:PRINT "F MUST BE LESS THAN 200 KHZ.
    INPUT A LOWER FREQUENCY.":GOTO 100
120 PRINT:INPUT "PERCENT DUTY CYCLE (>50%) ";D:D=D/100
130 IF D<=.5 THEN PRINT:PRINT "DUTY CYCLE MUST BE GREATER THAN 50%.
    INPUT A LONGER DUTY CYCLE.":GOTO 120
140 PRINT:INPUT "C (UF) ";C:C=C*1E-6
150 IF C<1E-9 THEN PRINT:PRINT "CAPACITANCE MUST BE GREATER THAN
    100 PF.  INPUT A LARGER CAPACITANCE.":GOTO 140
160 RA = (2*D-1)/(LOG(2)*C*F)
170 RB = (1/(2*LOG(2)*C*F))-(RA/2)
180 X = C*(RA+2*RB):F=(1/LOG(2))*1/X
190 RA = INT((RA/1E3)*100+.5)/100
200 RB = INT((RB/1E3)*100+.5)/100:C=C/1E-6
210 D=D*100
220 PRINT:PRINT "  RA = ";RA;"K-OHMS";"   RB = ";RB;"K-OHMS"
230 PRINT:INPUT "CHANGE INPUT VALUES (YES/NO) "; E$
235 PRINT
240 IF E$="YES" THEN 100 ELSE PRINT:PRINT"    GOODBYE!":END
```

```
250 CLS:PRINT:PRINT"    MONOSTABLE OPERATION"
260 PRINT:PRINT:INPUT "TIME DELAY (SECONDS) ";T
270 IF T<1E-3 THEN PRINT:PRINT"TIME DELAY MUST BE GREATER THAN
    ONE MILLISECOND.  ENTER A LONGER TIME DELAY.":GOTO 260
280 PRINT:INPUT"C (UF) ";C
290 IF C<.001 THEN PRINT:"CAPACITANCE MUST BE GREATER THAN .001
    UF.  ENTER A LARGER VALUE OF CAPACITANCE.":GOTO 280
300 R = INT(((1E3*T)/(1.1*C))*100+.5)/100
310 PRINT:PRINT"    R = ";R;"K-OHMS"
320 PRINT:INPUT"CHANGE VALUES (YES/NO) ";B$
330 IF B$="YES"THEN 260 ELSE PRINT:PRINT"    GOODBYE!"
340 END
```

Glossary

Absolute-value circuit

A full-wave precision diode circuit.

Active filter

A filter that contains amplifying devices in addition to passive devices.

Active tone control

Same as *tone control* except that operational amplifiers are used with passive components.

Adder

An electrical/electronic circuit that performs the mathematical function of summing.

All-pass filter

A filter that passes all frequencies at a relatively constant amplitude yet provides desired phase shift.

Amplification

The control of a large amount of voltage, current, or power by a smaller amount of voltage, current, or power.

Analog device

A device that displays something in terms of something else.

Analog multiplier

An op amp circuit (or maybe a separate IC) that performs the mathematical function of multiplication.

Analog signal-processing subsystem

A special IC containing two input amplifiers that may be electronically switched to hold information. A comparator is also included.

Antilog amplifier

A circuit whose output is proportional to the antilog of the input. Function is accomplished by interchanging the position of the logarithmic element and the input resistor of an op amp.

Astable multivibrator

A digital circuit that has unequal off and on times. It can be used as a pulse generator.

Audio amplifier

An amplifier that processes AC signals in the frequency range of 20 Hz to 20 kHz.

Automatic gain control (AGC)

A control voltage used to automatically adjust amplifier gain to maintain a constant output.

Band-pass filter

A filter that passes only a band of frequencies within the desired range, blocking all other frequencies both above and below the desired passband.

Band-reject filter

A filter that rejects a band of frequencies within the desired range, passing all other frequencies both above and below the desired rejection band.

Bandwidth

The band of frequencies between the lower and upper 3 dB points on a gain versus frequency graph. In referring to op amps, the number of cycles per second from DC to the cutoff frequency.

Bessel filter

A filter with a very gradual roll-off characteristic and a drooping passband.

Beta (β)

Percentage of output fed back to the input.

Bipolar junction transistor

A solid-state amplifying device that operates due to the existence of both positive and negative charge carriers.

Biquadratic filter

A filter that solves an expression containing quadratic equations in both the numerator and the denominator of a fraction. This filter uses two integrators and an inverting amplifier.

Bistable and astable flip-flop

A digital circuit with two and only two stable conditions.

Bode plot

A frequency response graph that uses straight-line approximations to simplify data.

Boost-mode regulator

A voltage regulator with an output greater than its input.

Buck-mode regulator

A voltage regulator with an output less than its input.

Butterworth filter

A filter with a relatively flat passband characteristic.

Capacitive load compensation

A type of frequency/phase compensation in which resistance is inserted in series with the output terminal of the amplifier to isolate capacitive loads.

Capture range

The bandwidth over which PLL capture is possible.

Capture state

A PLL state when the output frequency is changing.

Cascade

In amplifiers, one stage following another.

Center frequency

The geometric mean of the upper and lower 3 dB frequency points of a filter.

Chebyshev filter

A filter with dips and peaks in its passband characteristic.

Clamp

To limit a voltage to a predetermined value.

Closed-loop gain

Gain of an amplifier with feedback.

Closed-loop system

Any system in which a portion of the output is fed back to the input as control.

Colpitts oscillator

An oscillator circuit that obtains the required feedback and phase shift from a capacitive divider in an *LC* tuned circuit.

Common-mode gain

Same as *difference-mode gain* except that the input signal is connected to both amplifier input terminals. Theoretically, common-mode gain is 0 since the difference between the two inputs is 0.

Common-mode rejection ratio (CMRR)

The ratio of open-loop gain to common-mode gain. CMRR is often expressed in decibels (dB). It is ideally infinite.

Compandor

A combination audio frequency compressor-expandor used in audio applications.

Comparator

A special op amp that accepts linear inputs but provides digital outputs.

Complementary emitter follower

An electronic circuit that uses both NPN and PNP transistors in the emitter follower configuration.

Conditionally stable

An amplifier condition such that oscillation can occur under certain gain/ frequency combinations.

Constant current source

A source of energy that supplies constant current to a load despite changes in load resistance.

Constant-time-delay filter

Filter that does just what the name implies: provides constant time delay. A Bessel filter shape provides this capability.

Counter analog-to-digital (A/D) converter

A circuit that changes the output of a counter to an analog value to be compared with the analog value to be converted.

Cutoff frequency (f_c)

The frequency at which the gain or amplification of a circuit has dropped 3 dB from its constant gain value. Term is also used synonymously with the term *corner frequency*.

Cosine wave

A *sine wave* shifted 90°.

Critically damped

A term used to describe the characteristics of an *LC* circuit (or its equivalent) with properly selected *L, C,* and *R*. Being critically damped results in a response similar to that of an *RC* circuit.

Current-to-voltage converter

An op amp circuit that converts changing current flow to a changing voltage and that is used with moving-coil meters to measure small currents.

Current difference amplifier

An op-amp-like device that operates on the difference of input currents rather than input voltages.

Cross-talk

Information from one channel of a stereo audio system that is heard in the other channel.

Damping factor (*D*)

A number used to describe the degree of damping of an *LC* circuit or its equivalent.

Darlington configuration

A transistor circuit connection that improves power-handling capabilities.

Decade

A ten-fold change, such as frequency changing from 10 Hz to 100 Hz.

Demultiplexer

A circuit that reconstructs channels of information earlier combined by a multiplexer.

Detection bandwidth

Same as *capture range*.

Detector

A circuit that recovers information from a modulated carrier wave.

Difference-mode gain

Same as *open-loop gain* except that input voltage is the difference between the two input voltages.

Differential amplifier

An amplifier with two inputs and an output that results from the amplified difference between the two inputs.

Differentiating circuit

A circuit that performs the mathematical operation of differentiation. It allows only fast-rising leading edges of nonsinusoidal waves to pass; the remainder of the wave is not allowed through the circuit.

Differentiation

A mathematical operation that finds the instantaneous rate of change of an input.

Digital device

A device that displays something in terms of symbols.

Diode

A two-terminal semiconductor device that permits unidirectional current flow.

Duty cycle
On-off ratio, as used when speaking of pulse-type applications.

Elliptical (Cauer) filter
A variation of the *notch filter*.

Emitter follower
A transistor circuit configuration with a very high input resistance, low output resistance, unity voltage gain, and appreciable current gain.

Equal-component-value Sallen-Key filter
A special case of the *Sallen-Key filter*.

Equalizer amplifier
Same as *preamplifier* but with a tailored rather than flat frequency response.

Equivalent circuit
A simplification of a complex electrical/electronic circuit such that the minimum number of components have the same characteristics as the original circuit.

Exclusive-OR circuit
A digital circuit that provides an output only when one or the other of the inputs is active.

Feedback
A technique that uses a part of an amplifier's output as its input. Feedback is used to modify performance of the amplifier circuit.

Feedback factor (β)
A number that indicates what percentage of the output of an amplifier is fed back to the input.

Feedforward compensation
A type of frequency/phase compensation using AC coupling of high frequencies around the highest-gain portion of the circuit.

Filter
An electrical circuit or device that discriminates in favor of some frequencies and against certain other frequencies.

First-order filter
A filter that contains only a single reactive element.

Flash analog-to-digital (A/D) converter
A very fast A/D converter that uses a voltage comparator for every possible bit combination.

Flicker ($1/f$) noise
Noise caused by material imperfections.

Four-quadrant multiplier
An analog multiplier that will operate when both of the two numbers to be multiplied have positive and negative signs.

Free-running state
A PLL state when the output frequency is determined only by external components.

Frequency modulation

Transferring of information by varying the frequency of a radio frequency carrier.

Frequency response

The manner in which some characteristic of an electrical/electronic device responds as the frequency of the input signal changes. What happens to op amp gain with changing input frequency, for example.

Frequency selective

A term used to describe a characteristic of an electrical/electronic circuit that responds to only a narrow range of frequencies.

Frequency-shift keying (FSK)

A technique for sending and receiving data by using one frequency to represent a binary 1, then shifting to a different frequency to represent a binary 0.

Frequency synthesizer

A circuit that uses a phase locked loop and digital dividers to generate a number of frequencies from a single-frequency source.

Function generator

A circuit that supplies multiple output waveforms, such as sine waves, square waves, and triangular waves. Often a single large-scale IC.

Gain-bandwidth product

A measure of how much gain can be obtained at a specified maximum frequency.

Half-power point

The 3 dB point. Widely used method of describing amplifier and filter characteristics.

Half-splitting

A method of troubleshooting that separates a circuit into progressively smaller halves during identification of a problem.

Hartley oscillator

An oscillator circuit that obtains the required feedback and phase shift from a tapped inductor in an *LC* tuned circuit.

Highly damped

A term used to describe the characteristics of an *LC* circuit (or its equivalent) with large *L* and small *C*. Being highly damped results in a droopy roll-off characteristic.

High-order filter

A filter of third or higher order that is obtained by combining groups of first- and second-order filters.

High-pass filter

An electrical/electronic circuit that allows high frequencies to pass but restricts the passing of low frequencies.

Hum

A low-frequency audio signal that appears in an amplifier's output due to AC power picked up by wiring and components.

Hysteresis
> The property of a circuit that switches from one condition to another under one input condition but does not switch back until a different condition exists.

IC voltage regulator
> An integrated circuit assembly that contains all components necessary to perform voltage regulation.

Input bias current
> The small but finite current required to operate the input stage of an operational amplifier.

Input offset current
> External current that must be applied to equalize input bias currents.

Input offset voltage
> The voltage that must be applied to the input terminals to cause 0 output voltage. It is made necessary by inherent unbalance in the differential amplifier input stage of the operational amplifier.

Input resistance
> The resistance seen by the signal or controlling power source "looking into" the amplifier input terminals.

Insertion loss
> The losses suffered due to insertion of a filter in a circuit.

Instrumentation amplifier
> A special op amp that has high common-mode rejection ratio, high input impedance, low output impedance, stable gain, low drift and offset, and good linearity.

Integrated circuit (IC)
> A solid-state (as opposed to vacuum tube) device that contains many transistors and other components. ICs may be as simple as one or two transistors or may contain complete electronic systems.

Integrating analog-to-digital (A/D) converter
> A circuit that uses an active integrator circuit to perform A/D conversion.

Integration
> A mathematical operation that effectively provides the area under the curve defined by the input function.

Integrator
> A circuit that performs the mathematical operation of integration with an op amp and a capacitor.

Intermediate frequency (IF) amplifier
> A tuned amplifier used in superheterodyne radio receivers.

Internally compensated
> A term used to describe an op amp that is manufactured so as to control the roll-off characteristic.

Ions
> Atoms that have either gained or lost one or more electrons.

Inverting amplifier

An operational amplifier circuit configuration in which the signal to be amplified is applied to the inverting (−) input. A portion of the output is also fed back to the inverting (−) input, and the noninverting (+) input is grounded. Gain varies from near 1 to very high values. Input resistance is generally determined by resistor values, while output resistance is low.

Level detector

A zero-crossing detector that operates at some voltage level other than 0.

Linear integrated circuit

A general term that defines all nondigital integrated circuits, including not only op amps but also many of the complete-system ICs.

Linear ramp output voltage

A voltage that either increases or decreases linearly, such as a triangular wave.

Lock range

The frequency range over which the PLL output frequency can follow changes in input frequency.

Logarithmic amplifier

A circuit whose output is proportional to the logarithm of the input. Function is accomplished by using semiconductor diodes or transistors in the feedback path of an op amp.

Logarithmic scale

A scale in which the points are plotted logarithmically rather than linearly and that is used with frequency response and other types of graphs. Logarithmic scales compress the range of information so that more data may be shown in a given length on the graph.

Loop gain

The reduction of open-loop gain by closed-loop gain. It is the ratio of open-loop gain to closed-loop gain and is used in many op amp calculations.

Low-pass filter

A filter that passes low frequencies and attenuates high frequencies.

Miller effect

Apparent amplification of capacitor value by circuit amplification.

Mixer

A summing circuit used in audio applications.

Modulation

The process of combining information to be transmitted with a radio frequency carrier.

Monostable multivibrator

A digital circuit that provides an output for a predetermined time period upon receipt of an input signal. The output then is removed until another input signal is provided.

Multiple-feedback filter

A filter configuration that uses both capacitive and resistive feedback to the inverting input of an op amp.

Multiplexing

An operation that sequentially selects a number of different inputs for amplification.

Narrow-band

A term used to describe an electrical/electronic circuit that processes a narrow range of frequencies centered about a selected frequency. All other frequencies are rejected.

Negative ramp

A linearly decreasing waveform, such as the negative-going portion of a triangular wave.

Noise

Any unwanted random signal variation.

Noninverting amplifier

An operational amplifier circuit configuration very similar to the voltage follower. Only a portion of the output is fed back to the inverting (−) input, however. Gain varies from as little as 1 to as high as 1000. High input resistance and low output resistance are typical.

Norton amplifier

Same as *current difference amplifier.*

Notch filter

Same as a *band-reject filter.*

Octave

A two-fold change, such as frequency changing from 10 Hz to 20 Hz.

Open-loop gain

Gain of an amplifier without feedback. Output voltage divided by input voltage.

Operational amplifier (op amp)

Usually an integrated circuit assembly that contains a complete amplifier system having very high amplification, high input resistance, and low output resistance.

Optical coupler

An electronic device that isolates data-gathering equipment from recording equipment. It is a combination light source and photodiode.

Oscillation

A circuit condition in which the output frequency no longer depends on its input frequency. In other words, the circuit is providing its own input signal.

Oscillator

An electronic circuit that provides an AC output with no external AC input.

Output resistance

The resistance seen by the load "looking back into" the amplifier output terminals.

Output short-circuit current

The maximum output current that an operational amplifier can supply.

Passband

Those frequencies between the lower and upper 3 dB points on a gain versus frequency graph.

Passive filter

A filter that contains only resistors, capacitors, or inductors.

Peak detector

An electronic circuit that passes only the positive or the negative half-cycle of a radio wave and stores the peak value of each half-cycle until the next half-cycle arrives.

Peak-to-peak detector

Same as *peak detector* except that it uses both half-cycles.

Phase comparator

A circuit that provides an output voltage whose amplitude is proportional to the amount of phase difference between two input signals and whose polarity depends on whether a leading or a lagging phase angle exists.

Phase detector

Same as a *phase comparator.*

Phase-lag network

A compensation network that modifies the phase response of an operational amplifier to improve stability.

Phase-lead compensation

A compensation method that moves the point at which internal phase shift reaches 180° to some higher frequency.

Phase-locked loop (PLL)

An integrated circuit or combination of integrated circuits with an output "locked" to the frequency and phase of the input.

Phase-locked state

A PLL state when the output frequency equals the input frequency.

Phase margin

The number of degrees of phase shift allowed between unconditionally stable and conditionally stable circuit conditions.

Phase response

The manner in which the phase shift of an electrical/electronic device responds as the frequency of the input signal changes.

Phase shift oscillator

An oscillator circuit that obtains the required phase shift from output to input by using *RC* networks.

Pinchoff voltage

The value of control voltage for a FET that allows the highest drain-to-source resistance to exist.

Pole

A mathematical term that can be equated to an equivalent resonant circuit in a filter.

Popcorn noise

A sudden change in DC level at the output of an op amp.

Positive ramp

A linearly increasing waveform, such as the positive-going portion of a triangular wave.

Power amplifier

An amplifier with a primary purpose of providing power output.

Preamplifier

An amplifier used to accept very low-level input signals and to amplify with a minimum of noise. It usually has flat frequency response.

Precision diode

A circuit that uses a diode in the feedback path of an op amp to compensate for the nonlinearity of the diode at small voltage inputs.

Programmable op amp

An op amp whose characteristics such as power dissipation, slew rate, and gain-bandwidth product may be varied by adjusting current into a special input.

Pulse

A nonsinusoidal wave with unequal off and on times.

Q

The quality of a filter. Usually an indication of a filter's selectivity.

Quadrature oscillator

An oscillator circuit that provides both sine and cosine wave outputs.

Quartz crystal

A piezoelectric material that vibrates at a stable frequency when a voltage is applied across its terminals. A quartz crystal is used in controlling the frequency of oscillators.

Radio frequencies

Frequencies that are used to communicate information by propagation of electromagnetic waves rather than by movement of air molecules.

Reference diode

A precision *zener diode*.

Resolution

The ability to discriminate between two values.

RIAA playback equalization curve

Record Industry of America frequency response required to compensate for deficiencies in the recording process.

Roll-off characteristic

A graph that shows the change in gain of an amplifier as frequency increases above the cutoff frequency.

R-2R resistor network

A resistor network used in D/A converters in which only two resistor values are used, R and $2R$.

Sallen-Key filter

A filter configuration that uses capacitive feedback to the noninverting input of the op amp to simulate the inductive component of an LC circuit.

Sample-and-hold circuit

An op-amp-related circuit that samples the value of a voltage or current and holds it until needed. The sample-and-hold function may be accomplished with op amps and capacitors.

Saturation voltage

The maximum output voltage that an operational amplifier can supply while still responding linearly to input voltage change. Sometimes called *output voltage swing*.

Sawtooth wave

A triangular wave with different positive-going and negative-going rise/fall times.

Scaling

A technique used to allow solution of equations with terms having multipliers, such as $2x + 3y + z$. Scaling is accomplished by changing the series resistor in a summing circuit.

Schmitt trigger

A circuit that provides a single output pulse when the input exceeds a preset level.

Second-order filter

A filter that contains two reactive components or their equivalent.

Sensitivity

When referring to electromechanical meter movements, an indication of meter current required to rotate the coil assembly. Sensitivity is most often defined in terms of ohms per volt (Ω/V).

Series-pass transistor

A transistor connected in series with a source of voltage and a load as in a voltage regulator.

Shape option

Another name for *damping factor*.

Shot noise

Noise caused by charge carriers crossing a potential barrier, such as in transistors and diodes.

Shunt regulation

A method of voltage regulation where the regulating device is connected across or "in shunt with" the load.

Sidebands

Additional frequencies generated by the modulation process.

Signal-conditioning amplifier

An amplifier that scales inputs to values acceptable to A/D converters.

Signal-to-noise ratio (S/N)

The ratio of desired signal to noise.

Silicon-controlled rectifier (SCR)

A semiconductor device that is turned on by a small control voltage or current and is capable of controlling large amounts of power. It operates on either the positive or the negative half-cycle of an AC wave but not on both.

Sine wave

The most familiar form of an electronic signal. A wave whose form is obtained by graphing the trigonometric sine of a function.

Sinusoidal

Of a sine form.

Skirts

The sides of a graph showing frequency selectivity.

Slew rate

A number that describes the op amp's ability to supply large, rapid changes in output voltage. Slew rate is expressed in terms of volts per unit time.

Slope

Another word for *roll-off rate*.

Spectrum

A range of frequencies, such as the audio spectrum.

Spectrum diagram

A graph that displays all frequencies present for a specific application on the horizontal axis while displaying amplitude on the vertical axis.

Square wave

A nonsinusoidal wave that is symmetrical about some axis (perhaps 0 V). Both positive and negative amplitudes are equal, and both halves of the complete cycle have the same period.

State-variable filter

A multiple-feedback universal filter that employs at least three op amps and provides high-pass, low-pass, and band-pass outputs simultaneously.

Stopband

That portion of the frequency spectrum not passed by a filter.

Subtractor (difference amplifier)

An electrical/electronic circuit that performs the mathematical function of subtraction. Subtraction is accomplished by using both the inverting and noninverting inputs of an op amp.

Successive-approximation analog-to-digital (A/D) converter

A circuit that changes the output of a shift register to an analog value to be compared with the analog value to be converted.

Summing amplifier

A special case of the inverting amplifier with the inverting input connected to a summing point.

Summing point

A point in a circuit where two or more inputs combine, such as where two resistors join.

Supply voltage sensitivity

Output voltage change caused by power supply voltage changes. It is sometimes defined as a ratio called the *supply voltage rejection ratio*.

Switched-capacitor filter (SCF)

A circuit that filters by varying the rate at which capacitors are charged and discharged.

Switched-mode regulator

A type of voltage regulator in which load current is applied in the form of variable time duration pulses.

Thermal (Johnson) noise

Noise generated by the random movement of charge carriers in a circuit.

Thermistor

A temperature-sensitive resistor whose primary function is to change resistance with changing temperature.

Thermocouple

A temperature transducer that converts a change in temperature into a change in voltage.

Time constant

The product of R and C in a circuit.

Tone control

Electrical/electronic circuits that allow continuous adjustment of the amplifier's frequency response, thus varying the amplitude of high and low frequencies to suit the tastes of the listener.

Tone detector

An electronic circuit that provides an indication of the existence of a specified tone.

Tracking

A term that refers to resistors changing value equally as some other parameter, such as temperature, varies.

Tracking analog-to-digital (A/D) converter

Same as a *counter A/D converter.*

Transconductance amplifier

A special op amp with conventional input characteristics but with a current rather than a voltage output.

Transducer

A device that converts one form of energy into another.

Triac

A device similar to an SCR but operating on both AC wave half-cycles.

Triangular wave

A nonsinusoidal wave that is symmetrical about some axis (perhaps 0 V). Both positive and negative amplitudes are equal. The wave rises linearly from its maximum negative amplitude to its maximum positive amplitude and then falls linearly to the maximum negative amplitude.

Twin-T filter

A common *notch filter* that employs two RC T networks.

Twin-T (parallel-T) network

An RC network that consists of two T networks connected to supply near-zero transmission at some frequency. This network is used in oscillator circuits and filters.

Two-quadrant multiplier
An analog multiplier that will operate when only one of the two numbers to be multiplied has both positive and negative signs.

Ultrasonic frequencies
Frequencies higher than audio frequencies that can cause movement of air molecules.

Unconditionally stable
An amplifier condition such that oscillation cannot occur under any gain/frequency combination.

Underdamped
A term used to describe the characteristics of a high-*Q LC* circuit or its equivalent. Being underdamped results in a peaked response.

Unipolar (field effect) transistor
A solid-state amplifying device that operates due to the existence of either positive or negative charge carriers.

Unity gain frequency
The frequency at which the open-loop gain of an amplifier has dropped to 1.

Unity gain VCVS filter
A special case of the *Sallen-Key filter.*

Universal time constant curve
A graph of the exponential equation used to solve for voltage/current relationships in an *RC* circuit.

Video amplifier
Same as *wide-band amplifier* except that it is most often used in television and video applications.

Virtual ground
One of the inputs of an operational amplifier appearing to be grounded because the other input is grounded. This is due to the fact that the voltage difference between the two inputs of an op amp is assumed to be 0.

Voltage amplifier
An amplifier with a primary purpose of amplifying a small voltage input.

Voltage-controlled oscillator (VCO)
An oscillator whose frequency is controlled by an external voltage.

Voltage-controlled-voltage-source (VCVS) filter
Another name for *Sallen-Key filter.*

Voltage follower
An operational amplifier circuit configuration in which the signal to be amplified is applied to the noninverting (+) input. Op amp output is returned directly to the inverting (−) input, resulting in very high circuit input resistance, very low circuit output resistance, and unity voltage gain.

Voltage regulation
The capability of maintaining a constant voltage despite changes in load

resistance and source voltage. Voltage regulation is sometimes expressed in terms of percentage regulation.

Voltage regulator

A device that supplies constant voltage to a load despite changes in load resistance or source voltage.

Voltage sensitivity

An indication of how much voltage is required to obtain full-scale deflection of a moving-coil meter.

Voltage-to-current converter

An op amp circuit that converts input voltage to an output current. This circuit is used with moving-coil meters to improve their voltage sensitivity.

Voltage transfer characteristic

A graph of an op amp's input voltage versus output voltage.

Voltage-variable resistor (VVR)

A circuit element whose resistance changes as a function of an input voltage. A field effect transistor (FET) is often used for this purpose.

Weighted resistor network

A resistor network used in D/A converters in which resistor values are related in a binary manner.

Wien bridge oscillator

An oscillator circuit that obtains the required phase shift by using identical series and parallel *RC* networks in a bridge connection.

Wide-band amplifier

Any amplifier that is required to operate over a frequency range greater than two or three decades of frequency.

Window comparator

A comparator circuit that establishes that an input voltage is between an upper and a lower limit.

Zener diode

A semiconductor diode designed to maintain constant voltage despite changes in load resistance and source voltage.

Zero-crossing detector

A comparator circuit that detects when the input waveform crosses 0 V in either a positive or a negative direction.

Bibliography

Active Filters. Heath Co., Benton Harbor, MI, 1979.

Applications Data Book. Exar Integrated Systems, Sunnyvale, CA, 1979.

Audio/Radio Handbook. National Semiconductor Corp., Santa Clara, CA, 1980.

Bell, David A. *Electronic Devices and Circuits,* 2d ed. Reston, VA: Reston Publishing Co., Inc., 1980.

Berlin, Howard M. *Circuit Design Problems for the TRS-80*. Indianapolis, IN: Howard W. Sams & Co., Inc., 1980.

Berlin, Howard M. *Design of Op-Amp Circuits with Experiments*. Indianapolis, IN: Howard W. Sams & Co., Inc., 1980.

Berlin, Howard M. *Design of Phase-Locked Loop Circuits with Experiments*. Indianapolis, IN: Howard W. Sams & Co., Inc., 1984.

Boyce, Jefferson C. *Modern Electronics: A Survey of the New Technology*. New York, NY: McGraw-Hill Book Co., 1982.

Boylestad, Robert, and Nashelsky, Louis. *Electronic Devices and Circuit Theory,* 3d ed. Englewood Cliffs, NJ: Prentice-Hall, Inc., 1982.

Carr, Joseph. *Op Amp Circuits and Applications*. Blue Ridge Summit, PA: Tab Books, 1976.

Cirovic, Michael M. *Basic Electronics,* 2d ed. Reston, VA: Reston Publishing Co., Inc., 1979.

Coughlin, Robert F., and Driscoll, Frederick F. *Operational Amplifiers and Linear Integrated Circuits,* 3d ed. Englewood Cliffs, NJ: Prentice-Hall, Inc., 1987.

Data Conversion/Acquisition Handbook. National Semiconductor Corp., Santa Clara, CA, 1980.

Deboo, Gordon J., and Burrous, Clifford N. *Integrated Circuits and Semiconductor Devices: Theory and Application,* 2d ed. New York, NY: McGraw-Hill Book Co., 1977.

Dungan, Frank R. *Linear Integrated Circuits for Technicians*. Boston, MA: PWS-KENT, 1984.

Faulkenberry, Luces M. *An Introduction to Operational Amplifiers with Linear IC Applications,* 2d ed. New York, NY: John Wiley & Sons, 1982.

Gayakwad, Ramakant A. *Op-Amps and Linear Integrated Circuit Technology*. Englewood Cliffs, NJ: Prentice-Hall, Inc., 1983.

IC Master. Hearst Business Communications, Inc., Garden City, NJ, 1987.

Jacob, J. Michael. *Applications and Design with Analog Integrated Circuits*. Reston, VA: Reston Publishing Co., Inc., 1982.

Jung, Walter G. *Audio IC Op-Amp Applications,* 2d ed. Indianapolis, IN: Howard W. Sams & Co., Inc., 1980.

Jung, Walter G. *IC Op-Amp Cookbook,* 2d ed. Indianapolis, IN: Howard W. Sams & Co., Inc., 1980.

Lancaster, Don. *Active Filter Cookbook.* Indianapolis, IN: Howard W. Sams & Co., Inc., 1980.

Linear Applications Handbook. National Semiconductor Corp., Santa Clara, CA, 1980.

Linear Databook. National Semiconductor Corp., Santa Clara, CA, 1980.

Linear Op Amp Databook. Fairchild Camera & Instrument Corp., Mountain View, CA, 1979.

McMenamin, J. Michael. *Linear Integrated Circuits.* Englewood Cliffs, NJ: Prentice-Hall, Inc., 1983.

McWane, John. *Introduction to Electronics and Instrumentation.* North Scituate, MA: Breton Publishers, 1981.

Meiksin, Z.H., and Thackray, Philip C. *Electronic Design with Off-the-shelf Integrated Circuits.* West Nyack, NY: Parker Publishing Co., Inc., 1980.

Mims, Forrest M., III. *Engineer's Notebook.* Fort Worth, TX: Radio Shack, 1979.

Nashelsky, Louis, and Boylestad, Robert. *Devices: Discrete and Integrated.* Englewood Cliffs, NJ: Prentice-Hall, Inc., 1981.

Noll, Edward M. *Linear IC Principles, Experiments, and Projects,* 2d ed. Indianapolis, IN: Howard W. Sams & Co., Inc., 1978.

Nonlinear Circuits Handbook. Analog Devices, Inc., Norwood, MA, 1976.

Operational Amplifiers. Heath Co., Benton Harbor, MI, 1980.

Reference Data for Radio Engineers, 6th ed. Howard W. Sams & Co., Inc., Indianapolis, IN, 1977.

Rutkowski, George B. *Handbook of Integrated-Circuit Operational Amplifiers.* Englewood Cliffs, NJ: Prentice-Hall, Inc., 1975.

Shacklette, L.W., and Ashworth, H.A. *Using Digital and Analog Integrated Circuits.* Englewood Cliffs, NJ: Prentice-Hall, Inc., 1978.

Shrader, Robert L. *Electronic Communication,* 5th ed. New York, NY: McGraw-Hill Book Co., 1985.

Solid State Devices Manual. RCA Corp., Somerville, NJ, 1975.

Voltage Regulator Handbook. Fairchild Camera & Instrument Corp., Mountain View, CA, 1978.

Voltage Regulator Handbook. National Semiconductor Corp., Santa Clara, CA, 1980.

Wojslaw, Charles. *Integrated Circuits: Theory and Applications.* Reston, VA: Reston Publishing Co., Inc., 1978.

Young, Thomas. *Linear Integrated Circuits.* New York, NY: John Wiley & Sons, 1981.

Answers
to Selected Problems

Chapter 1

    1. $V_o = 47$ V   3. $V_o = 23.75$ V   6. $V_f = 11.875$ V

Chapter 2

1. $A_{cl} = 1$	$R_i' = 400{,}000$ MΩ	$R_o' = 1 \times 10^{-3}$ Ω
3. $A_{cl} = -10$	$R_i' = 10$ kΩ	$R_o' = 0.01$ Ω
7. $A_{cl} = 2.74$	$R_i' = 3{,}894{,}433$ MΩ	$R_o' = 1.08 \times 10^{-4}$ Ω

Chapter 3

    1. (a) $V_{be} = 701.25$ mV   (b) $V_{be} = 656.25$ mV
       (c) $V_{be} = 611.25$ mV   (d) $V_{be} = 566.25$ mV
       (e) $V_{be} = 521.25$ mV   (f) $V_{be} = 476.25$ mV
    5. $V_i = 0.01$ V
    8. % regulation $= 2.6\%$

Chapter 4

    1. (a) S $= 0.157$ V/μs   (b) S $= 0.314$ V/μs   (c) S $= 0.471$ V/μs
      (d) S $= 0.785$ V/μs   (e) S $= 2.355$ V/μs   (f) S $= 18.84$ V/μs
    5. (a) $A = 100{,}000$ or 100 dB   (b) $A = 19{,}612$ or 85.85 dB
      (c) $A = 6{,}652$ or 76.46 dB   (d) $A = 1{,}000$ or 60.00 dB
      (e) $A = 20$ or 26.00 dB

Chapter 5

    1. The circuit of Figure 5–3 depends on the R_a/R_b divider to establish the reference of $V^+/2$. If the negative half-cycle is distorted, probably the divider ratio is upset. First check V_o with $V_i = 0$ V. V should be $V^+/2$. If not, check the junction of R_a, R_b, and C_a. If it is not $V^+/2$, the most likely failed component is C_a.

7. There should be no change in low frequency response with changes in C_x and C_y values.

10. If the amplifier shown in Figure 5–11 has developed poor low-frequency response, the 0.05 μF capacitors may be shorted. Circuit operation depends on the capacitive reactance of the 0.05 μF capacitors to look like open circuits so that the bass control can control feedback.

Chapter 6

2. $A_{cl} = 1 + \dfrac{R_8}{R_7} = 1 + \dfrac{22 \times 10^3}{220} = 101 = 40$ dB

4. $Q = 16.67$ kHz

6. $A_{cl} = 26$ dB

10. An FM broadcast intermediate frequency amplifier operates near 10.7 MHz. An op amp capable of supplying gain at that frequency is required. Typical op amps discussed in this chapter are the LH0024, CA3038, and LH0032.

Chapter 7

1. (a) 0 dB (b) 0 dB (c) − 14 dB (d) − 20 dB (e) − 30 dB

3. (a) − 26 dB (b) − 20 dB (c) 0 dB (d) 0 dB (e) 0 dB

6. In (a) through (e) gain is increased by approximately 20 dB: $A_{cl} = 20$ dB.

Chapter 8

1. (a) Passband gain $= 1$ (b) $f_c = 2.275 \times 10^3$ Hz
   (c) $D = 1.414$

4. Any $R_1 C_2$ combination whose product is ½ of the RC product in Problem 3 will increase f_c by a factor of 2 as long as the restrictions for this circuit are observed.

9. Changing R_b changes only the band-pass gain (Q): $Q = 2.3$.

Chapter 9

1. (a) $f = 774$ Hz (b) $A_v = 32.14$

4. $f = 483$ Hz

9. (a) On time $= 1 \times 10^{-5}$ s; off time $= 1 \times 10^{-4}$ s
   (b) On time $= 4.7 \times 10^{-3}$ s; off time $= 4.7 \times 10^{-2}$ s
   (c) On time $= 3.3 \times 10^{-4}$ s; off time $= 3.3 \times 10^{-3}$ s

Chapter 10

1. $V_o = -10$ V

4. $V_o = -\left[V_x \left(\dfrac{R_f}{R_x} \right) + V_y \left(\dfrac{R_f}{R_y} \right) + V_z \left(\dfrac{R_f}{R_z} \right) \right]$

$\qquad = -[4V_x + 2V_y + 0.5V_z]$

6. Voltage change = 1 V/second due to the 1-second time constant of R_iC_f. Therefore, it will take 15 seconds to reach saturation.
9. Since the circuit of Figure 10–14 functions as a band-pass filter between 995 Hz and 4423 Hz, a 2500 Hz sine wave should be faithfully reproduced, but shifted in phase.

Chapter 13

3. Resistors in a weighted resistor network increase in a binary manner, each value doubling from the MSB resistor. Thus,

MSB	5 kΩ
	10 kΩ
	20 kΩ
	40 kΩ
	80 kΩ
	160 kΩ
	320 kΩ
	640 kΩ

Chapter 14

2. $f_o = 16.666$ kHz

Index